Handbook of Concrete Culvert Pipe Hydraulics

Handbook of Concrete Culvert Pipe Hydraulics

PORTLAND CEMENT ASSOCIATION *Old Orchard Road • Skokie, Illinois 60076*

Printed in the United States of America
Fourth Printing

Library of Congress catalog card number 64-22189

EB058.01W

Price: $6.00

Preface

HIGHWAY CULVERTS INVOLVE A SIGNIFICANT INVESTMENT IN engineering design, field surveys, preparation of drawings, materials, labor, and inspection. However, design practices vary from place to place and are largely dependent upon the emphasis placed upon hydraulics. As larger, longer, and costlier drainage structures are specified, hydraulic design becomes imperative for reasons of economy and increased potential for flood damage. Hydraulic principles apply to all culverts and are important in minimizing the costs. Any additional cost there may be for hydraulic design is minor when compared with the total cost of the installation.

This *Handbook of Concrete Culvert Pipe Hydraulics* supplies up-to-date information necessary for the proper design of circular culverts. It is intended to assist the culvert designer in understanding hydrology and hydraulics and in applying these principles to design. Engineers will find much of the information in this handbook to be of value in designing all types of drainage installations. Material is presented in a form that is practical and usable for both the practicing engineer and the student. Principles of operation are fully explained and easy-to-use design aids are provided.

Individual chapters have been devoted to the various major phases of hydraulic design. Special problems not covered in the book can be solved by applying these principles with local experience to arrive at satisfactory design.

This handbook was prepared by the staff of the Water Resources Bureau, Portland Cement Association, under the general supervision of E. P. Sellner, manager. Ralph M. Weaver, hydraulic engineer, was the principal author. The handbook was reviewed and contributions to its contents were made by Dasel E. Hallmark, hydraulic engineer. Many sources of information were consulted in preparing this book. However, particularly valuable information and data were obtained from the Bureau of Public Roads, the National Bureau of Standards, the U.S. Army Corps of Engineers Waterways Experiment Station, the American Concrete Pipe Association, the St. Anthony Falls Hydraulic Laboratory of the University of Minnesota, and other universities.

It is believed that engineers throughout the United States and Canada will find this handbook useful in designing well-planned and efficient culverts, in reducing the time required for hydraulic design, in making full use of the capability of concrete pipe, and in building economical drainage installations.

PORTLAND CEMENT ASSOCIATION

Contents

Concrete pipe stockpiled on the job site for culvert construction.
Courtesy of Texas Highway Department.

Introduction

PIPE CULVERTS ARE STRUCTURES REQUIRING PLANNING AND engineering design. Every culvert installation performs an operative function determined by hydrology and hydraulics, and a load-carrying function determined by structural considerations and construction procedures.

Culvert design, therefore, involves two independent design problems: hydraulic design and structural design. The intent of the hydraulic design is to determine the most economical installation by realistically anticipating the effects of hydrology in establishing satisfactory hydraulic operation. The intent of the structural design is to assure the construction of an installation with sufficient strength to support the loads without adversely affecting the hydraulic operation. However, structural design information is more readily available than is information on hydraulics. Therefore, this handbook is devoted entirely to updating published material on hydraulics. A list of structural design references is given in Appendix E.

The results of much new engineering research have become available in recent years, making it possible to design culverts in closer conformance with individual requirements. Recent hydraulic research has developed scientifically sound techniques that replace the empirical formulas previously used. Up-to-date information, in many cases applicable to box culverts as well as pipe culverts, is included in every chapter of this handbook.

Information on preliminary planning, hydrological investigation, and hydraulic design has heretofore been available from widely scattered

High fills require long culverts and high-strength culvert pipe. This is a 48-in. culvert under a 60-ft. fill.

sources. This handbook has been prepared to assemble the most recent information and to apply it to the design of pipe culverts. The subject of hydraulics has been treated extensively to provide a basis for a complete understanding of the hydraulic operation of culverts. Many new design aids are included, among which are the culvert capacity charts for circular pipe recently completed by the Bureau of Public Roads.

Since engineering judgments should be based on complete information, design data and some design aids have been provided for culvert materials other than concrete pipe. This increases the usefulness of the handbook and permits ready evaluation of comparative design.

1

Location and Alignment of Culverts

The economics of culvert design is greatly influenced by location and alignment. When feasible, the culvert should be located to maintain the natural drainage. The natural location is at the bottom of a ravine and often at an angle skewed to the roadway. Inasmuch as this will usually result in maximum loading and maximum length of culvert, it may be desirable to consider several alternatives. The purpose of this chapter is to acquaint the designer with the various methods of locating a culvert and some major considerations involved in each.

No set rule can be given for the location and alignment of culverts. The following discussions are for the purpose of pointing out major factors in certain general design situations. The final location and alignment of culverts are at the discretion and good judgment of the designer, who, armed with a knowledge of hydrology, hydraulics, and structural aspects of culvert design, will be able to place the culvert so as to achieve maximum economy, utility, and safety.

Culverts in modern highways may be classified according to two general uses. The first and predominant use is maintaining the natural drainage channels. In this application, culverts are used to maintain natural streams to prevent ponding in artificially created depressions. The other use is in continuation of ditch drainage through access roads to connect with natural drainage channels. In such cases very little choice in locating the culvert is possible since the alignment and grade of the ditch must be maintained. Prime importance is the selection of a culvert that is compatible with the hydraulic characteristics of the ditch.

Location of Culverts

Natural drainage is maintained by following the original drainage grade. Minor channel relocations essentially maintain the natural drainage grade. Care must be exercised in the latter case because of the possibility of introducing objectionable secondary effects and even interfering with desirable hydraulic operating characteristics. Essential hydraulic features should not be sacrificed in the effort to reduce first cost by alternate culvert location. Experience and good judgment suggest some rules and considerations which should be helpful in establishment of the location and alignment of culverts.

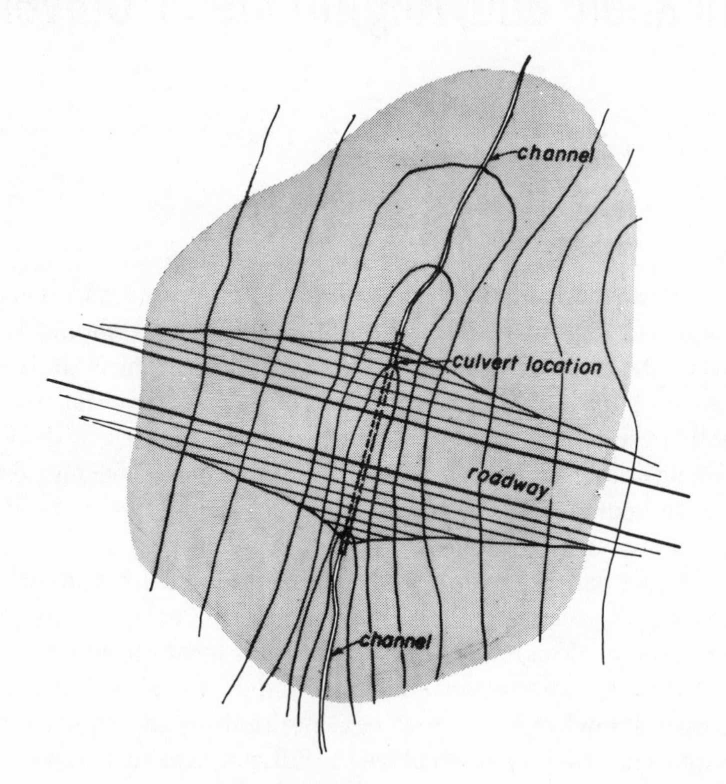

Fig. 1. Culvert in natural drainage channel.

In general, the best overall drainage operation will occur when the culvert is located in the original flow channel (Fig. 1). This may result in some curvature and possibly one or more changes in grade in order to obtain satisfactory bedding. Culverts installed in the natural stream channel will generally be under the widest portion of the embankment and under the maximum loading. These conditions usually result in higher pipe costs. Cost comparison with other locations should include consideration of headwalls, spillways, energy-dissipation structures, channel changes, revetments, extra maintenance, and possible damage due to upsetting natural conditions.

Long culverts are required for modern expressways. This is a long 48-in. culvert near Chicago, Ill.

In cases of steep channels, it may be possible to reduce the length and required strength of the culvert by modification of the natural slope and alignment. In such cases (Fig. 2), the culvert inlet is located in the natural drainage channel, but the slope and alignment of the culvert deviate so that the outlet is displaced from the natural channel both vertically and horizontally. In order to raise the slope as shown, the alignment follows the hillside so that satisfactory bedding can be obtained in undisturbed earth. This results in horizontal as well as vertical displacement.

While this may seem to be an economical expedient, there are certain objections that must be overcome. Some means must be provided at the outlet to return the flow to the natural drainage channel. This requires an auxiliary channel and necessary protection to prevent erosion. In some instances, a form of spillway will be required, particularly if the return channel is steep. In other cases it may be feasible to project the culvert beyond the toe of the embankment and allow the water to drop into a pool. Special construction will be required for the support of the exposed pipe. The pool in this case should be designed and constructed to dissipate the energy of the falling water.

Culverts also may be located to one side of the natural channel, as shown in Fig. 3, thereby shifting the location of both the inlet and the outlet. In these cases, short sections of channels may need to be relocated at the culvert inlet, outlet, or both.

Certain structural advantages and improved working conditions may

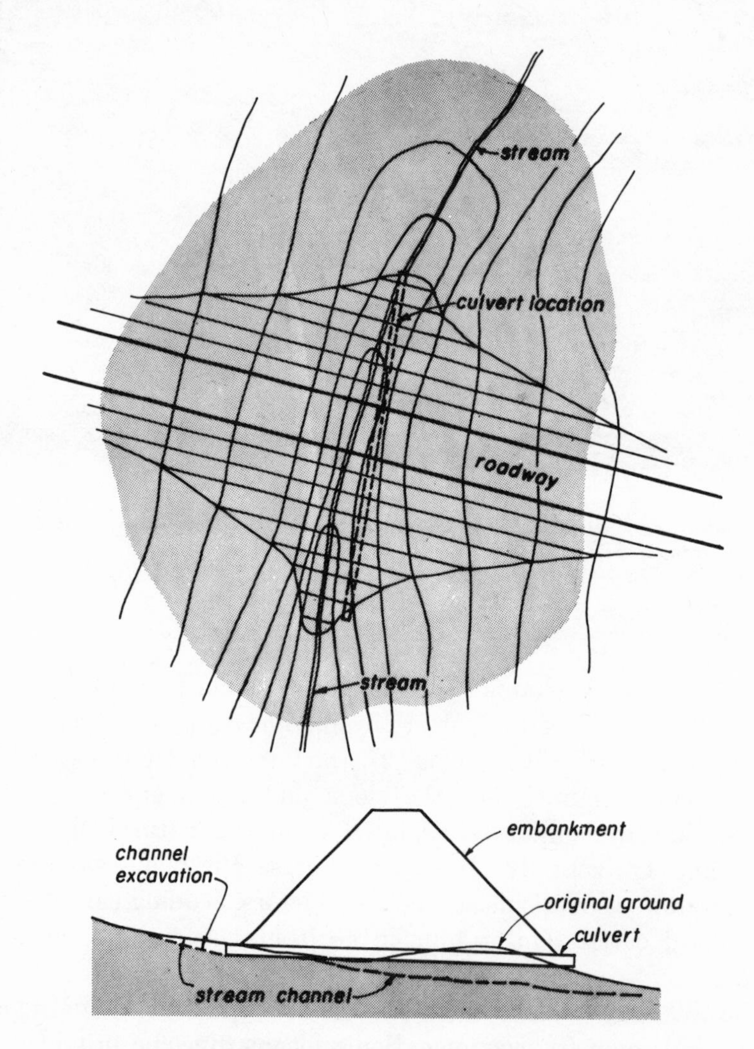

Fig. 2. Displacement of culvert outlet to reduce grade and earth loading.

be achieved by this method. With the culvert placed in a trench dug in undisturbed soil, the embankment load on the pipe is reduced. This is a particularly satisfactory construction method in gradually sloping terrain where only moderate channel changes are needed to re-establish natural drainage. Channel realignment should be done with great care.

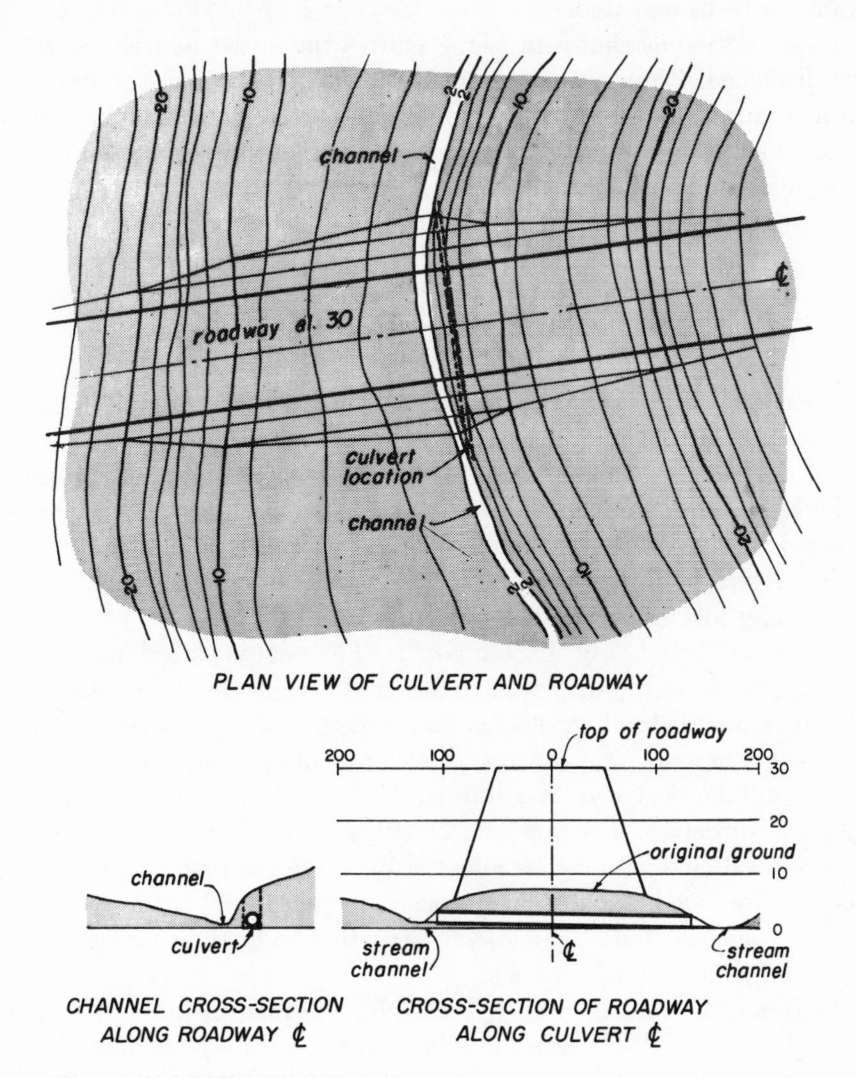

Fig. 3. Sidehill culvert location.

It may be desirable in the case of installations such as shown in Fig. 3 to locate the inlet at an elevation above the natural stream bed. This increase in culvert inlet elevation will create a pond and affect the upstream stage for some distance. These results may actually be beneficial.

On a continuously flowing stream the pond would be an asset to conservation and recreation. If the stream is rapid and erosive, the impoundment will be a settling basin that will eventually fill, raising the stream bed in the vicinity of the culvert. On intermittent watercourses the impoundment may become stagnant and catch debris, which must be tolerated if the entrance is to be elevated.

Construction as shown in Fig. 3 causes the outlet as well as the inlet to be displaced. Proper provision must be made to return the flow to the natural channel. If the return channel is steep, paving may be required. Whatever solution is adopted, channel realignment and maintenance must be considered as part of the cost.

Channel Diversions

If the natural watercourse crosses the roadway obliquely, it may be economical to divert the natural flow through a shorter culvert by crossing the roadway at a right angle. As in other cases, channel realignment will be required and should be included in the total cost when compared to the cost of longer installation in the natural drainage channel or skewed crossing as shown in Fig. 4, Plan No. 1. Channel diversions, such as Fig. 4, are normally located in one of three ways:

Outlet Diversion, Fig. 4, Plan No. 2—The inlet is placed in the natural channel with the outlet displaced to one side as illustrated. A characteristic of this diversion is the longer total flow length with the consequent reduction in average grade. Entrance and outlet structures and channel realignment should be designed to minimize the effect, on the flow, of abrupt changes of direction. The size of this culvert as compared to the culvert in the natural channel may be affected by these factors. Extra considerations to be included in a cost comparison are the special entrance diversion structure, special outlet diversion structure, channel realignment at outlet, and channel maintenance.

Entrance Diversion, Fig. 4, Plan No. 4—The entrance is displaced so that the outlet discharges directly into the natural channel. In order to prevent ponding, the entrance must be below the natural ground line and the channel cut to divert the flow to the culvert. Good practice requires that this approach channel should be direct and aligned with the culvert barrel. In this case no special entrance or outlet structure is required. The size of the culvert may be affected since the length of the flow path has been increased with a consequent reduction in grade. Extra cost will be incurred in channel construction and maintenance and possible larger culvert diameter.

Entrance and Outlet Diversion, Fig. 4, Plan No. 3—An alternative to each of the foregoing locations is to place the culvert with both the inlet and the outlet displaced from the natural channel. No hydraulic advantage is gained and special structures may be required, as well as channel realignment at both the entrance and outlet. However, if the new channel is aligned for direct entrance and discharge of flow, special headwall and

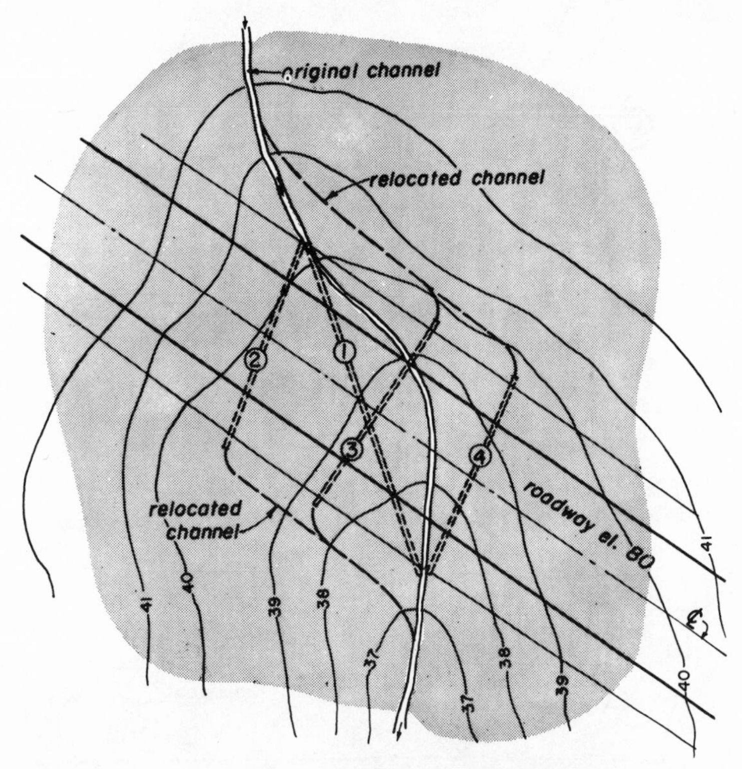

PLAN NO. 1. skewed crossing, no channel relocation required.

PLAN NO. 2. inlet in original channel, downstream channel relocated.

PLAN NO. 3. inlet and outlet displaced with upstream and downstream channel relocation.

PLAN NO. 4. outlet in original channel, upstream channel relocated.

Fig. 4. Possible channel relocation to reduce length of culvert.

endwall structures may be eliminated. This location may be an advantage if right-of-way limitation restricts channel realignment. Extra cost features will be special headwall and endwall structures; possible larger culvert section due to reduced grade; channel realignment; and channel maintenance.

Moderate diversions from the natural channel, as shown in Fig. 5, may sometimes be made without excessive expense for special structures or channel realignment. The purpose of a diversion of this type is to reduce

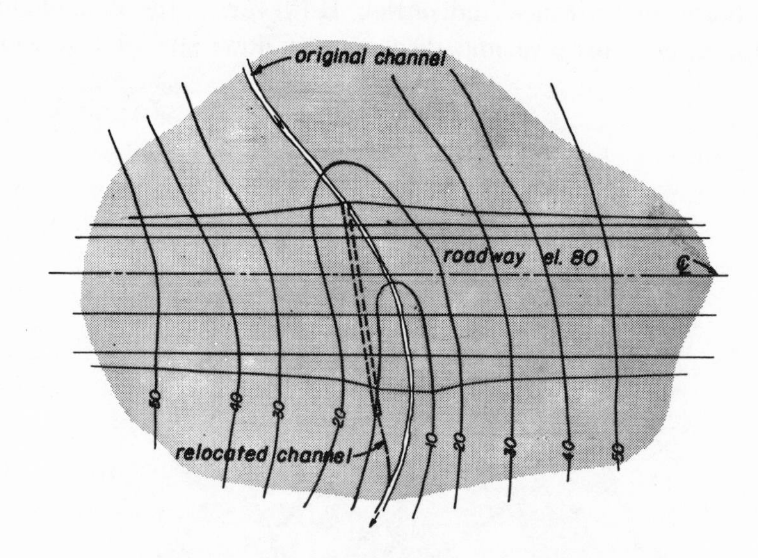

Fig. 5 (above). ***Correction of moderate skew.***
Fig. 6 (below). ***Slight adjustment of skewed channel.***

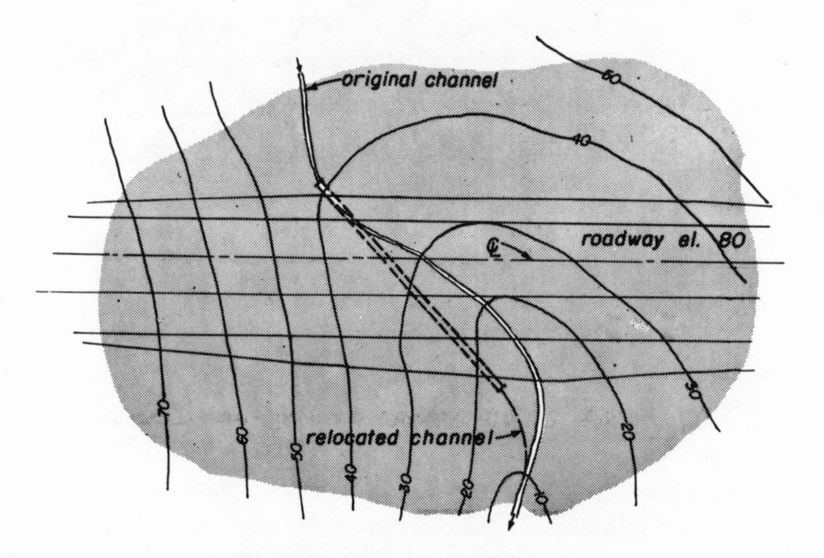

the total required length of culvert pipe. The resulting culvert will still be skewed with respect to the right-of-way, but not nearly as severely as the natural channel. Where the natural channel is only slightly skewed, the culvert may be aligned at right angles to the embankment without introducing adverse effects.

As long as only moderate corrections in alignment are made, no special headwall or endwall structures will be required. Major corrections require special structures and will therefore raise the cost. Some minimum amount of channel realignment will be required for moderate corrections.

A small degree of skewness in the natural channel (Fig. 5) may be corrected to a right-angle crossing, while a large skew (Fig. 6) may be reduced. Experience has shown that there is no significant saving in reducing a moderate skew. The extent to which a skew may be modified without special structures or channel work must be left to the judgment of the designer.

Transverse Interceptor Culverts

Culverts that are used as interceptors operate and function much the same as culverts used for continuation of ditch drainage under access roads or intersecting highways. Culverts of this type (Fig. 7) are usually required to handle only small flows; therefore, small pipe sizes will generally suffice.

An interceptor culvert is located where it is necessary to drain low portions of drainage ditches. Normal practice is to place an interceptor at controlled intervals to drain gutters or roadside ditches. High flows are not encountered, but the hydraulic efficiency of the culvert is still of prime importance. Culvert entrances at right angles to the ditch flow will generally serve satisfactorily. Flow over the roadway is dangerous; therefore this type of installation deserves careful attention. Flow that is not picked up by one culvert may overload the next culvert along the interceptor ditch.

Channel Relocation Factors

Natural channels exist as a result of adjustments of factors that eventually produce a natural balance. The more important of these are channel grade, velocity, and transportability of the channel material. Any channel relocation must contend with the same factors. Any alteration in one factor will be compensated by changes in another. These changes should be anticipated and any detrimental effects guarded against.

Changes in channel grade will cause changes in stream velocity.

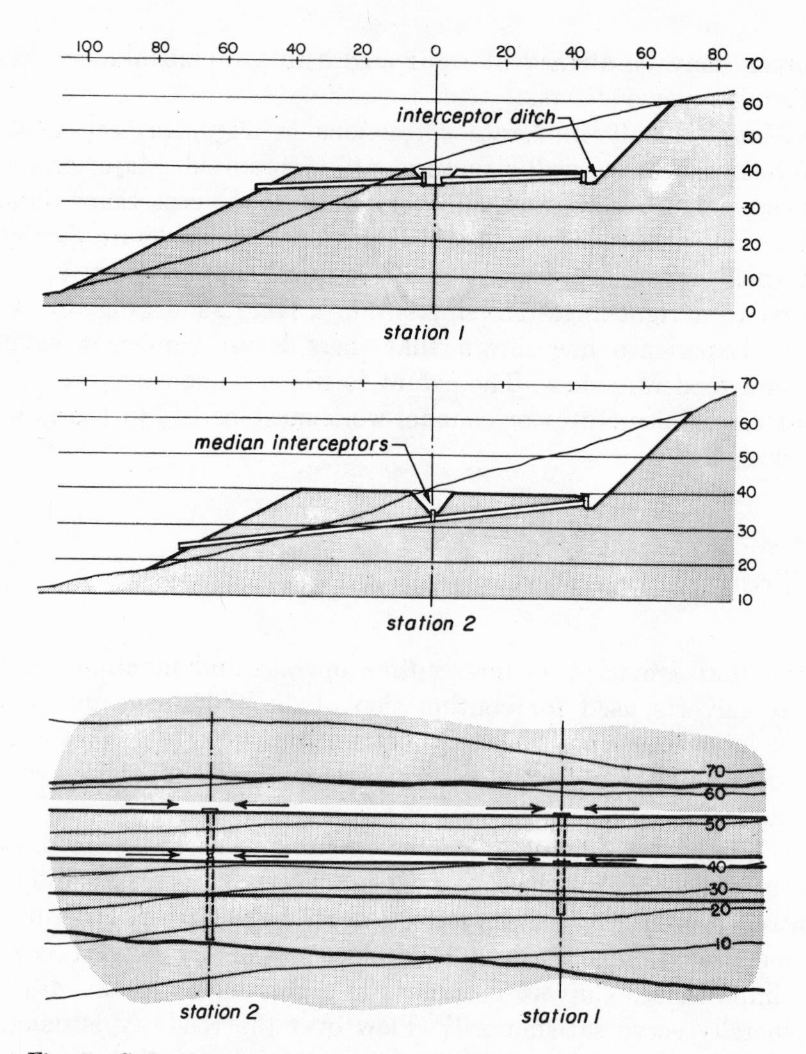

Fig. 7. Culverts under divided highway.

Shortening a long channel increases the grade and consequently increases the stream velocity. An increase in stream velocity has the secondary effect of increasing erosion of the stream bed and banks. This enlarges the channel until additional frictional effects compensate for the increased grade and reduce the velocity below that which causes erosion. The alternatives to prevent erosion are to shape the new channel to regulate stream velocity, provide additional roughness (either natural or artificial), or stabilize the bank by paving.

If relocation effectively lengthens the channel, the reverse situation may occur. Lengthening causes a reduction in grade and consequently a lessening of velocity. The ability of the water to hold transported material in suspension is reduced and the suspended material tends to settle out. This tends to clog the channel and may eventually cause flooding. Clogging is particularly objectionable during periods of high flow since unusually high water levels may occur due to reduced culvert capacity.

Channel relocations which reduce the natural grade should include corrective measures to maintain the existing stream velocity. This is best done by smoothing the channel by: removing rocks, providing straight clean sides, or paving. Channel velocity can also be increased by proper channel shaping to provide a minimum surface area for the flow.

All bends in a channel should be smooth and gradually curved. Sharp bends will not guide the flow and will be subject to erosive action, partic-

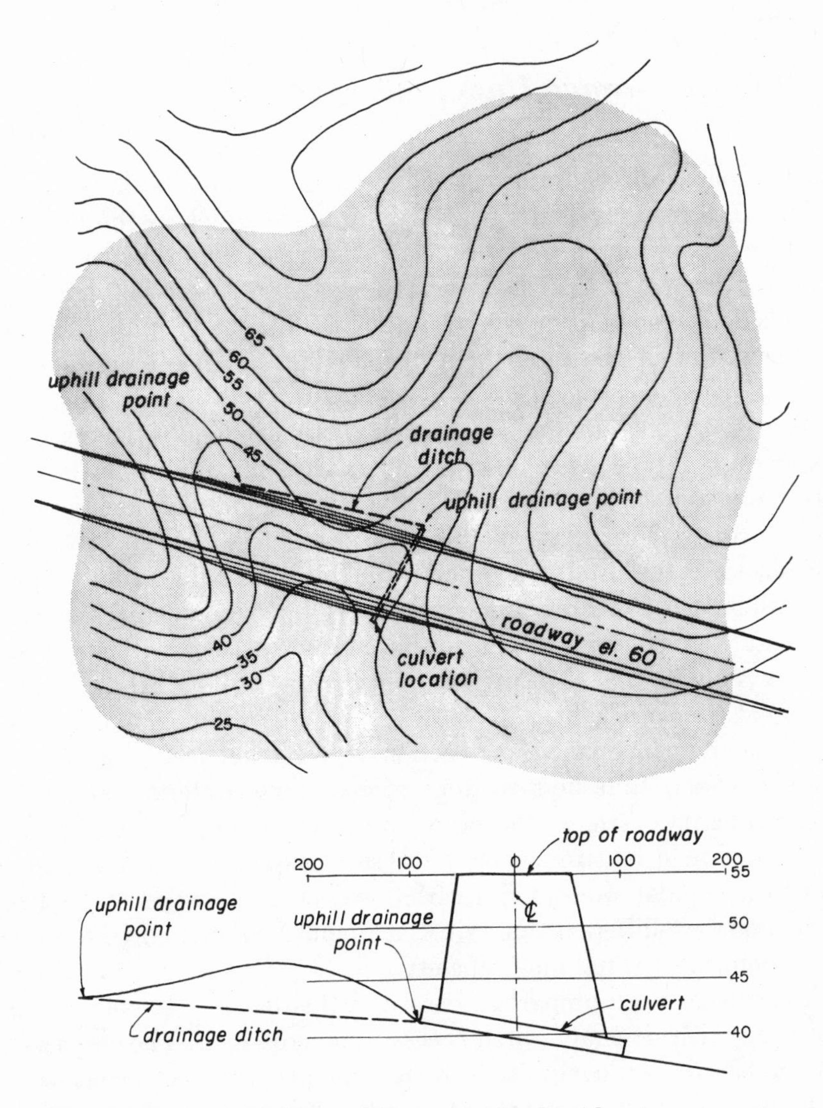

Fig. 8. Diversion of drainage areas to single culvert.

ularly during high flows. It is not unusual for the flow to erode the bank on the outside of the curve and deposit material on the inside of the curve. Bends are sources of energy loss and retard the flow. This undesirable condition can be alleviated to some extent by making the bend as gradual as possible. In general, a radius of curvature equal to 2.5 times the width of the stream will produce satisfactory results. Bends with greater radii of curvature are desirable and should be used if space permits.

Another form of channel relocation exists when a stream is diverted into another stream as shown in Fig. 8. This is sometimes advisable for very small areas in order to reduce the number of culvert installations. The cost savings must be balanced against the drainage ditch costs.

Ditch Drainage Under Access Roads

Continuation of ditch drainage systems under access roads is an important function for culverts. The design problem involves the design of a culvert to maintain natural drainage. Hydrology and hydraulics must also be considered in this case to establish the cross-section and grade of the roadside drainage ditch. Culvert design is for the purpose of achieving continuous flow in the ditch with as little interference or change in the water surface as possible.

The design criteria for culverts in ditch drainage systems preclude the selection of pipe sizes that will operate at maximum efficiency. The location of ditch culverts is fixed by the ditch alignment and the location of access roads. The grade of this type of culvert is fixed by the grade established for the ditch. In order to maintain maximum flow efficiency in the ditch, the headwater on the culvert must not greatly exceed the normal water surface elevation established by ditch flow. Culvert design generally requires that the flow capability of the culvert (the conveyance) must equal that of the ditch.

The conveyance of a flow section is a geometrical property, which means, in effect, that flow sections of the same materials and different shapes will carry water at the same rate at equal slopes. Thus, a circular pipe culvert must be sized to have the same capacity as a drainage ditch, usually trapezoidal. Inasmuch as frictional characteristics of ditches and pipe sections are different, an adjustment must be applied to the conveyance to determine equal flow capacity.

Table 1 has been prepared to assist in the selection of culvert sections to be used with drainage ditch-access road crossings. The values in the table are based on a comparison of the flow properties of trapezoidal and circular sections with a correction applied for friction difference of the

Concrete pipe culverts provide minimum interference to ditch flow, yet are capable of carrying large live loads with practically no cover over the pipe.

ditch-lining material and concrete pipe. This table has been designed for maximum utility by expressing the ditch and pipe dimensions in terms of ratios of depth of flow. To use the table it is merely necessary to enter the table corresponding to the side slope z of the ditch and the ratio of d/b, depth of flow divided by the bottom width of channel, and select the corresponding ratio of d/D, depth divided by pipe diameter. The correct pipe diameter is then determined by dividing the depth by the selected ratio, d/D. See the example at bottom of Table 1.

Pipe sizes determined by use of Table 1 will give pipe culvert sections with flow characteristics similar to the ditch. This pipe will flow unsubmerged under the design conditions. The maximum depth in the pipe permitted by the table is 95 per cent of the pipe diameter. Roughness characteristics of the ditch are assumed as having n value* of 0.030, corresponding to a straight, fairly clean ditch with some weed growth. The pipe roughness

***See "Manning Formula," Chapter 3, p. 63.**

chosen is that of normal concrete pipe with roughness value of $n = 0.012$.

In some cases, limited headroom may necessitate using smaller pipe to handle the expected ditch flow. For these cases the table provides for the use of two parallel pipe culverts, usually permitting the use of smaller pipe.

The development of Table 1 is based on mathematical relationships that do not necessarily yield results corresponding to pipe sizes commercially available. The proper procedure is to select the pipe size next larger than the theoretical size computed by use of the table. This procedure will provide a margin of safety and help reduce changes in water surface elevation due to entrance configuration.

TABLE 1. Access Road Culvert Size Determination, d/D Values

d/b	$z = 1$		$z = 1\frac{1}{2}$		$z = 2$		$z = 3$		$z = 4$	
	No. of pipes		No. of pipes		No. of pipes		No. of pipes		No. of pipes	
	1	2	1	2	1	2	1	2	1	2
.4	.465	.821	.400	.758	.350	.702	.277	.611	.224	.533
.6	.640	.950	.550	.890	.489	.830	.364	.718	.294	.625
.8	.755	.950	.640	.950	.552	.896	.421	.778	.328	.677
1.0	.830	.950	.709	.950	.606	.932	.460	.815	.357	.710
1.2	.880	.950	.754	.950	.647	.950	.490	.842	.376	.731
1.4	.913	.950	.788	.950	.677	.950	.510	.860	.391	.747
1.6	.942	.950	.814	.950	.702	.950	.526	.872	.405	.760
1.8	.950	.950	.835	.950	.719	.950	.540	.884	.416	.772
2.0	.950	.950	.850	.950	.734	.950	.552	.893	.421	.778
2.5	.950	.950	.880	.950	.762	.950	.572	.908	.436	.792
3.0	.950	.950	.900	.950	.780	.950	.585	.918	.448	.804
3.5	.950	.950	.914	.950	.783	.950	.596	.926	.454	.810
4.0	.950	.950	.924	.950	.803	.950	.602	.929	.460	.815
5.0	.950	.950	.939	.950	.818	.950	.615	.939	.466	.821

Example Problem: Ditch Drainage

Select a concrete pipe culvert to carry the flow in a trapezoidal ditch with a bottom width of 1 ft. and with side slopes of 1 vertical to 3 horizontal.

The maximum depth of flow in the ditch has been determined to be 2 ft.
Solution:

Compute the depth-over-width ratio d/b of the ditch,

$$d/b = 2/1 = 2.0.$$

From Table 1, for $z = 3$ select the corresponding d/D value for one pipe,

$$d/D = 0.552.$$

The required pipe diameter is then computed,

$$D = \frac{2.00}{0.552} = 3.6 \text{ ft.}$$

The required size of pipe to carry the flow adequately is the next standard size, or a 48-in. pipe.

If sufficient headroom is not available for a 48-in. pipe, it will be necessary to use two parallel pipe culverts. The pipe size for this installation may also be determined from the table by selecting the d/D ratio for two pipes. In this case, for a value of d/b of 2.0,

$$d/D = 0.893.$$

Then

$$D = \frac{2.00}{0.893}.$$

The required pipe diameter D is 2.22 ft. The required size of standard pipe will then be 30 in.

Also note that the two 30-in. pipe require more channel width than the original channel. This will require some channel shaping to provide a transition into the pipe inlets and from the pipe outlets.

References

1. Bruce, A. G., and Clarkeson, J., *Highway Design and Construction*, Scranton, Pa., International Textbook Co., third edition, 1950.
2. *California Culvert Practice*, State of California, Department of Public Works, Division of Highways, second edition, 1955.
3. *Bank and Shore Protection in California Highway Practice*, State of California, Department of Public Works, Division of Highways, November 1960.

2

Hydrology

A HYDROLOGICAL ANALYSIS OF THE AREAS TO BE DRAINED IS AN essential element in the design of culverts. This type of study supplies the designers with information on runoff and stream flow characteristics which is used as a basis of the hydraulic design. In applying the principles of hydrology, design discharges are established which will assure satisfactory culvert operations for all but a few occasions. This chapter enables the designer to select the average frequency and magnitude of storm events and to determine the probability of exceeding the design flood.

Undesirable flooding is understood to mean the occurrence of headwater pools which exceed a predetermined safe level at the entrances of culverts. In this handbook the safe level is referred to as the maximum permissible headwater depth. Balanced design requires that the selected culverts operate with a headwater equal to or less than the maximum permissible headwater depth for the design discharge. The design discharge is the flow established by the risk of being exceeded which is acceptable to the design engineer.

It must be realized that a culvert is an artificial flow channel and does not in any case duplicate the natural drainage channel that originally existed. In establishing flow in a culvert, a headwater depth greater than the natural stream flow depth for the same flow will be created. Inasmuch as floods existed before the construction of the culvert, they can be expected afterwards as well. The culvert designer cannot be expected to design for the most extreme condition. All parties concerned must be satisfied with culvert designs that minimize the occurrence of flood damage to an acceptable probability.

One major responsibility of the engineer is the decision that determines the flood magnitude and flood stage with the related probability of the flood being exceeded for any period of time. The risk of having larger flows enables the engineer to evaluate the annual flood damage costs for the life of the structure. A fundamental knowledge of hydrology permits the engineer to make this evaluation on a sound basis.

Factors in Establishing Design Criteria

In some respects, the hydrologic analysis required for the design of culverts is relatively simple. On the other hand, the analysis is handicapped by a lack of information pertaining specifically to the smaller watersheds drained by culverts. This is due to the prime importance of research for the large flood-control projects and water supply problems that involve watershed areas of hundreds and thousands of square miles. However, many of the working principles that apply to large watersheds also apply to small watersheds. These principles do not provide all the information required for small watersheds because of the importance of variations which are insignificant in large areas. For the purpose of this analysis, it will be necessary to present reasonable methods of approximation which should be recognized as such and should be used to assist engineering judgment.

The design flow is established by selecting the proper combination of rainfall and runoff characteristics that can reasonably be expected to occur. This is usually further restricted by establishing an interval of time or frequency period as the basis of design. The design criteria would then be the maximum flow carried by the culvert with no flooding or a limited amount of flooding, to be exceeded on the average of once during a designated design period.

The amount of flooding or ponding within reasonable damage limits at a culvert entrance determines the permissible headwater. As shown in Fig. 9, the interrelated facts of flood discharge and discharge through the culvert determine actual resulting headwater at the culvert entrance. This operating headwater is controlled by the hydraulic performance of the culvert once the discharge is selected. The flood discharge, with its related frequency and probability of occurrence in a given period of time, is related to the damage that would result from greater discharges exceeding the permissible headwater.

Flood damage may occur in various ways. One type of damage may

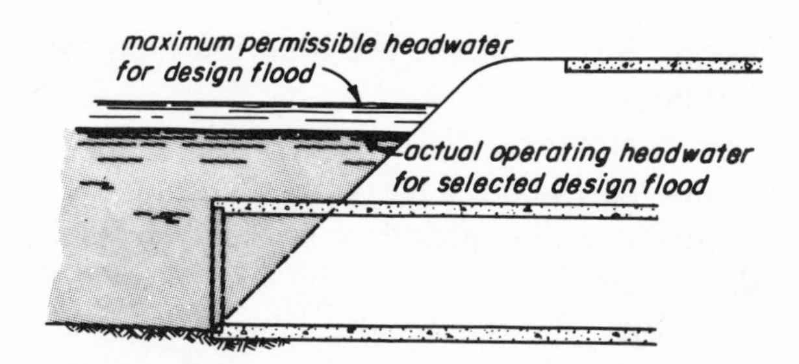

Fig. 9. Relationship of actual operating headwater to maximum permissible headwater.

result from ponding of buildings, crops, or other commercial enterprises. Another type of damage may result from scouring the roadway. Still another type of damage may result from the floodwater going over the roadway, affecting traffic and the roadway itself. These different types of damage probably begin at different headwater elevations and therefore any one or combination determines the maximum permissible headwater. Once the permissible headwater is established, a design discharge is selected that will keep the damage costs within reasonable limits.

In its broadest sense, hydrology is the study of the disposition of all

Confined upstream areas permit ponding at high permissible headwater depths to reduce the required pipe size.

Low fill heights minimize the permissible headwater depth and pipe size, requiring a dual installation as in this case.

the precipitation which falls on the land. However, in culvert design, it is only necessary to consider hydrology to the extent of predicting the maximum flow rate at which water can be expected to run off past the proposed location of the culvert. This will require a prediction of the storm that is capable of producing the design discharge. The complete analysis is one involving the interdependence of rainfall characteristics and runoff characteristics for a particular watershed in producing flood flows.

The Hydrologic Cycle

In applying the principles of any science, it is necessary to obtain a fundamental understanding of the interrelationships of the contributing factors. The principles of hydrology can best be illustrated by a description of the hydrologic cycle in which the water falling on the land as rain is retained in either temporary or permanent storage, or disposed of as runoff or atmospheric moisture.

The rain distributed over an area is likely to fall on many different surfaces. As shown in Fig. 10, some of the rain falling on forests will be intercepted by the leaves of trees and shrubs. That which reaches the forest floor will fall on a spongy mat of leaves, plants, and rotting twigs. This type of surface is highly absorbent and will retain a large amount of water which infiltrates into the mat and then into the soil below. Other surfaces exhibit more or less of this same absorbing capacity, ranging from the highly absorbent forest floor, to the less absorbent cultivated agricultural land, to impermeable paved surfaces such as streets. Excess water which is not absorbed or otherwise used in wetting leaves, grasses, and other plants must be either retained in surface depression storage or run off to streams and rivers.

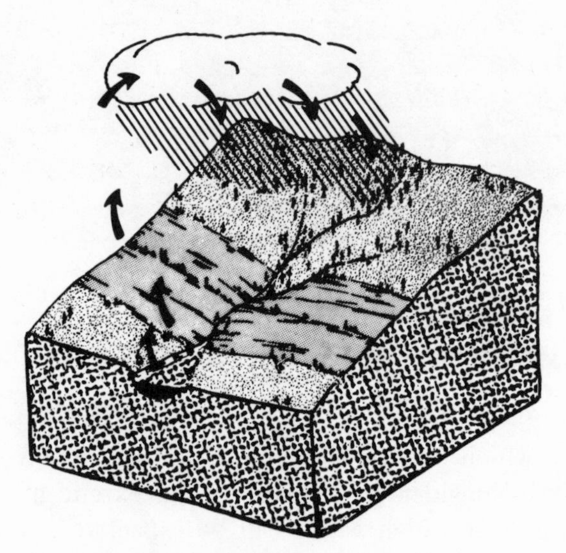

Fig. 10. The hydrologic cycle.

A form of temporary storage must exist on the surface of the land in order to create the flow which is observed as runoff. A large amount of surface storage will exist in flat lands, while there will be less surface storage where water runs off steep slopes. Surface roughness is another factor that tends to increase surface storage by imposing high resistance to flow and thus slowing the rate of runoff. Water which is retained on the surface is subject to capture by infiltration into the soil. However, the soil can only absorb water at a limited rate which varies with the type of soil and the amount of moisture present. Runoff will occur when the rainfall intensity exceeds the soil's infiltration rate and after all of the depression storage requirements have been satisfied.

The hydrologic cycle continues after the rain. This is the period in which water in depression storage is ultimately either absorbed into the soil or evaporated into the atmosphere. A large amount of the water captured by infiltration moves from the area by groundwater flow or by transpiration. In groundwater movement, the water is slowly released to stream flow or continues to percolate to recharge deep water-bearing rock strata. Transpiration is the release of water to the atmosphere by trees and plants as a result of growth.

Stream Flow

The flow in a stream consists of that portion of precipitation that reaches the stream either by runoff from the surface of the soil or by flowing through the soil as groundwater. The resultant stream flow is total runoff and the rate of such flow is referred to as rate of runoff. The hydrograph illustrated in Fig. 11 is a representation of the runoff process in chronological order. Discharge in cubic feet per second (cfs) is the ordinate, and time (in minutes, hours, days, or months) is the abscissa.

In examining a hydrograph of stream flow hour by hour, it is found that the rate of runoff is seldom, if ever, constant. It may rise rapidly to a peak as a result of some storm and fall more slowly in the interval between

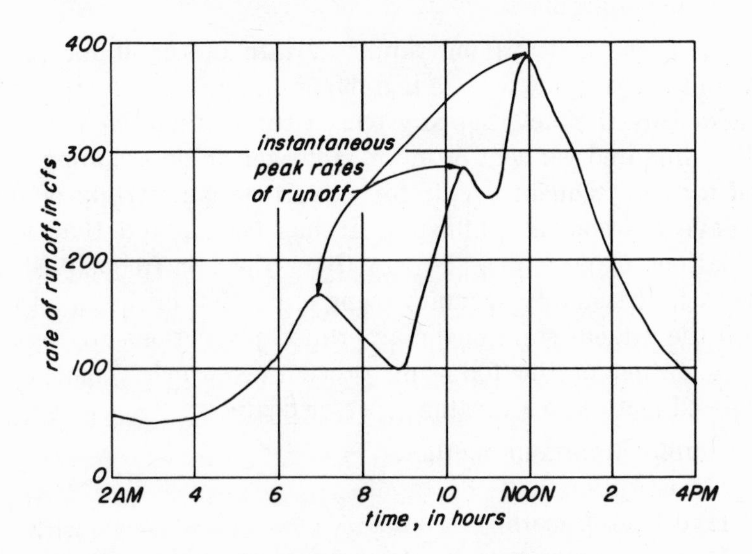

Fig. 11. Typical hydrograph of stream flow.

storms. Not only does the rate of runoff vary with time, but the magnitude of instantaneous peak rates of runoff varies from one storm to another. If the hydrograph in the illustration could be extended to cover several years of stream flow history, it would be apparent that the pattern of stream rises varies with time, not only in magnitude of the peak rates, but also as to the sequence and time of year of their occurrence.

The fluctuations of the hydrograph are explained by the factors that affect the runoff process. These factors can be separated into two categories: climatic and topographic. The climatic factors are:

1. Type of precipitation—intense storms or continuous rain
2. Rainfall intensity
3. Duration of rainfall
4. Distribution of rainfall on drainage basin
5. Direction of storm movement
6. Antecedent precipitation and soil moisture
7. Climatic conditions that affect evaporation and transpiration

The topographic factors that influence the runoff are:

1. Land use
2. Type of soil
3. Area
4. Shape
5. Elevation
6. Slope
7. Orientation
8. Type of drainage net
9. Extent of indirect drainage
10. Artificial drainage

An equation to determine runoff or rate of runoff for the various climatic and topographic factors is difficult to derive. A further complication is added by the fact that any one of the factors listed can influence runoff by a hundred per cent or more. However, in determining peak rates of runoff for less frequent events for culvert design, certain of the above factors have a secondary influence. It has been found that reasonable approximations of peak rates of runoff for the less frequent storms can be made with satisfactory accuracy using only a few of the listed variables.

With the present state of the art, runoff predictions are made by one or a combination of the following procedures which consider the previously listed factors to a greater or lesser degree:

1. Empirical formula method
2. Statistical method
3. Hydrograph method
4. Rational method

Empirical Formulas

Empirical formulas have been used extensively in computing the rate of runoff. Most formulas of this type were derived near the end of the 19th Century or early in the 20th Century. Since limited records were available to substantiate this work, these formulas cannot be expected to account adequately for the frequency factor. And in many cases these formulas were derived only for specific areas. However, these limitations have been generally ignored and the formulas have been used for locations and under conditions for which they were not applicable. Most formulas of this type do not specifically consider rainfall, which is an important variable and must otherwise be inconspicuously included in the formula. The variability of rainfall is either ignored or is included in a coefficient to be selected.

Most empirical formulas are based on the area of the drainage basin and a coefficient to be selected on the basis of topographic features. These formulas are of two types. The first type is a waterway formula for the direct determination of the area of cross-section of the culvert. This is of the form

$$a = CA^n$$

in which a is the waterway area of the culvert cross-section, A is the area of the drainage basin, C is a coefficient depending on units and basin characteristics, and n is an empirically determined exponent.

Talbot's formula is an example of a waterway area formula in which a specific value is assigned to n, leaving C to be selected. A formula of this type presupposes the hydraulic design and limits the flexibility in design afforded by modern hydraulic research.

The second type of empirical formula commonly used is of the form

$$Q = C\sqrt{A}$$

in which Q is the runoff in cubic feet per second, A is the area of the drainage basin, and C is a coefficient selected to give peak discharge based on observed peak discharges in the particular locality. An example of this is Myer's formula in which A is expressed in square miles and C is equal to 100 p. p is the ratio of Q to the ultimate maximum flow Q_u for all streams. This formula is written as

$$Q_u = p10{,}000\sqrt{A}.$$

Other empirical formulas of slightly different forms have been proposed to account specifically for various rainfall and watershed factors which affect runoff. Among formulas of this type is the McMath formula developed for the St. Louis area. This formula is for the purpose of accounting for rainfall intensity and slope of the watersheds as well as the area of the drainage basin. It is written in the form

$$Q = CiA^aS^b.$$

Another well-known formula of the same form proposed to account for the factors affecting runoff is the Burkli-Ziegler formula. This formula is different only in the evaluation of C, a, and b.

An empirical formula developed to consider the frequency of flooding is the Fuller formula. This formula is meant to be applicable to the entire United States and expresses the expected runoff for any chosen frequency period. The Fuller formula is

$$Q = CA^{0.8}(1 + 0.8 \log T)(1 + 2A^{-0.3})$$

in which Q and A are runoff and drainage area, respectively. T is the number of years in the flood return period, and C is a varying factor depending upon the locality.

Statistical Method

The statistical approach predicts the future stream runoff based on its past performance. This procedure possesses fundamental merit provided that sufficient records are available and that the stream has not changed regime of flow sufficiently during or subsequent to the period of record. This approach, often referred to as frequency analysis, requires data over a sufficiently long period (period of record) to assure the establishment of a statistical trend. The reliability of an estimate of flow is related to a large extent to the length of time for which the data are available. There are several methods available for analyzing the stream flow data.

The frequency approach provides the designer with a guide in determining the size of structure where it is permissible to take a calculated risk, and a means of estimating probable damage during the life of the structure. The usual procedure followed in deriving a frequency relationship for the annual flood peaks consists of three principal steps.

The magnitudes of the annual floods are first tabulated in order, starting with the largest and assigning a position number starting with one. The average time interval between flood peaks of equal magnitude is designated as the recurrence interval or frequency period T and is computed by a formula. One formula that is commonly used is

$$T = \frac{N + 1}{M}$$

where T is the recurrence interval, N is the length of continuous record, and M is the order of magnitude of the annual flood peak. The final step involves plotting the recurrence interval against the flood peak on probability or logarithmic paper. A plot of recurrence interval *versus* flood peak

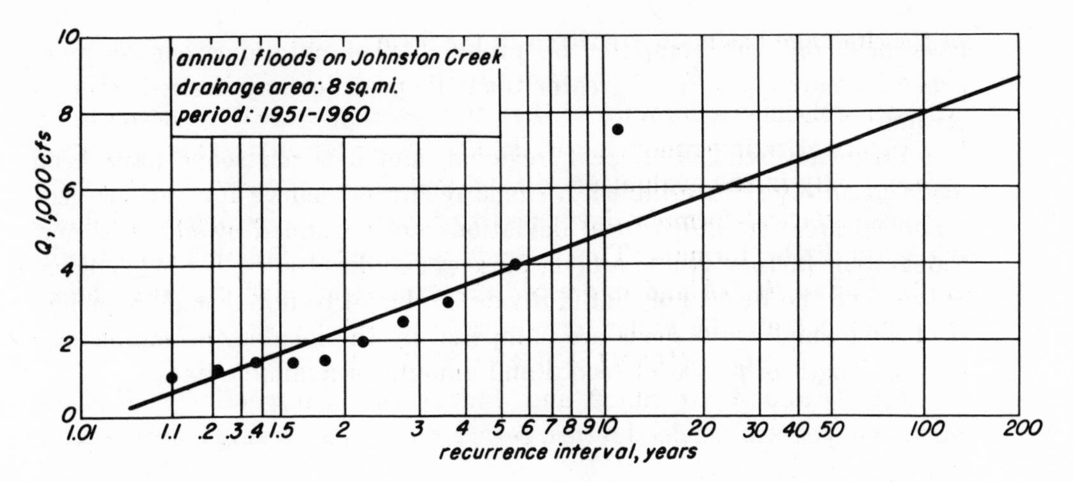

Fig. 12. Frequency curve plot for Johnston Creek.

makes possible an estimate by extrapolation of larger size storms with longer recurrence intervals. An example of this procedure is illustrated in Table 2 and plotted in Fig. 12. This technique enables the designer to establish a sufficiently large recurrence interval to minimize the risk of damage. By knowing the average recurrence interval for any particular

TABLE 2. Example Computation for Plotting Flood Frequency

Date of annual peak flow*	Peak discharge	Order no.	Frequency period**
6/11/60	7,500	1	11.0
5/20/52	4,000	2	5.5
6/3/55	3,000	3	3.67
6/20/58	2,500	4	2.75
5/25/56	2,000	5	2.20
6/15/57	1,500	6	1.83
6/2/59	1,450	7	1.57
6/2/59	1,400	8	1.37
5/28/53	1,200	9	1.22
5/10/51	1,100	10	1.10
N = 10 years—period of record			

*Flood data may be obtained from U.S. Geological Survey, Water Supply Papers.

$$**T = \frac{N+1}{M} = \frac{(10+1)}{1} = 11.0$$

peak flow, one can compute the probability of obtaining one or more peaks that are equal to or greater than the peak for any desired interval of time.

Frequency studies of local, regional, and national scope have been made in an effort to establish a single recurrence curve for various geographical areas in which local deviations are explained by climatic and topographic factors. Noted among these are studies by the U.S. Geological Survey and the Bureau of Public Roads. It should be noted that frequency studies on small watersheds are hampered by the insufficient sample size both in length of period of record and amount of available data.

Hydrograph Method

The hydrograph method is one of the most satisfactory techniques developed for flow determinations. This procedure is usually preferred by engineers planning water resource facilities in large watersheds. In its most elementary forms the hydrograph graphically describes the runoff characteristics of the watershed. The basic hydrograph may be applied to rainfalls of varying intensities and durations to develop composite hydrographs showing peak discharges and changes in the discharge. A hydrograph is applicable to the particular watershed for which it is developed. Its reliability is predicated upon accurate rainfall and runoff observations for the area for which it is established. It is well suited for runoff studies for watersheds of all sizes, and is particularly well suited for projects involving water supply, water power, irrigation, and flood control.

The hydrograph is an accounting system relating rainfall rates to runoff rates. In order to establish this relationship, information is collected on rainfall, infiltration, surface storage, basin size, length of main channels, and time for stream flow to reach maximum after rainfall begins.

The data required for the development of a hydrograph are seldom available for the small watershed that can be drained with culverts. However, hydrograph analysis has revealed certain fundamental relationships that can be applied to the analysis of runoff characteristics of small watersheds. In determining required culvert capacities it is not necessary to obtain the detailed runoff information provided by the hydrograph. Peak discharge is a major consideration for culvert design and may be estimated by the simplified rational approach employing some of the relationships established by the hydrograph, such as time of peak flow after the start of rainfall, infiltration rates, surface storage, rainfall factors, and other basic data.

Rational Method

The rational method is one of the most used techniques for estimating peak runoff. Although it uses an empirical equation, certain modifications based on scientific knowledge provide a direct and feasible method of predicting flood peaks for culvert design. It is now possible to evaluate some of the major factors affecting runoff, with subsequent application of the factors to the rational equation. This method is particularly applicable to watersheds of the size drained by culverts, and is the method generally applicable to the requirements of present-day culvert design.

Several methods have been developed to investigate the hydrology of watersheds. As yet, no one method appears to be clearly superior to all others. The rational method, however, possesses serious shortcomings which limit its usefulness. Wherever data or techniques are available that are superior to the rational approach, their use is preferred. Where neither data nor other reliable hydrological methods are available, the rational method has been found to be the most applicable. The remainder of this chapter discusses the rational method in detail in a manner that permits the designer to account for the hydrological variables that are important in culvert design.

Applications of the Rational Method

The rational formula is fundamentally a ratio in which the total quantity of water falling at a uniform rate on an area is related by simple proportion to the total quantity that appears as runoff. This can be expressed in instantaneous form as

$$Q = CiA$$

where Q is runoff in cubic feet per second, i is rainfall intensity in inches per hour, A is the area of the drainage basin in acres, and C is the ratio expressing the proportional amount of the rainfall that appears as runoff. Each of these factors is a variable that must be evaluated. The formula makes use of the fact that one acre-inch per hour of rainfall equals 1.008 cfs runoff. This formula is only applicable where the rainfall intensity can be assumed to be uniformly distributed over the area at a uniform rate throughout the duration of the storm. This assumption applies fairly well to areas of less than 200 sq.mi.

The design rainfall intensity is determined in one of the first steps in applying the rational formula. The selection is based on climatology, time of concentration of flow at the culvert location, and the size of the area. The value of the coefficient C must be based on several factors that are not entirely characteristic of the area. Since C is a proportionality factor, it must be based upon the rainfall intensity and the retention characteristics of the basin. Basin retention is a function of the infiltration rate, depressive storage, and surface detention.

The area of the basin is easily obtained by delineating the watershed on a topographic map and measuring the area with a planimeter. If maps of the area are not available, it will be necessary to establish the area by other means, such as a survey, aerophotographs, or a good estimate. The factors affecting C and i are discussed in more detail in the following sections.

Precipitation

Precipitation is the most variable factor affecting runoff. It varies from year to year and from season to season. Precipitation is nonuniform, varying in intensity with time and from point to point during the same storm. The highly variable nature of precipitation would preclude the possibility of practical hydrologic analysis if it were not for the accumulation and analysis of data of many years of rainfall measurements.

Certain useful generalizations have been discovered:

1. The most intense rainfalls occur less frequently.
2. The most intense rains occur over small areas; rainfall distributed over large areas is much less intense.
3. Rainfall of high intensity is of short duration.

As a result of statistical analysis, certain relationships between rainfall frequency, duration, and intensity have been established. Depending upon the purpose of the hydrologic analysis, it is possible to establish the rainfall that will occur at various average frequencies. As an example, the mean annual rainfall is a prediction of total accumulation in a year's time without regard to the manner in which it is distributed. By the same token, the maximum five-year storm is the storm with a rainfall intensity that will be equaled or exceeded on the average of one time in five years without regard to the number of these storms that may occur in any one period.

Rainfall intensity may be considered a function of three major factors directly related to the runoff characteristics of a particular watershed. One of these, climatology, is also related to the frequency with which particular intensities can be expected to be exceeded. Once the design period has been selected, the rainfall intensity for the particular drainage basin which will produce the maximum runoff for design purposes can be established.

Rainfall intensity has been found to be a function of the climatology of the geographical area, the duration of the storm, and the storm area.

Climatology. Rainfall is distributed throughout the country in greatly varying proportions, depending upon the movement and interaction of air masses. Rain in the Midwest is generally produced as a result of the interaction of warm, moisture-laden air from the Gulf of Mexico moving north and cold, dry air moving southeast from the Pacific Northwest. Air masses follow the same general course time after time, with the same general results. The climatology of various regions is thus established, with local features such as mountains or lakes causing deviations in the general pattern. From time to time exceptional conditions occur which produce exceptional rainfall intensities. These conditions are usually restricted to relatively small areas within the general region, and are equally likely over relatively large areas.

As the result of a statistical analysis of a large number of rainfall records, it has been found that exceptional rainfall intensities do not necessarily occur with a regular frequency. They are, however, more or less predictable in that certain intensities are exceeded with an average

Fig. 13. One-hour rainfall intensities (map series).

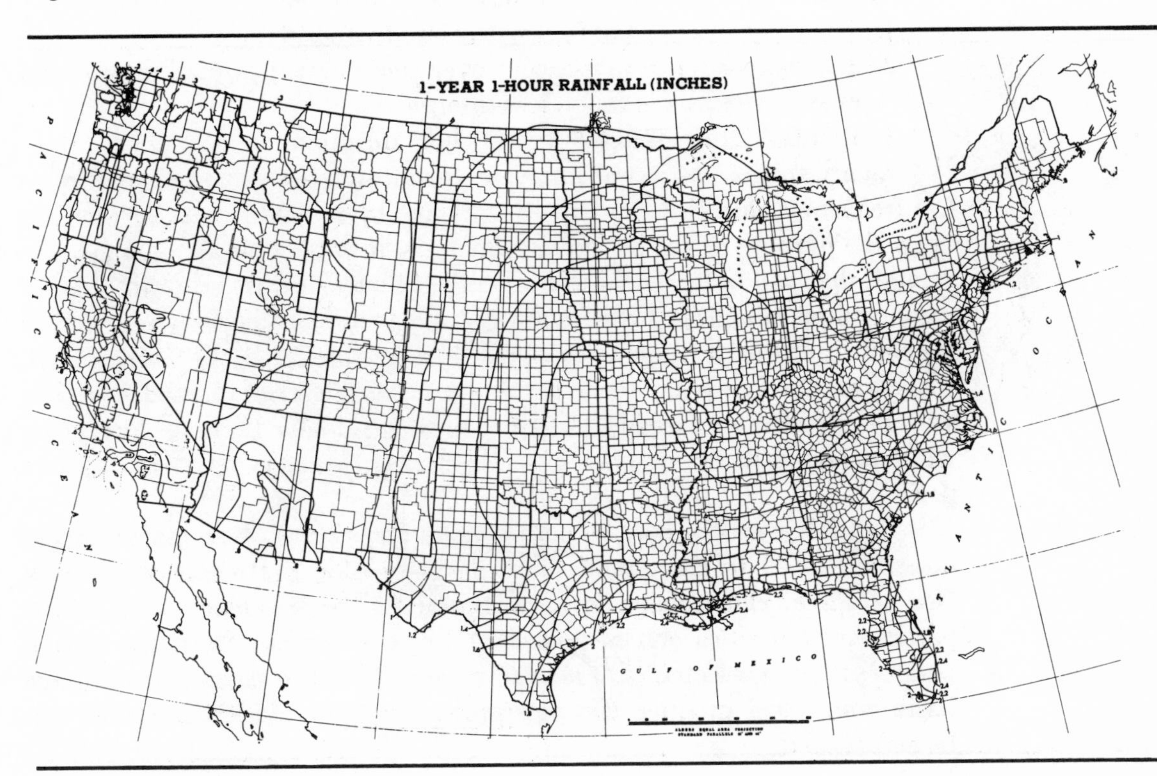

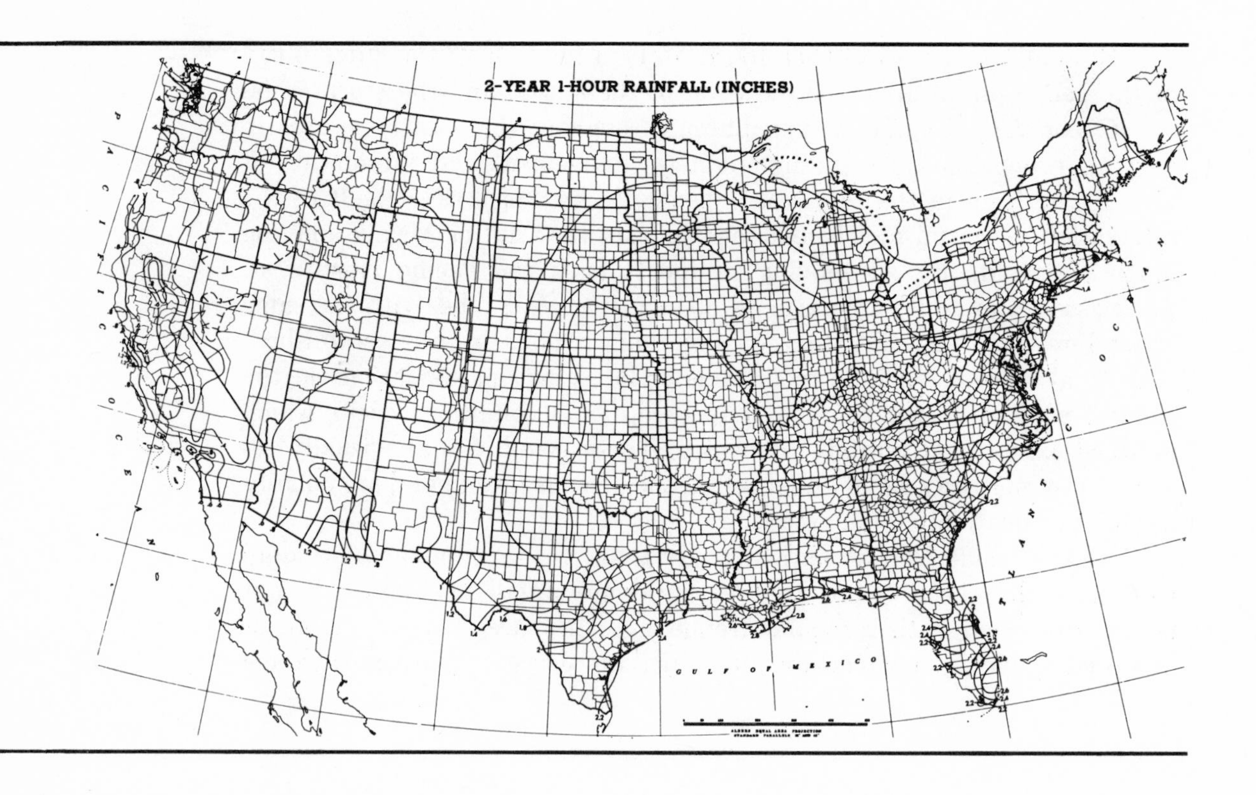
2-YEAR 1-HOUR RAINFALL (INCHES)
GULF OF MEXICO

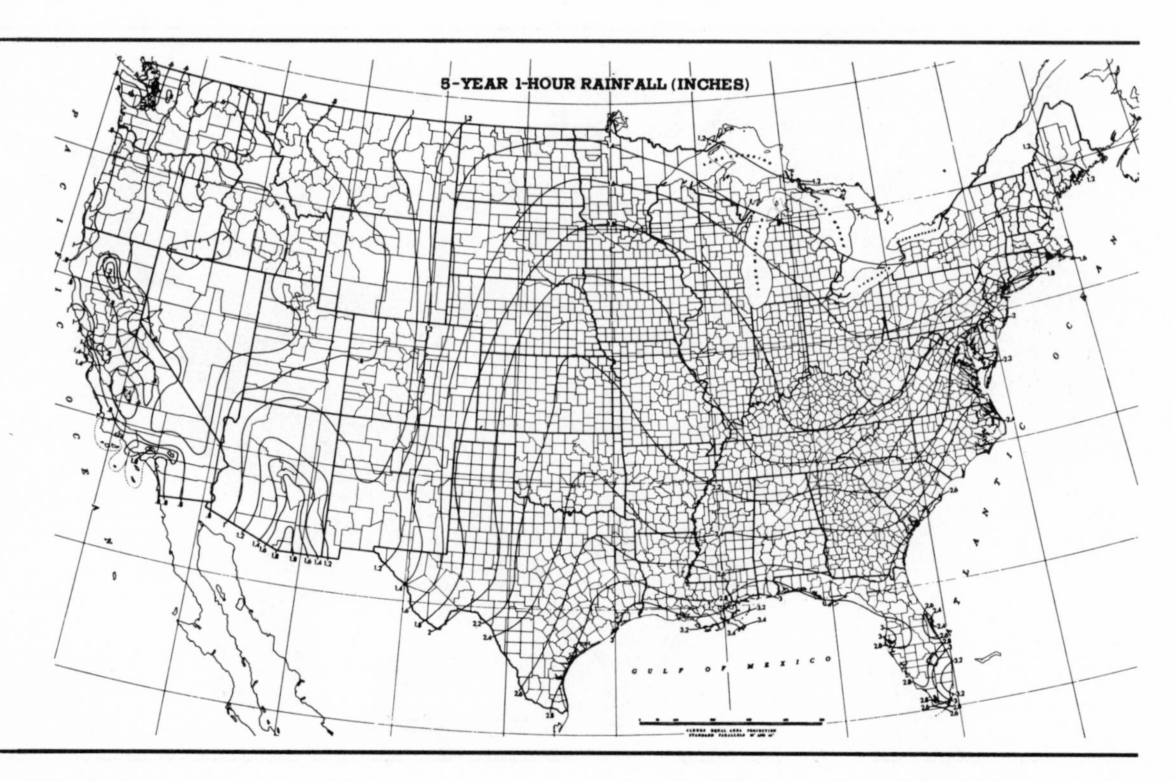
5-YEAR 1-HOUR RAINFALL (INCHES)
GULF OF MEXICO

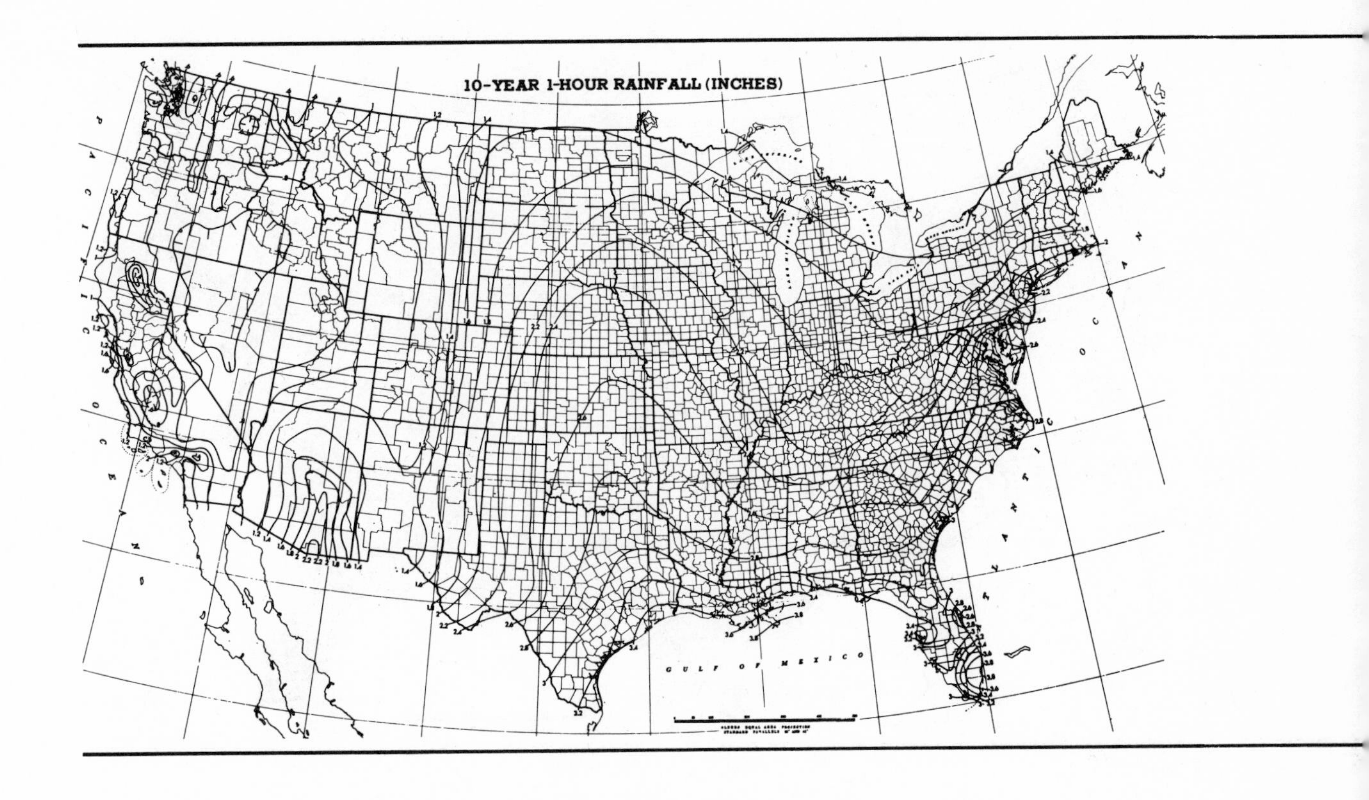
10-YEAR 1-HOUR RAINFALL (INCHES)
GULF OF MEXICO

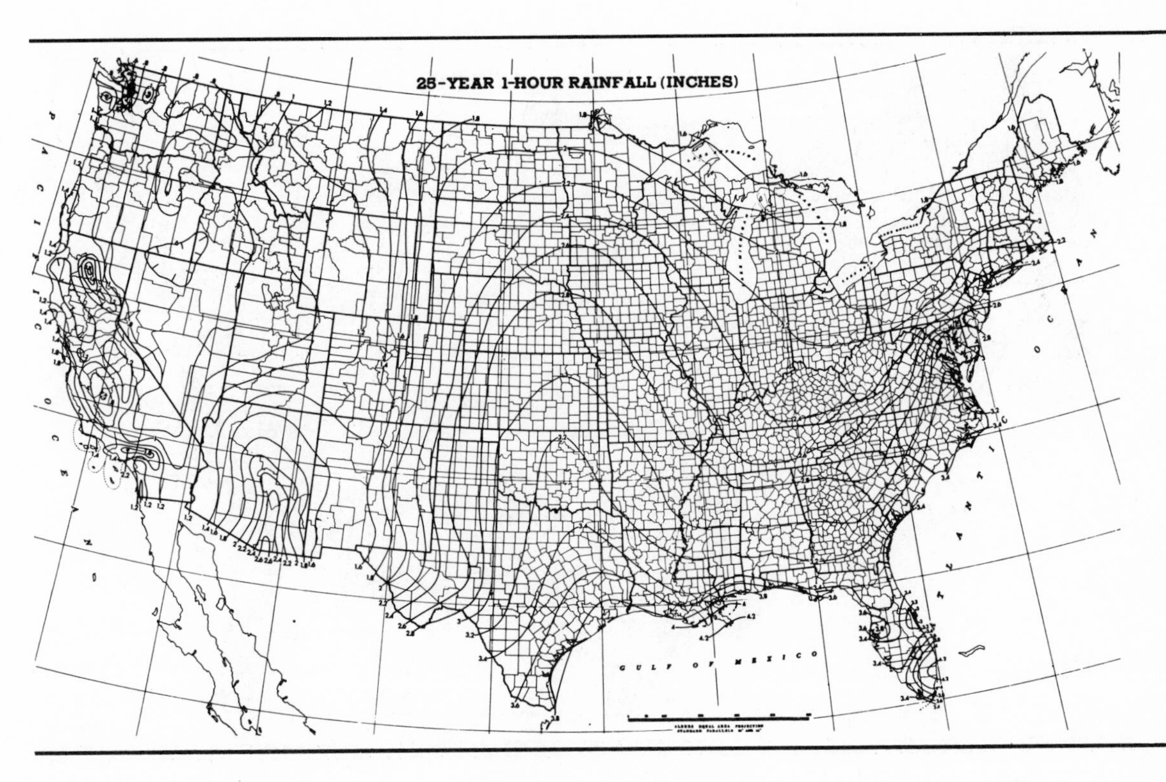
25-YEAR 1-HOUR RAINFALL (INCHES)
GULF OF MEXICO

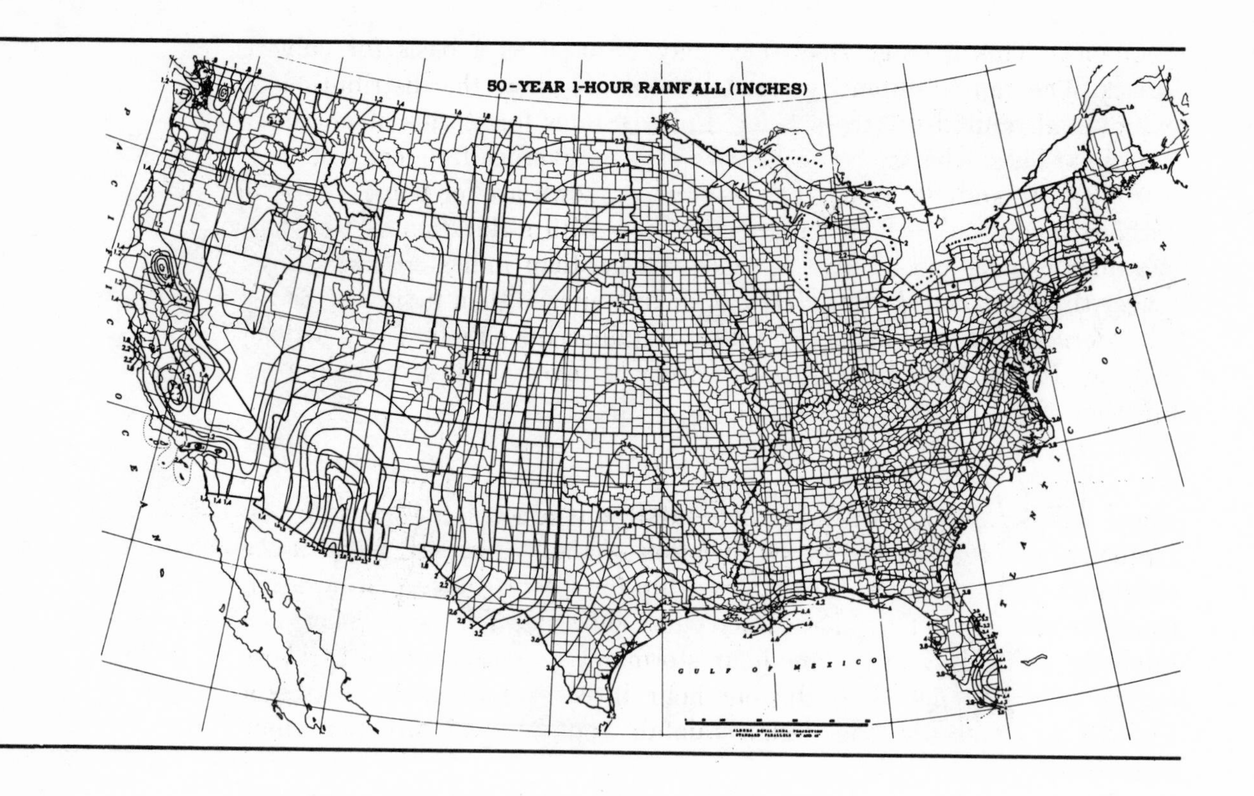
50-YEAR 1-HOUR RAINFALL (INCHES)
GULF OF MEXICO

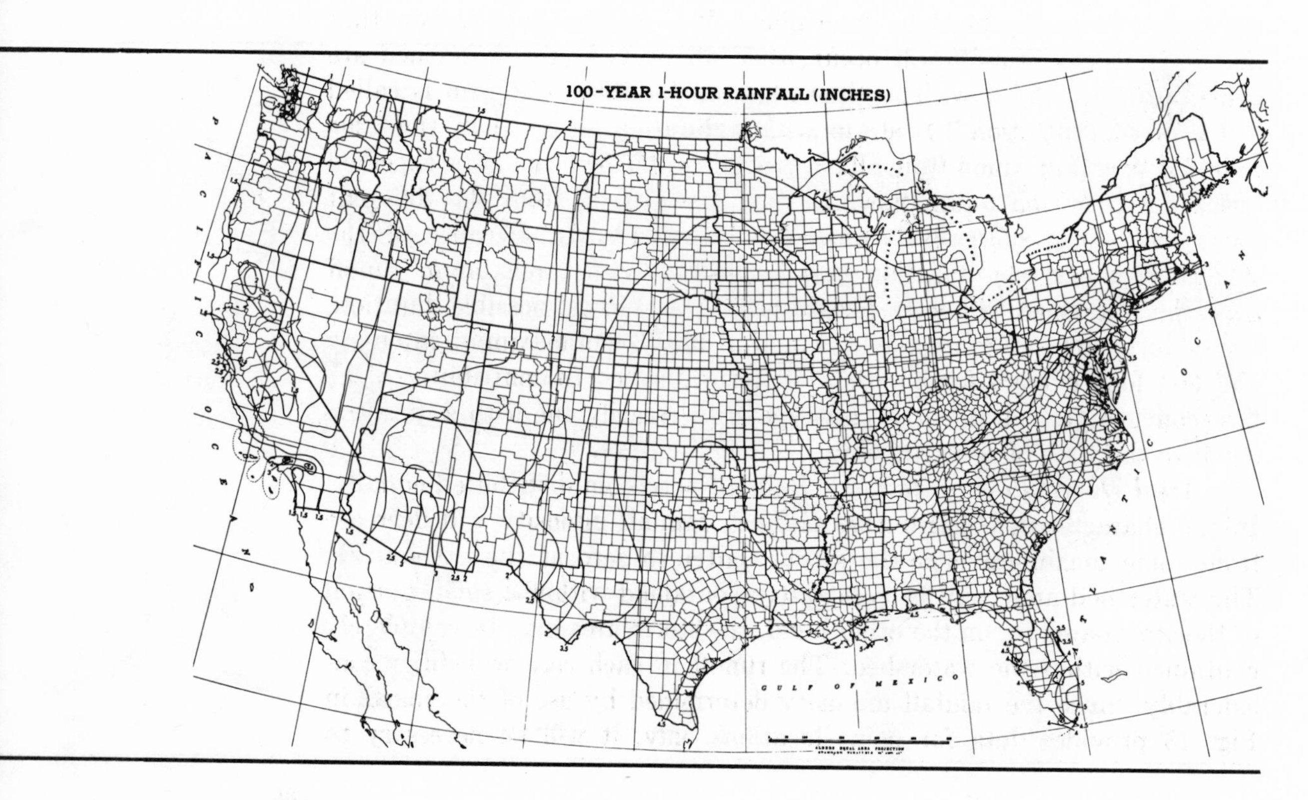
100-YEAR 1-HOUR RAINFALL (INCHES)
GULF OF MEXICO

frequency. This average frequency may be used as a basis for culvert design. The rainfall-intensity charts of Fig. 13 show the distribution of exceptional rainfall throughout the United States for storms of one-hour duration. These charts are for storms with an average frequency of 1, 2, 5, 10, 25, 50, and 100 years. The intensities shown are for point locations without regard to areal distribution. Storms with a duration of less than one hour can be expected to be more intense than indicated and storms longer than one hour in duration will be less intense than indicated.

Storm Duration. The most intense rainfall occurs only for short periods of time. It has been found that intensity is inversely proportional to a function of the duration in which

$$i = \frac{c}{(d + t)^n}$$

where i is the average intensity of rainfall, c is a constant depending on frequency of occurrence, t is the duration of the storm, and d and n are constants. Fig. 14a shows this relationship for storms varying in duration from five minutes to four hours. Each curve shows the relationship between intensity and duration for one-hour storms of various intensities. These curves may be applied to the one-hour intensities from the charts of Fig. 13 to determine the design rainfall applicable to any particular watershed.

To assure adequate design, the maximum runoff that may occur with the design frequency must be determined. It is reasonable to assume that maximum (peak) runoff will occur when all parts of the watershed are contributing to the flow. The time required for this to happen is called "time of concentration." A storm with a duration of less than the time required to collect runoff from all parts of the watershed cannot be expected to produce the maximum flow. In this case, runoff from the different parts will occur successively instead of concurrently. Because of the relationship between duration and rainfall intensity, maximum runoff from the watershed will occur for storms of the shortest possible duration. For a storm to produce maximum runoff, it must be of maximum intensity and last long enough for all parts of the watershed to contribute to the flow concurrently. A storm of this type is necessarily one with a duration equal to the time of concentration.

Areal Distribution of Rainfall. Rainfall is seldom distributed equally. In the characteristic distribution pattern, rainfall intensity will decrease from some maximum near the storm center to zero at the extremities. The watershed area may be completely contained within a small portion of the storm area or, on the other hand, the storm area may be completely contained within the watershed. The runoff in each case will differ considerably. Since the rainfall intensity determined by use of the charts in Fig. 13 provides data for point locations only, it will be necessary to

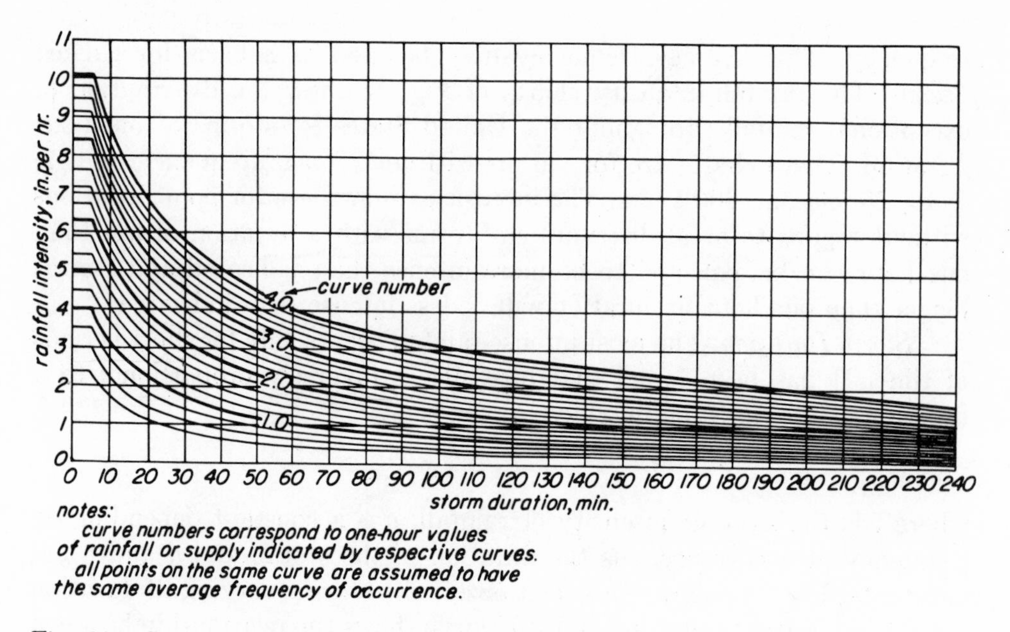

Fig. 14a. Standard duration—rainfall intensity curves.

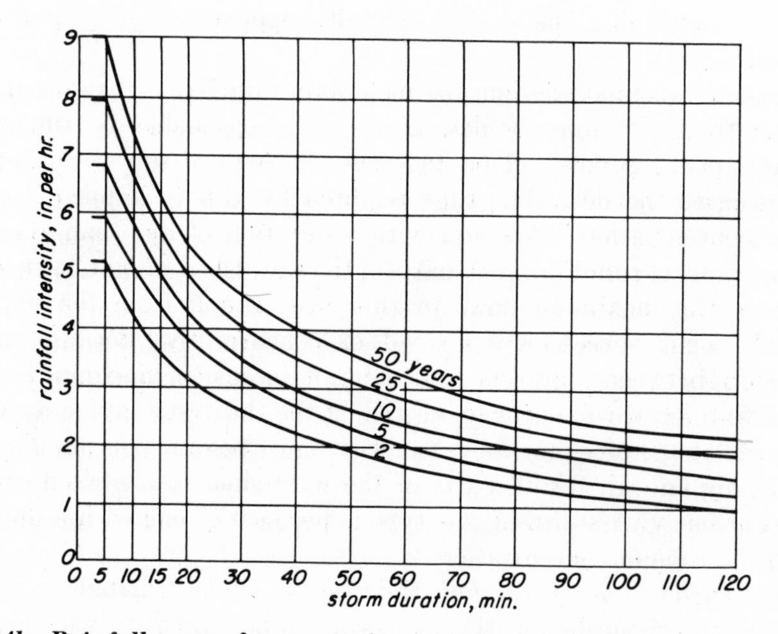

Fig. 14b. Rainfall curves for storms in vicinity of example site.

make an adjustment in the design data to account for the areal distribution of the rainfall.

The rational formula is an idealized equation for computing runoff

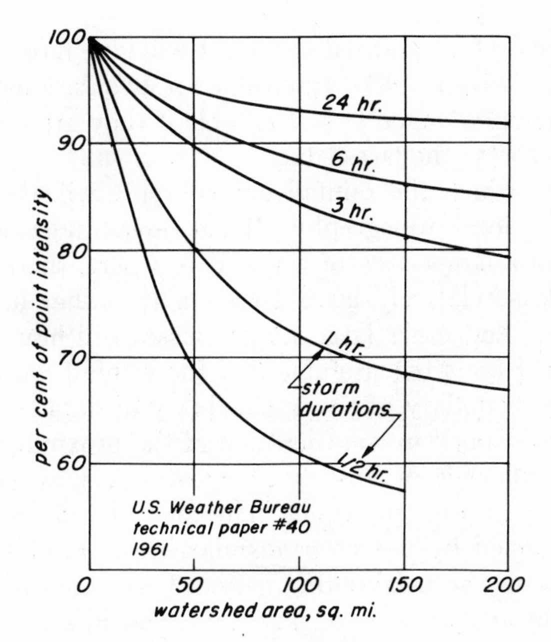

Fig. 15. Variation of rainfall intensity with area.

for storms of nonvarying intensity which are uniformly distributed over the watershed area. Average intensity for a point location may be determined by use of Figs. 13 and 14. The curve of Fig. 15 provides an adjustment of rainfall intensities at point locations to an average intensity uniformly distributed over the watershed. This curve is based on typical storm patterns where climatic conditions prevail. It cannot be used in areas subject to orographic influences.

For watersheds with an area of less than 1 sq.mi., point rainfall intensities data may be used for the entire area. For areas greater than 1 sq.mi. and smaller than 200 sq.mi., the point rainfall intensity should be adjusted for areal distribution. Fig. 15 may be used to provide a reasonable approximation of rainfall intensity uniformly distributed over the watershed area. An adjusted intensity is obtained by applying the "per cent of point intensity," corresponding to the area of the watershed, to the intensity of the design storm.

Local Precipitation

The most reliable curves for expected precipitation are those that are based upon local data. While this approach will require considerably more effort than the use of generalized curves, it will give more realistic results. The curves thus derived will be applicable for all subsequent requirements and will become more valuable and reliable if they are revised from time to time to incorporate the latest data.

The area to which the rainfall curves apply will depend to a great extent upon the local topography. If the area under consideration is representative of a larger area of which it is a part, the rainfall data will be applicable to a relatively large area. On the other hand, mountains, the Great Lakes, and other large water masses will have a decided local influence and will limit the usefulness of the rainfall data to local areas.

The general boundary of the applicability of data from any one rain gage can best be defined in consideration of the proximity of other gages. The extent of influence of any rain gage station may be taken as one-half the distance to adjacent gages. The area of influence is defined as the enclosure formed by the perpendicular bisectors of the lines joining the central gage to the neighboring gages. There are other equally good methods used in analyzing rain gage data, and in all cases local topography must be considered in determining the area of influence of any one gage.

The rainfall-duration-frequency curves pertaining to a specific area will be of the form shown in Fig. 14b. Individual curves will be different for each locality. However, it has been found that all rainfall intensity data follow the same general relationship expressed by

$$i = \frac{CT^x}{(t + d)^n}$$

The factors i, t, and T are, respectively, rainfall intensity in inches per hour, storm duration in minutes, and recurrence interval in years. The factors C, x, d and n are constants determined from the local rainfall data. The final results may be expressed by a family of curves as shown in Fig. 14b in which intensity and duration are plotted for each frequency period.

The data for establishing local rainfall curves may be available from locally monitored rainfall gages. In order for this data to be of the greatest use, the period of record should be several times longer than the desired frequency period. If such records are not available or do not extend over a sufficiently long period, other data from nearby rainfall gages can be used and may be obtained from rainfall gages operated by the U.S. Weather Bureau.

For hydrological information in Canada, inquiries may be addressed to Department of Transport, Meteorological Branch, Toronto, Ont.

The following types of information may be obtained from any field office of the U.S. Department of Commerce, or from U.S. Department of Commerce, Special Business Service Desk, Washington 25, D.C.:

1. Climatological data (U.S.)

2. Climatological data (national summary)
3. Climatological data (local), specify section desired
4. Hourly precipitation data, specify section desired
5. Rainfall frequency atlas (U.S.)

Generalized rainfall curves are established from a summary of the rainfall data. However, it is not necessary to consider storms with an intensity less than that indicated by the following empirical formulas:

$$i = 0.6 + \frac{12}{t} \text{ for northern U.S.}$$

$$i = 1.2 + \frac{18}{t} \text{ for southern U.S.}$$

where i = intensity, in. per hr.
t = duration, min.

The summary may be prepared according to any of several forms. Two suggested procedures are given here:

1. One of the simplest summaries is a tabulation of excessive storms with a given duration. In this summary, the storms are listed in descending order of magnitude for total depth of rainfall for the entire period of record, with the exception of the lesser storms. A tabulation is made for various storm durations according to the design requirements. An order of magnitude is assigned to each storm, beginning with 1 for the greatest total rainfall, 2 for the next, etc. The frequency of each is computed from the formula

$$T = \frac{N + 1}{M}$$

where T = frequency period in years
N = total number of years of record
M = order of magnitude

Hence, a storm in 39 years of record with an order of magnitude of 4 will have a frequency period of 10 years; that is, a storm equal in intensity to the fourth greatest storm of record will be equaled or exceeded on the average of once in 10 years. This data may then be used to plot intensity-duration-frequency curves summarizing the complete experience record. This is the method illustrated by Table 2 and Fig. 12.

2. Another procedure in establishing the summarized data is to prepare a table listing the number of storms that equal or exceed certain definite limits of intensity and duration. It is suggested that durations be listed vertically in ascending order, and intensities be listed horizontally in ascending order. Table 3 is an example of such a tabulation.

Intensity-duration-frequency curves may be established from a tabulation of this type by determining the number of storms in the period of record that corresponds to a particular frequency period. Curves that are slightly conservative will result by computing the number of storms from

$$M = \frac{N}{T}$$

where M = number of storms in period of record corresponding to frequency period
N = number of years of record
T = frequency period in years

TABLE 3. Example Tabulation of Number of Storms Exceeding Given Intensity-Duration for 40-Year Period

Duration, min.	Intensity, in. per hr.						
	0.25	0.50	0.75	1.0	1.25	1.5	1.75
5				45	29	17	10
10			54	34	22	12	7
15		66	44	27	17	9	5
20	68	41	26	16	9	4	2
30	39	24	14	8	4	2	1

Note: Interpolate for 20 storms corresponding to 2-year frequency along diagonal line to establish values in Table 4.

Intensities and durations corresponding to each frequency period are interpolated from the tabulation on the basis of M, the number of storms associated with each frequency period.

An illustration of this technique may be made by considering an example. Suppose that it is desired to construct the intensity-duration curve for a frequency period of two years. With the data in Table 3 representing a period of record of 40 years, the number of storms representing a two-year frequency is computed to be

$$M = \frac{N}{T} = \frac{40}{2} = 20.$$

Intensities and durations are interpolated from Table 3 and tabulated in Table 4. The data in Table 4 should then be plotted on either rectilinear or log-log graph paper and a smooth curve best representing the data drawn through it.

The final curves are made by fitting the intensity-duration data from either type of tabulation to a straight line on log-log graph paper. This is done by plotting log i vs. log $(t + d)$, since the general expression for intensity-duration $i = CT^x/(t + d)^n$ reduces to $\log i = \log A - n \log (t + d)$. The factor A is equal to CT^x and will be constant for any given frequency period. It will be necessary to determine the factor d by trial and error since this is an unknown constant. The proper value of d will be established when the plot of $\log i$ vs. $\log (t + d)$ is a straight line and when similar plots for all frequency periods are parallel. The factor d is a constant which applies to all data for all frequency periods and may vary from 0 to 30 for North America. The slope of the straight line determines the value of n, which has been found to vary from 0.4 to 1.0 for North America.

If desired, values of C and x may also be determined by establishing the family of curves on the logarithmic plot. The value of A for each frequency period is determined by the value of i when $(t + d)$ is equal to 1, the intercept. The plot of the A values vs. T will also be a straight line on a logarithmic plot, $\log A = \log C + x \log T$. The slope of the resulting straight line will determine the value of x and the intercept of the line will establish the value of C. (On the logarithmic plot, C will equal A when T is equal to 1.) For North America C has been found to vary from 5 to 50 and x from 0.1 to 0.5.

The foregoing operation has a smoothing effect which accounts for sporadic data and unusual storms, resulting in a family of curves that express the average conditions. The logarithmic plot may be converted to the usual arithmetic form in which i is plotted against t for each frequency period. These curves will be similar to those in Fig. 14b. The same information may also be expressed in the generalized equation $i = CT^x/(t + d)^n$ in which the proper values of C, x, d, and n for the particular area have been substituted.

The intensity-duration-frequency curves derived for a particular

TABLE 4. Example Tabulation of Intensity and Duration Corresponding to 2-Year Frequency

Horizontal interpolation					
Duration, min.	5	10	15	20	30
Intensity, in. per hr.	1.44	1.30	1.18	0.90	0.60

Vertical interpolation							
Intensity, in. per hr.	0.25	0.50	0.75	1.0	1.25	1.50	1.75
Duration, min.	>30	>30	25	18	12	<5	<5

locality should be used in preference to the generalized information contained in Figs. 13 and 14. As a check, the derived curves should be reasonably close to the generalized curves, which can be used as a guide in the curve-fitting process. The rainfall expectancy curves thus derived are generally applicable within the area represented by the original data and become more reliable as revisions are made on the basis of new data. These curves will also be helpful in establishing similar curves for adjacent areas.

Time of Concentration

The time of concentration is defined as the interval of time required for the flow at a given point to become a maximum. This occurs when all parts of the catchment area are contributing to the flow in the channel. In other words, the time of concentration is the interval of time, from the beginning of the storm, for water from the most remote portion of the watershed to reach the measuring station.

The time of concentration will be different for all watersheds, depending on:

1. Area of the watershed
2. Shape of the area
3. Average slope of the land
4. Length and slope of the main channel
5. Length and slope of the tributary channels
6. Channel roughness
7. Type of ground cover
8. Overland distance runoff must travel before reaching a channel
9. Directional movement of the storm

Obviously, the flood-producing capability of identical storms will vary depending on the watershed. As an example, a steeply sloped, well-builtup residential area will be more subject to flooding than would a prairie farm of equal area. This is due to the shorter time required for water to flow from the most remote point in the residential area. Culverts draining the residential area will, therefore, be more subject to flooding due to intense short storms than would those draining farmland. In the latter case, short storms are likely to pass before water from the most remote point has had an opportunity to concentrate.

The usual procedure in the selection of a design storm is to estimate the time of concentration and then determine the storm intensity consistent with recurrence frequency and with the duration equal to the time of concentration. This estimate is undoubtedly one of the most serious weaknesses in making a hydrologic analysis by any method. An error in judgment has a direct effect on the rainfall intensity. The error in rainfall intensity due to an error in estimating rainfall duration will be proportional to and opposite in sign to the error in duration. It should be noted that this same error is inherent in empirical formulas, in some cases to a great degree, since all formulas of this type must include presumed rainfall relationships.

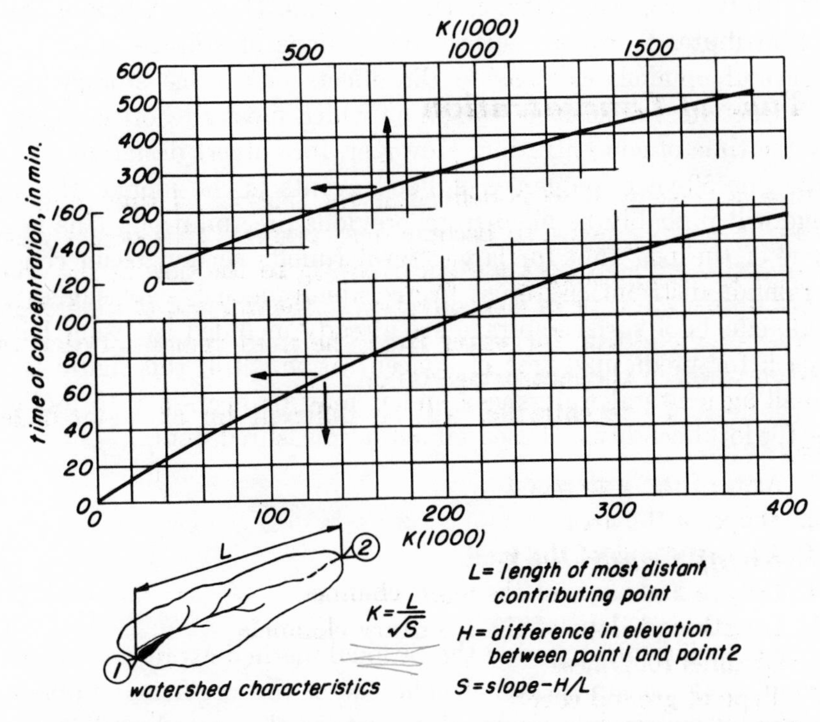

Fig. 16. Time of concentration as a function of watershed length and slope.

Fortunately, error in time of concentration selection for storm durations greater than one hour will not be serious because the rainfall intensity does not change rapidly for long durations. On the other hand, time of concentration for short-duration storms is more critical in that a small change in duration (time of concentration) causes a considerable change in rainfall intensity. Studies of runoff by the use of hydrographs provide information for a better estimate of time of concentration.

Kirpich[9]* developed a relationship between time of concentration, t_c, and watershed characteristics of length and slope. Fig. 16 shows this rela-

*Numbers refer to references at end of chapter.

tionship, in which L is the maximum length of travel and S is the average slope over this length. Actually, the relationship expresses the time from the beginning of rainfall until the peak flow at the point in question is reached. This relationship accounts for time lag caused by surface travel time and surface storage. Furthermore, the basin characteristics of length, slope, and soil cover are included in the determination of this relationship.

As rainfall commences, some of the rain is used to satisfy the infiltration capacity of the soil. As the rainfall intensity becomes greater than the infiltration capacity, surface runoff occurs. However, before the total area contributes to runoff, surface depressions or storage must be filled.

Several opinions exist as to the effects of surface storage on peak runoff. One effect of surface storage on which most authorities agree is to delay the time of concentration. However, for culvert design in which the 10-, 25-, or 50-year frequency of flood events is considered, the surface storage will probably be filled from previous precipitation. This is stated in view of the fact that for large storm runoffs certain basin conditions and rainfall distributions must occur simultaneously. As suggested by Fig. 16, effects of surface storage are already included by using Kirpich's approach for predicting time of concentration. Still, this figure is based on small agricultural watersheds and it may be necessary to modify the curve for local conditions based on actual measured data.

Runoff Coefficient

The runoff coefficient as used in the rational method expresses the per cent of rainfall that appears as runoff. The use of the coefficient implies that conditions of equilibrium eventually exist. In the preceding discussions it was pointed out that runoff occurs when rainfall is in excess of the natural storage capabilities of the watershed. The coefficient C combines the effects of infiltration and surface storage of the watershed.

In the rational formula $Q = CiA$, the factor C is related to the unit runoff as shown by $Q/A = Ci$. The coefficient C and the rainfall intensity are directly related by the factors that influence the time of concentration, namely, topographic conditions. From the unit runoff concept, the discharge at a point is some percentage of the rainfall intensity.

In contrast to storm drain design, culvert design considers less frequently occurring flood runoff events which, in essence, are larger floods. Large floods on small drainage basins are primarily dependent on the simultaneous occurrence of high intensity rainfall, low infiltration capacity, and full basin surface storage. The selected C values for these conditions must necessarily be greater than for a yearly flood event. The high rainfall

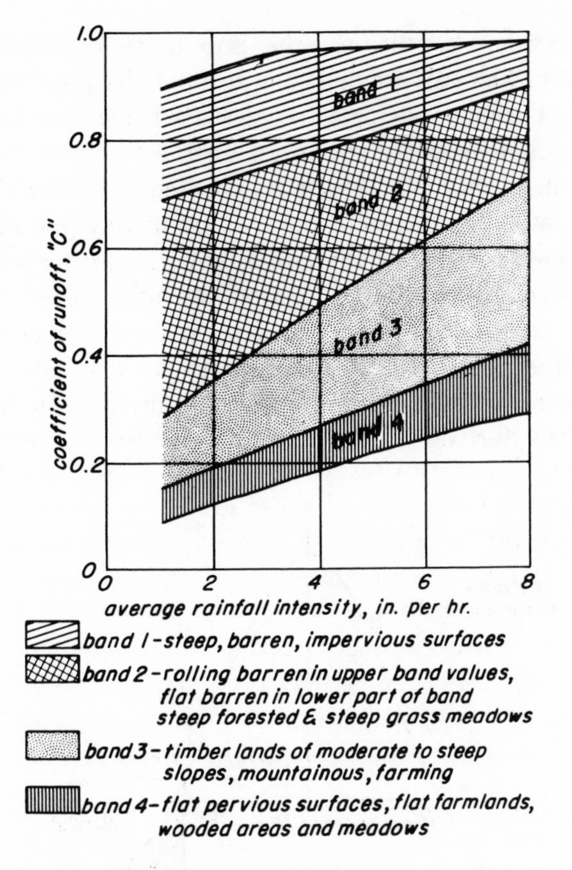

Fig. 17. Runoff coefficient C related to rainfall intensity and topography.

intensity is considered by selecting an average intensity i (Fig. 13).

As an aid in selecting C values, Fig. 17 has been prepared. The series of bands shows runoff coefficients for varying rates of rainfall with typical soil types and land uses. The bands are an adaption of several current methods of determining C values. The runoff coefficient thus determined may be substituted into the equation $Q = CiA$. Adjustment of these curves for local conditions based on measured data may be necessary. The curves are given as a guide in selecting the runoff coefficient.

Determination of Flood Risks

An element of risk is associated with the operation of every culvert. Although the engineer may wish to design a culvert with a capacity equal to the most extreme conditions, the possibility of even more extreme conditions exists. The culvert designer accepts the possibility of extremes in excess of the design capacity as a calculated risk.

It is a common practice to design on the basis of frequency period. This implies a flood or storm which is expected to be equaled or exceeded on the average of at least once during the frequency period. However, the useful life of the structure or the embankment may be less than, greater than, or equal to, the frequency period. As an economic consideration, it is necessary to evaluate the damages caused by floods exceeding the magnitude of the design flood. In order to do this, an estimate of the chances of obtaining larger floods permits a more reliable flood risk evaluation and may be derived from a statistical analysis of natural events.

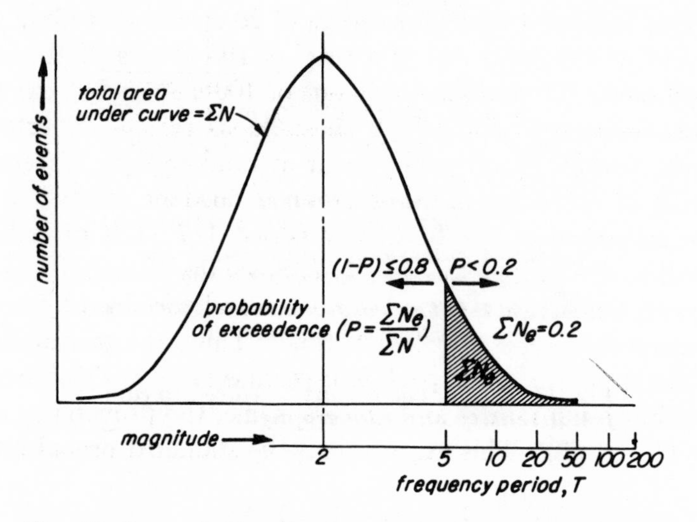

Fig. 18. Normal distribution curve for maximum annual peaks.

Flood data or rainfall data may be plotted to establish a pattern showing the occurrence of events of different magnitudes. The pattern takes the shape of the normal distribution curve illustrated in Fig. 18. In this curve the number of events for various magnitude ranges is plotted against magnitude. From the curve it is evident that few events of either very low or very high magnitude occur. It is also possible to use the curve to determine the magnitude of the events that occur most frequently. The area under the curve represents the total number of all events that were used in constructing the curve. Conversely, the area of any portion of the curve represents the number of events occurring from some minimum magnitude to some maximum magnitude. This curve is useful also in establishing the number of events that exceed a certain magnitude of interest to the analyst. By comparing the number of events that exceed a given magnitude to the total events, a ratio is determined that establishes the probability of exceedence.

The culvert designer is interested in the probability of floods or rainfalls exceeding a predetermined amount. From the area relationships established for the normal distribution curve, the magnitude of a flood or rainfall with a predetermined probability or risk of being exceeded is established. An example is illustrated in Fig. 18 for a probability of exceedence of 20 per cent. This means that the area (shaded) under the curve to the right of the reference line is 20 per cent of the total area under the curve. Furthermore, this means that the chance of exceeding the magnitude represented by the reference line in any one event is 20 per cent. This indicates that an average of 20 events exceeding the referenced amount would occur out of a total of 100 events. If the events are annual flood peaks, 20 annual floods out of 100 will exceed the reference. The average frequency with which these floods can be expected is once in a five-year period. Flood peaks occur at random with respect to time.

The risk of exceeding a predetermined flood or rainfall in any one year is the reciprocal of the frequency period $1/T$. The probability that the flood will not be exceeded is $1 - 1/T$. Since the probability is the same for every year, the risk in a period of n years is determined by multiplying the one-year probabilities together n times. Thus, the probability of not exceeding the stipulated flood peak in n years is $(1 - 1/T)^n$. Since the sum of the probabilities of failure and success is one, the probability of exceedence is $1 - (1 - 1/T)^n$. This expression is the standard probability theory equation

$$P = 1 - (1 - 1/T)^n$$

in which P is the probability or flood risk factor for exceeding the flood peak having a frequency period of T years within the time of n years.

The use of the probability equation can be illustrated by calculating the probability (chances) of having a flood with a 25-year frequency in a 10-year period. Thus

$$P = 1 - (1 - 1/25)^{10}$$

from which the flood risk factor P is computed to be 0.34. It can also be shown that the risk of experiencing a flood with a 25-year frequency within a 25-year period is 64 per cent. The risk of experiencing a flood with a T-year frequency within a period of T years is also 64 per cent

The probability is computed for average frequency periods for various time intervals in Table 5, using standard probability theory. Further, the data are plotted on Fig. 19 to provide a better method of evaluating the selected design storm. As an example, assume that the expected life of

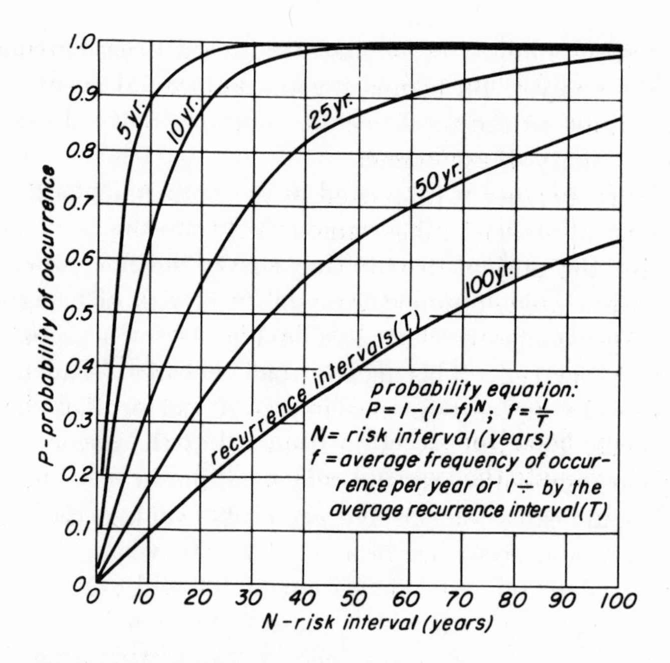

Fig. 19. Probability of flood occurrence in design period.

the structure is 50 years and that in this interval little damage is desired from flood flows. Entering the figure on the abscissa (time scale) with a 50-year life expectancy, read upwards to the 100-year frequency period curve, and at this intersection read the probability $P = 0.4$. This means that on the average at least one or more floods equal to or greater than the 100-year recurrence interval peak will have 4 out of 10 chances of occurring in the next 50-year period. Similarly, for this same 50-year

TABLE 5. Probability of Flood Occurrence in the Design Period

Average recurrence interval, years	Average frequency per year	Probability of occurrence in N years					
		$N=100$	$N=50$	$N=25$	$N=10$	$N=5$	$N=1$
100	0.01	0.64	0.40	0.22	0.09	0.05	0.01
50	0.02	0.87	0.64	0.41	0.18	0.09	0.02
25	0.04	0.98	0.87	0.64	0.34	0.18	0.04
10	0.10	1.00	0.99	0.93	0.64	0.41	0.10
5	0.20	1.00	1.00	0.996	0.89	0.67	0.20

period, read up to an assumed design based on a 10-year frequency flood. The probability of having one or more floods equal to or greater than the 10-year frequency flood is 0.99 or a near certainty. Design based on this condition (10-year frequency) would have to consider damage resulting in greater floods and occurring more often as weighed against a 100-year recurrence interval or intermediate design.

Fig. 19 is presented as an aid to the engineer in weighing the hydrologic factors in design. This figure applies equally well to any method of flood peak determination discussed in this text which has the connotation of frequency of occurrence. Fig. 19 does not directly indicate the size of the flood. On the other hand, it indicates the risk involved in selecting a given frequency flood for design within selected periods of time. The designer must evaluate the type of traffic facility in relation to probabilities of greater flood events than selected for design.

Analytical Procedure Using Rational Method

Computation of the expected maximum runoff by the rational method requires the evaluation of each of three factors. As previously discussed, these factors are to some extent interrelated and will require an analysis of the effect of each on the other. The design runoff is computed after the engineer is satisfied that each of the major factors is representative of the conditions of the problem. The flow is evaluated by substituting in the rational formula the value for rainfall intensity, per cent of rainfall which will run off when equilibrium flow is established, and the area of the drainage basin. Each of these factors is represented in

$$Q = CiA$$

in which Q = runoff, cu.ft. per sec.
C = rainfall-runoff coefficient
i = rainfall intensity, in. per hr. for a given frequency storm
A = area of drainage basin, either acres or sq.mi. (Use proper conversion factors.)

This method for evaluation of runoff may proceed in any of several orders. The following is a logical procedure which may be used:

1. Establish the location of the culvert and determine the drainage area. Evaluate the importance of the culvert location to the damaging effect of floods both to the roadway and to affected property.

2. Survey the drainage area to determine soil type, type of cover, and average slope. Locate the drainage channels, determine the most remote point in the watershed, and map the course water would take from

that point in reaching the proposed culvert location. Measure the length of the watercourse and determine the average slope.

3. Establish the design period and flood frequency using Fig. 19 as a guide. This will be the average period of time the culvert will be expected to operate with a reasonable probability of not flooding. Thus, if a design period of 10 years is used with a 10-year frequency flood, the design will result in a structure that is expected to be exceeded in capacity on the average of at least once in 10 years. The chance or probability of getting this 10-year average frequency flood is 0.64 (64:100). This period may be chosen on the basis of the importance of the structure, the extent of damages resulting from flooding, or inconvenience resulting from temporary failure. In many cases, the design criterion is established by local practice.

4. Estimate the time of concentration for the drainage basin by use of Fig. 16. Determine the average rainfall intensities for the particular area and frequency period with a storm duration equal to the estimated time of concentration using a figure similar to Figs. 13 and 14.

5. Adjust the rainfall intensity to account for areal distribution on the basis of Fig. 15.

6. Select the proper runoff coefficient for the type of soil, cover, and rainfall intensity (Fig. 17).

7. Substitute the values of C, i, and A in the rational formula and compute the runoff. The product CiA should be multiplied by 1.008 if A is expressed in acres, and by 645 if A is expressed in square miles.

8. Compare the discharge of step 7 with measured records of streams in that area. In most parts of the United States, short records (less than 10 years) on small watersheds are available from USGS Water Supply papers.

Example Problem Using Rational Method

As an example of runoff computations by the rational formula, consider the design of a culvert near Chicago, Ill. The culvert is to be installed to drain the area shown in Fig. 20. The drainage basin consists of 125 acres of gently sloping pastureland. The average slope is estimated as 1 per cent. The most remote point of the drainage basin is 200 ft. from the end of the defined channel, which is 2,000 ft. long as measured from the culvert location. Because of the culvert location and type of traffic facility, a 10-year storm frequency is selected for design. The damage from flooding is expected to be low over the 50-year life of the structure; therefore, a high risk factor can be assumed. Even a 100-year flood for this site will cause little damage.

The culvert is 2,200 ft. from the most remote point of the watershed.

The average slope of the watercourse is computed by $S = H/L$ in which H is the difference in elevation between the culvert location and the most remote point. From Fig. 20 the slope becomes $S = 2/2{,}200$ or 0.0009 ft. per foot.

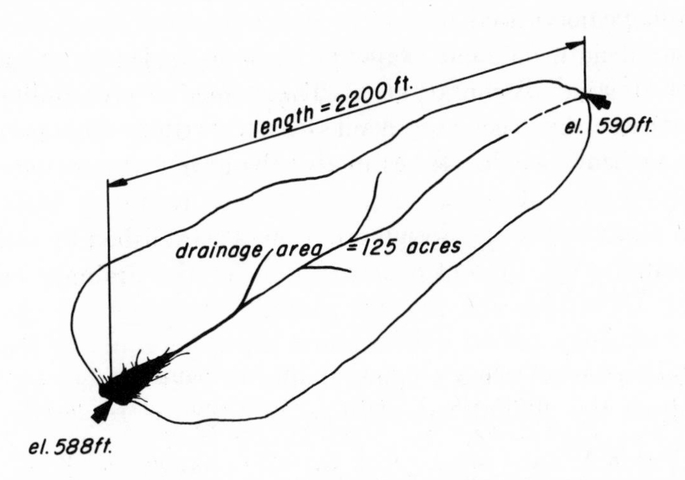

Fig. 20. Example problem of flood estimate by rational method.

The time of concentration is estimated by using Fig. 16. To use Fig. 16, the value of K must be computed from the length and slope of the watercourse. Since $K = L/\sqrt{S}$, by substitution $K = 2{,}200/\sqrt{0.0009} = 73{,}300$. Enter Fig. 16 with $K = 73$ (K on the chart is in thousands) and read an estimated time of concentration, $t_c = 42$ minutes.

On the basis of a 10-year frequency, the 1-hour rainfall intensity may be determined from Fig. 13 as 2 in. per hour. Converting the 1-hour rainfall intensity to a 42-minute duration storm by using Fig. 14, obtain 2.6 in. per hour for the 10-year frequency. Since the watershed area is quite small, the areal distribution correction of Fig. 15 is not applied. Therefore, rainfall intensity i is 2.6 in. per hour.

Next estimate the per cent of rainfall that appears as runoff at the culvert location C. As a guide use Fig. 17. With the rainfall intensity i of 2.6, read vertically to the average soil cover and slope conditions of the watershed. For this example the watershed was a flat pastureland; therefore, band 4, which provides average C values for flat pastureland, gives an upper limit of 0.2 for the runoff coefficient C.

Substituting the determined values of C, i and A into the rational formula, obtain an estimated 10-year frequency discharge:

$$Q = CiA = 0.2 \times 2.6 \times 125 = 65 \text{ cfs.}$$

The designer can expect at least one or more flood flow equal to or greater than 65 cfs in any consecutive period of 10 years on the average at this culvert location. Furthermore, the estimated value is based on general conditions, and local conditions can modify this estimate considerably. However, changes in this estimate should be made only on actual measured hydrologic conditions.

Measured data on small watershed runoff provide a means to compare the estimated discharge at a culvert location to similar drainage basins. As more data become available, the rational method should be modified to permit even better estimates than are now possible.

References

1. *Airport Drainage*, Washington, D.C., Civil Aeronautics Administration, 1960.
2. Davison, A. H., "Methods of General Application Developed Finding Peak Flood Flow," *Civil Engineering*, June 1952, pp. 56-58.
3. Fair, Gordon M., and Geyer, John C., *Water Supply and Waste-Water Disposal*, New York, John Wiley & Sons, Inc., 1954.
4. *Hydrology Handbook*, Manual of Engineering Practice No. 25, American Society of Civil Engineers, New York, 1949.
5. Linsley, R. K., Jr.; Kohler, M. A.; and Paulhus, J. L. H., *Applied Hydrology*, New York, McGraw-Hill Book Co., Inc., 1949.
6. Miller, W. C., "Evolving a Shortcut for the Design of Storm Sewers," *Municipal Utilities*, September 1951, pp. 42-54.
7. Ordon, Chester J., "A Modified Rational Formula for Storm Water Runoff," *Water & Sewage Works*, June 1954, pp. 275-277.
8. "Rainfall Frequency Atlas of the United States," Technical Paper No. 40, U.S. Weather Bureau, Washington, D.C., 1961.
9. Rouse, Hunter, *Engineering Hydraulics*, New York, John Wiley & Sons, Inc., 1949, Chapter IV, Hydrology.
10. Wisler, C. O., and Brater, E. F., *Hydrology*, New York, John Wiley & Sons, Inc., 1949.
11. Yarnell, David L., *Rainfall Intensity-Frequency Data*, Miscellaneous Publication No. 204, U.S. Department of Agriculture, Washington, D.C., 1935.

3

Hydraulics of Culverts

A CULVERT'S PURPOSE IS TO PROVIDE A WATER CHANNEL THROUGH an embankment. Proper design requires compatibility between inflow and allowable headwater elevation at normal and extreme operating conditions. This can only be assured by a hydraulic analysis considering all of the factors controlling flow through the particular culvert.

At one time, it was common practice to design culverts by formulas in which no attention was paid to hydraulic design. This method cannot be justified since no consideration is given to design variations that materially affect the flow. This technique assumes no difference in flow characteristics between a short culvert and a long culvert. Actually, flow can be affected by several hundred per cent. According to hydraulic theory and many recent experimental investigations, flow is dependent upon the effects of headwater depth, culvert slope, culvert length, entrance shape, shape of the conduit, conduit size, tailwater depth, and the roughness of the conduit material.

The designer is principally concerned with providing a culvert adequately sized and installed to carry some maximum flow of water without causing excessive ponding. If this is to be accomplished with a structure compatible with economy, adequacy, and other construction requirements, it is necessary to design on sound hydraulic principles.

A culvert flows in either of two ways. The usual way is as an open channel or part full. The other is as a full-flowing conduit, similar to flow in water mains. Sometimes a culvert will appear to flow full at the entrance but only part full at the outlet. To an engineer unexperienced in culvert operation, the general behavior seems confused and analysis seems hopeless. However, each of these modes of operation occurs in an orderly and predictable fashion and is simple to analyze.

The purpose of this chapter is to outline the hydraulic fundamentals underlying culvert operation and to provide practical design information. The fundamentals of conduits flowing part full and completely full are explained so that the culvert design charts and nomographs provided in the appendix may be used with understanding and good judgment.

Principles of Conduits Flowing Full

The flow of water in a culvert can take several forms. Because of this, the task of design may seem formidable and hopelessly confused. Fortunately, this is not the case. Flow in a culvert is predictable and occurs in accordance with established hydraulic principles. An understanding of the principles of conduits flowing full will assist the designer in his work.

CONTINUITY OF FLOW

The law of continuity of flow is fundamental to a clear concept of hydraulic phenomena and may be expressed as

$$Q = \text{constant.}$$

This law establishes a base for relating flow in one part of the system to another. The quantity of flow is measured in terms of discharge Q which is expressed as units of volume per unit time. The units of discharge may be expressed as gallons per minute, gallons per hour, cubic feet per second, etc. In engineering hydraulics it is most convenient to express units of discharge in cubic feet per second, as is done throughout this handbook unless

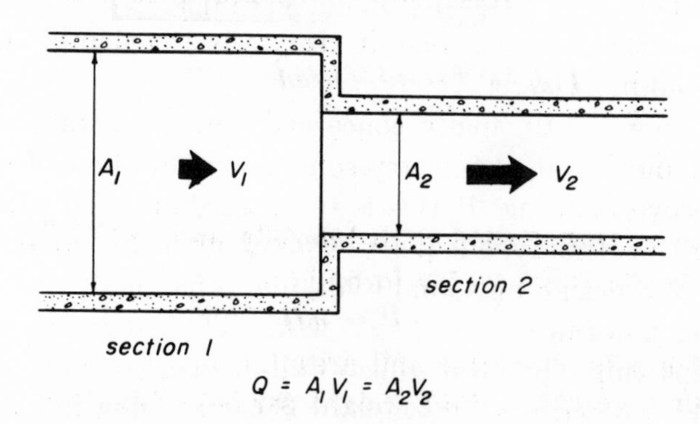

Fig. 21. Continuity of flow.

otherwise stated. The law of continuity of flow merely states that the discharge throughout a given flow system is the same. This principle is illustrated in Fig. 21 for flow in a system consisting of two different sizes of pipe. Discharge is determined by the local average velocity and cross-sectional area of flow, or

$$Q = VA$$

where Q = discharge, cubic feet per second (cfs)
V = velocity, feet per second (fps)
A = cross-sectional area, square feet (ft.²)

Since the discharge in section 1 must equal the discharge in section 2,

$$Q_1 = Q_2 = \text{constant}.$$

The velocities must vary in accordance with the cross-sectional area, thus

$$Q = V_1A_1 = V_2A_2$$

$$\text{or } V_2 = \frac{A_1}{A_2}V_1.$$

Pressure Head

A fluid has the unique ability to transmit pressure equally in all directions. Water at rest creates pressure in proportion to its weight. As illustrated in Fig. 22, pressure in a body of water increases directly with the depth of

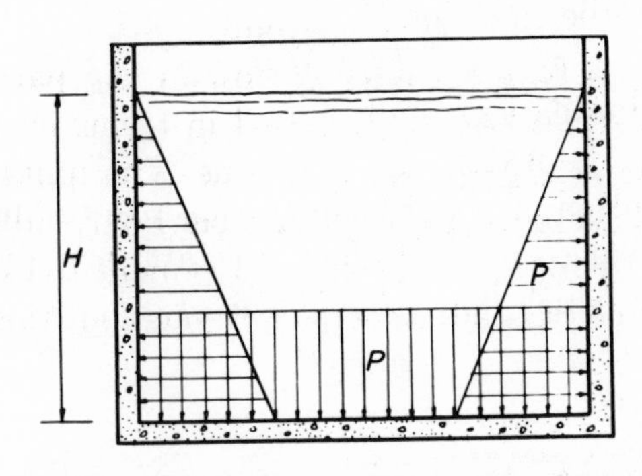

Fig. 22. Pressure head.

the water and is transmitted both laterally and vertically. The pressure thus created is expressed by the formula

$$P = wH$$

where P = pressure, force per unit area
w = unit weight of fluid, weight per unit volume
H = depth of fluid, length

If the unit weight w is expressed as pounds per cubic foot (lb./ft.^{3}) and the depth as feet, the pressure will be expressed in pounds per square foot (psf). The unit weight of water is 62.4 lb./ft.^{3}, therefore

$$P = 62.4H.$$

Inasmuch as pressure and depth are related by a constant factor, the magnitude of one will be defined by the other. Since depth is easily measured and directly significant, pressure is conveniently expressed as depth or head. As an example, water in a tank 10 ft. deep has a head at the bottom of 10 ft. and a pressure of 624 psf. The significance of head also applies to closed sections. The head in a pipe is the height to which water will rise in a vertical tube attached to the pipe at the pressure-measuring point.

VELOCITY HEAD

Kinetic energy in a hydraulic system may be expressed in terms of velocity head. This is a convenient term in which the flow energy is expressed in terms of equivalent head. Velocity head may be defined as the equivalent relationship between potential energy and kinetic energy, or the head required to produce a velocity of given magnitude. This term is important in expressing flow relationships and establishes the basis for determining losses due to flow in a hydraulic system.

The relationship between velocity and head is developed from consideration of the second law of motion in which the force required to cause flow is expressed by the equation

$$F = Ma$$

where F = force obtainable from head
M = mass of the water
a = acceleration of water from static state to final velocity

The force F available to produce flow is established by the head acting on the area through which flow takes place, or

$$F = PA$$

where F = total force
P = pressure
A = cross-sectional area of flow stream

Expressing pressure in terms of head from the pressure depth relationship $P = wH$, the equivalence of potential and kinetic energy is given by

$$wHA = Ma.$$

In order to be useful, the right-hand side of the equation must be evaluated in easily measured terms. Mass M is given by

$$M = \frac{W}{g}$$

where W = total weight
g = acceleration of gravity

The total weight is obtained from

$$W = w\int Q dt$$

where Q = discharge, cfs

dt = element of time

In this case, total weight is the integral of the unit weight of water, the discharge, and time. Acceleration is expressed by

$$a = \frac{dV}{dt}.$$

By substituting these quantities in the basic equation for the equivalence between head and kinetic energy, the equation

$$H = \frac{1}{g}\int V dV$$

is obtained, which when integrated yields the equation for the static head equivalent in energy content of the flowing water. The expression for velocity head is thus

$$H = \frac{V^2}{2g}.$$

Bernoulli's Equation—Energy Concept of Flow

The well-known Bernoulli equation is useful in establishing the interrelationship of the various factors in a hydraulic system. Energy may exist as potential or kinetic energy in the form of elevation head, pressure, velocity, or heat. In energy form, Bernoulli's equation is expressed as

$$(E_p)_E + (E_p)_P + (E_k)_V + (E_p)_H = \text{constant}$$

where $(E_p)_E$ = potential energy due to water surface elevation

$(E_p)_P$ = potential energy due to pressure

$(E_k)_V$ = kinetic energy due to velocity

$(E_p)_H$ = potential energy due to heat

For the condition that potential energy due to heat is essentially constant throughout the system, Bernoulli's equation is written in terms of head as

$$H + \frac{P}{w} + \frac{V^2}{2g} = \text{constant}.$$

The energy may be equated between two sections of the same flow, disregarding energy losses, to give

$$H_1 + \frac{P_1}{w} + \frac{V_1^2}{2g} = H_2 + \frac{P_2}{w} + \frac{V_2^2}{2g}$$

in which the subscripts refer to section 1 and section 2. In practical application, section 1 may be a free water surface and section 2 may be a section of full-flowing pipe as illustrated in Fig. 23.

Hydraulic Losses

Energy losses occur in a flowing system due to friction or resistance to flow. In the strictest sense, these apparent losses are merely a conversion

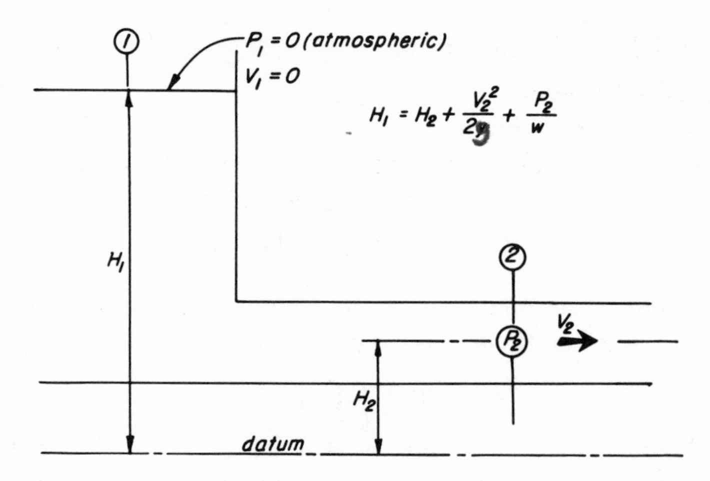

Fig. 23. Bernoulli's equation expressing energy relationship between sections.

of kinetic energy to heat. This process is irreversible and the energy thus converted to heat is lost for all practical purposes. Losses may be considered in Bernoulli's equation by substituting E_L for $(E_p)_H$ in the fundamental energy equation, so that

$$(E_p)_E + (E_p)_P + (E_k)_V + E_L = \text{constant}$$

Hydraulic losses are directly related to the velocity of flow and may be expressed in terms of velocity head as

$$H_L = K_L \frac{V^2}{2g}$$

where H_L = head loss

K_L = loss coefficient

The loss coefficient K_L may combine several loss factors. One major factor of energy loss is the normal resistance or frictional loss of flow in contact with a surface. The degree of this loss is associated with the surface roughness and discharge. Another major loss arises when flow expands downstream of an obstruction such as a culvert entrance. The losses at entrances to pipe culverts are considered to be directly proportional to the velocity head of the full pipe and are expressed by a constant value as the entrance loss coefficient. The value of this coefficient depends upon the type of entrance that is used for the particular installation. There are other losses expressed by coefficients for bends, expansions, transitions, etc.

HYDRAULIC GRADE LINE

In solving hydraulic problems it is often helpful to visualize the flow condition before any calculations are made. A useful approach for this purpose in full conduit flow is to roughly establish the hydraulic grade line. The hydraulic grade line is established from a graphical consideration of the Bernoulli equation.

By definition, the hydraulic grade line is the top surface of the water columns which would be established by open tubes located at all possible points along the pipe. Fig. 24a illustrates the hydraulic grade line as part of the Bernoulli equation.

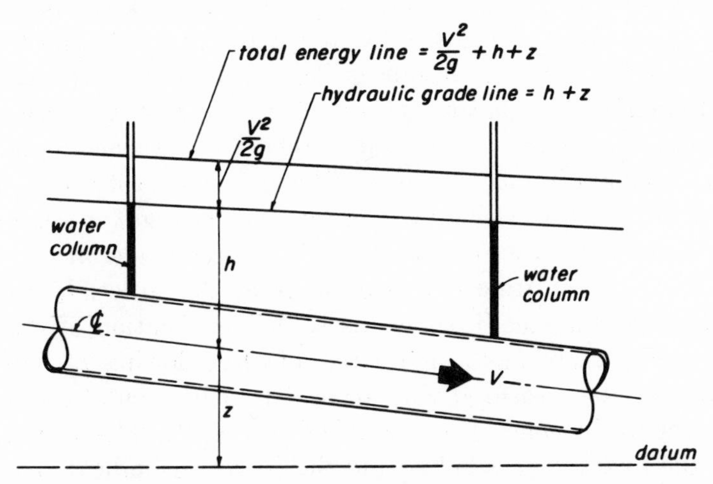

(a) definition sketch of total energy line and hydraulic grade line

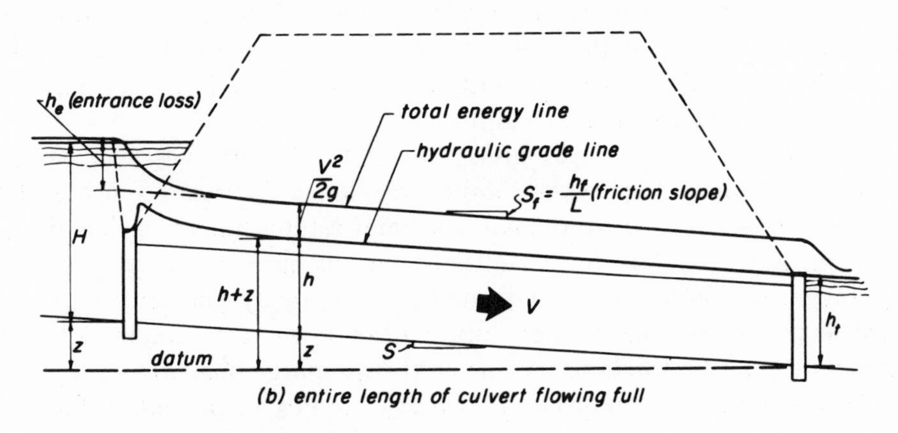

(b) entire length of culvert flowing full

Fig. 24. Definition sketch for the energy concept.

The example shown in Fig. 24b is a culvert through an embankment with the inlet and outlet submerged. The total energy line indicates the total energy remaining in the system at every point. This line accurately shows the losses that take place and the manner in which they occur. At the entrance to a culvert the flow is ponded to some degree and the velocity of flow becomes small; therefore, velocity head is so small that the energy line is essentially the same as the pool depth or headwater surface. At a submerged culvert outlet the flow expands to a man-made or natural channel in which the flow area is much greater than the culvert flow area; therefore, the velocity again may become rather small. The water surface again reflects the approximate position of the total energy line. If the outlet is unsubmerged, the elevation of the total energy line may be approximated by adding the velocity head to the elevation of the pipe crown.

The hydraulic grade line is located with respect to the total energy line. Each point of the hydraulic grade line is located a distance below the total energy line equal to the velocity head at that section. The hydraulic grade line does not necessarily reflect losses since its location will vary with changes in velocity head. Changes in velocity head are merely energy conversions which occur as a result of changes in section and are usually accompanied by some loss. The hydraulic grade line always terminates at the point of atmospheric pressure at the outlet. In Fig. 24b this is the tailwater surface. In some cases, the termination of the hydraulic grade line is not so obvious, as in the case of a free-flowing jet. The hydraulic grade line may be measured with respect to a horizontal datum plane or with respect to the conduit, as indicated in Fig. 24. The vertical distance between the hydraulic grade line and the conduit is indicative of the pressure in the pipe. The same measurement with respect to the datum plane is indicative of total potential energy in the form of elevation and pressure. Note that the slope of the conduit has no effect on the location of the hydraulic grade line when the outlet is submerged, but does have an effect on the pressure of the conduit.

Entrance losses or energy losses caused by the entrance may be indicated by an initial drop in the total energy line as illustrated in Fig. 24b. However, losses caused by the entrance and establishment of flow do not occur instantly but are fully realized some distance downstream of the entrance. Friction losses are indicated by the steady and uniform downward slope of the total energy line. Outlet losses are indicated by the sudden drop in the total energy line at the discharge point. In some cases, the flow may not expand or lose the energy directly at the outlet, but may require considerable distance to change the kinetic energy to potential energy. For this condition the energy line would have a gradual drop over a considerable length downstream of the outlet. It is important to realize that all of the available energy, as indicated by the elevation of the headwater surface above the tailwater, is completely expended in the flow process. This occurs as a natural adjustment in which flow rate will increase until no further energy is available to meet the increased demands of higher flow.

The Effect of Roughness

The effect of roughness is present to a greater or lesser degree in every hydraulic system. All surfaces produce energy losses attributable to the drag between the flowing fluid and the boundary which contains it. The presence of a rough surface increases the drag and thus causes an increase in the amount of energy that is expended in maintaining flow in contact with the surface. Roughness is particularly objectionable in long culverts where the energy losses due to roughness amount to several times the combined losses from all other sources. In short culverts roughness is of minor importance since the major energy losses are the entrance and outlet losses.

Effect of Pipe Size and Velocity on Friction

The effect of roughness is produced through the mechanics of fluid friction. All surfaces exhibit frictional characteristics depending upon the rate of flow (velocity), the area in contact with the flow, the shape of the flow cross-section, and the smoothness or roughness of the surface. The smoothest surfaces have frictional characteristics that decrease (friction factor in terms of Darcy f)* with an increase in Reynold's number, a significant dimensionless parameter. For a given size pipe, Reynold's number is directly proportional to velocity; for a given velocity, it is directly proportional to pipe size. The presence of roughness limits the extent to which friction coefficients can decrease with increasing Reynold's numbers. Very rough surfaces are characterized by high limiting friction factors, while the limiting friction factors for surfaces less rough are lower. Depending upon the Reynold's number, the friction factor may be larger than the limiting value, but it cannot be less.

Effect of Friction on Velocity Distribution

Energy losses due to friction are produced by the drag or retarding effect of the surface in contact with the flow. The surface drag is imparted throughout the flow by the drag of one fluid particle on the other. In a pipe, the net effect is to establish a variation in velocity from zero at the wall to a maximum value at the center. Drag due to extreme roughness will produce a velocity distribution which appears pointed when the velocity vectors are plotted as in Fig. 25. This type of velocity distribution is similar to the parabolic velocity distribution of laminar flow, illustrated in Fig. 26, where energy losses due to friction are quite high. The turbulent nature of flow such as occurs in culverts produces a more uniform type of velocity distribu-

---

*See "Darcy-Weisbach Equation," p. 64.

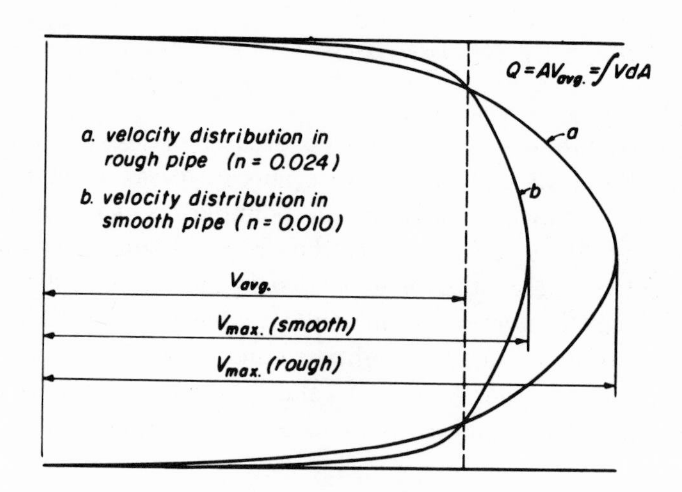

Fig. 25. Turbulent velocity distribution.

tion, also shown in Fig. 25. Curve *b* illustrates the velocity distribution in a relatively smooth pipe. Curve *a* shows the effect of an increased wall drag produced by a surface considerably rougher.

The quantitative effect of roughness is indicated by the slope of the velocity distribution curve at a pipe wall. Flat slopes such as curve *a* indicate high friction and consequently high losses. The steeper slope of curve *b* is indicative of a smooth pipe with much lower frictional losses.

Friction losses for fully developed frictional velocity distribution are minimized when the ratio of the maximum velocity to the average velocity approaches unity. High sidewall friction requires correspondingly high central velocities to maintain the total discharge and hence to maintain the average velocity. This is apparent from consideration of basic flow relationships in which $Q = VA$. The ratio of centerline velocity to average velocity for curve *a*, Fig. 25, is 1.39, while the ratio for curve *b* is 1.16 for a 3-ft.-diameter pipe. Energy losses as a result of the frictional effects producing the velocity distribution shown in curve *a* are 580 per cent greater

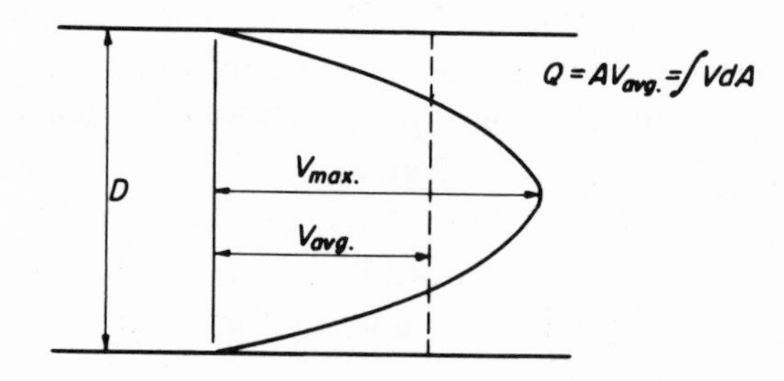

Fig. 26. Laminar velocity distribution.

than the losses associated with the velocity distribution of curve *b*. Curve *a* is based on a rough type of pipe normally used in culverts, and curve *b* is based on a smooth type available for culverts. Greater efficiency and better performance always result when the interior surfaces are smooth and straight. Such surfaces will make the best use of the flow area and the available energy.

Friction Formulas

Friction is always an important and often a controlling factor in the rate of flow. Formulas for evaluating frictional effects were among the first hydraulic formulas to be used. In the early days of hydraulic engineering, open channel flow was the primary mode of transporting water and provided the stimulus for the development of the first hydraulic friction formulas. The most useful of these were applicable to either flow in open channels or closed conduits.

Chezy formula

The earliest friction formulas were empirical and of limited usefulness. Chezy was the first to develop a formula which properly embodied the factors involved in friction-controlled flow. Modified forms of his formula are still in use. The Chezy formula is

$$V = C\sqrt{RS}$$

in which V = average velocity
R = hydraulic radius, ratio of flow area to wetted perimeter
S = channel slope
C = friction coefficient

Kutter formula

Chezy's original intention was to develop a formula in which the coefficient C was a constant. However, C was soon found to be dependent on other factors requiring a method of evaluation. Several formulas were developed, the most notable being the Kutter formula. It has been used extensively and is expressed as

$$C = \frac{41.65 + \frac{0.00281}{S} + \frac{1.811}{n}}{1 + \frac{n}{\sqrt{R}}\left(41.65 + \frac{0.00281}{S}\right)}$$

where the symbols are the same as previously defined, except that n is the friction factor.

Manning formula

The complex Kutter formula was difficult to use and prompted several attempts to simplify it. Robert Manning developed another formula for

C in which it was believed that the value of n was the same as in the Kutter formula. This is

$$C = \frac{1.486}{n} R^{1/6}.$$

It has been found, however, that the value of n is not identical in all cases. The deviation is particularly pronounced for full pipes at high values of n. Experiments have shown that the impressive Kutter formula is not as reliable as its complexity would indicate. Satisfactory results are achieved with the Manning form of Chezy's equation,

$$V = \frac{1.486}{n} R^{2/3} S^{1/2}.$$

In terms of discharge, this formula becomes

$$Q = \frac{1.486}{n} A R^{2/3} S^{1/2}.$$

The Manning equation is ordinarily used for open channel flow. It also has been adapted to pipes flowing full by expressing hydraulic radius in terms of pipe diameter and slope in terms of the slope of the energy grade line. For full pipes Manning's equation can be written to determine friction losses as

$$H_f = \frac{2.88 n^2 V^2 L}{D^{4/3}}$$

in which H_f = total head loss due to friction
n = friction factor
D = pipe diameter
L = length of pipe
V = average velocity

Darcy-Weisbach equation

As a matter of custom, empirical formulas have been used in determination of frictional effects in open channels. These formulas are closely paralleled by friction formulas rigorously derived for closed conduits. The one most commonly used is the expression derived by Darcy and Weisbach,

$$H_f = f \frac{L}{D} \frac{V^2}{2g}$$

in which H_f = total head loss due to friction
f = friction factor
L = length of pipe
D = diameter of pipe
V = average velocity
g = acceleration of gravity

The Darcy-Weisbach equation is the most convenient equation to use for full-flowing conduits. However, the friction factor for culvert pipe customarily used is in terms of the Manning n. Since both the Manning formula and the Darcy-Weisbach equation are different formulas for express-

TABLE 6. Roughness Coefficients for Various Types of Culvert Pipe

Type	n	Source
Concrete pipe (very smooth)	0.010	St. Anthony Falls Lab.
Concrete pipe (rough, including offset joints and misalignment)	0.012	St. Anthony Falls Lab.
Corrugated metal, ½-in. corrugations (coated or uncoated)	0.024	Corps of Engineers
25 per cent paved, full	0.021	Corps of Engineers
25 per cent paved, depth at 0.80	0.019	Corps of Engineers
50 per cent paved	0.018	Corps of Engineers
100 per cent paved	0.010	Corps of Engineers
Vitrified clay (good joints)	0.010	King's Handbook
Corrugated metal, 2x6-in. corrugations	0.033	Reference 4

ing the same quantities, an expression relating n and f may be determined. This is

$$f = 185\frac{n^2}{D^{1/3}}.$$

Values of n are assumed to be constant for a particular material regardless of size of pipe or depth of flow. Average values based on recent tests and experience are given in Table 6. The values of n for a full pipe were computed from the above conversion formula.

Other friction formulas

Many other formulas have been used to determine frictional effects. Among these is the Bazin formula for determining Chezy's C,

$$C = \frac{157.6}{1 + \dfrac{m}{\sqrt{R}}}$$

in which m is a friction coefficient similar to n.

Another well-known formula is the Hazen-Williams formula, which is also similar to the Manning formula. The Hazen-Williams formula is

$$V = C_1R^{0.67}S^{0.54}$$

The coefficient C_1 contains the friction factor and must be selected. This differs from the Manning formula in that slightly different exponents are used for R and S. The close similarity to the Manning formula and the convenience of the Darcy-Weisbach equation have precluded use of the Hazen-Williams formula in recent years.

The steep slope and smooth interior wall of this concrete pipe culvert assure inlet control operation at maximum flow as well as at this intermediate discharge.

EVALUATION OF FRICTION FACTORS

The selection of the proper friction factor is of great importance in establishing culvert performance. Conventional culvert practice is to select a value of Manning's n to use as a constant on the basis of the type of material forming the pipe wall. Once n has been selected, it is applied to all sizes of pipe without regard to possible variations in the effect of roughness with changing depth. It is well established that both wall roughness and flow depth have an important effect on the actual magnitude of the roughness factor. This has been shown by Straub at the St. Anthony Falls Hydraulic Laboratory in tests on full pipes, both concrete pipe and corrugated metal pipe. The results of these tests are shown in Fig. 27 for Darcy-Weisbach's f and Fig. 28 for Manning's n. These tests show that the friction factor for concrete pipe decreases with increasing Reynold's number and that the friction factor for corrugated metal pipe increases with increasing Reynold's number. Additional tests on corrugated metal pipe by the U.S. Army Corps of Engineers have supplied additional information so that the effect of size on the friction factor for both types of pipe can be expressed in generalized equations. For typical concrete pipe with moderately good installation the Manning's friction factor closely corresponds to

$$n = 0.0112D^{0.042}.$$

For corrugated metal pipe ($2\frac{2}{3}$x$\frac{1}{2}$-in. corrugations), it was found that Manning's n varied according to the formula

$$n = 0.0254D^{-0.053}.$$

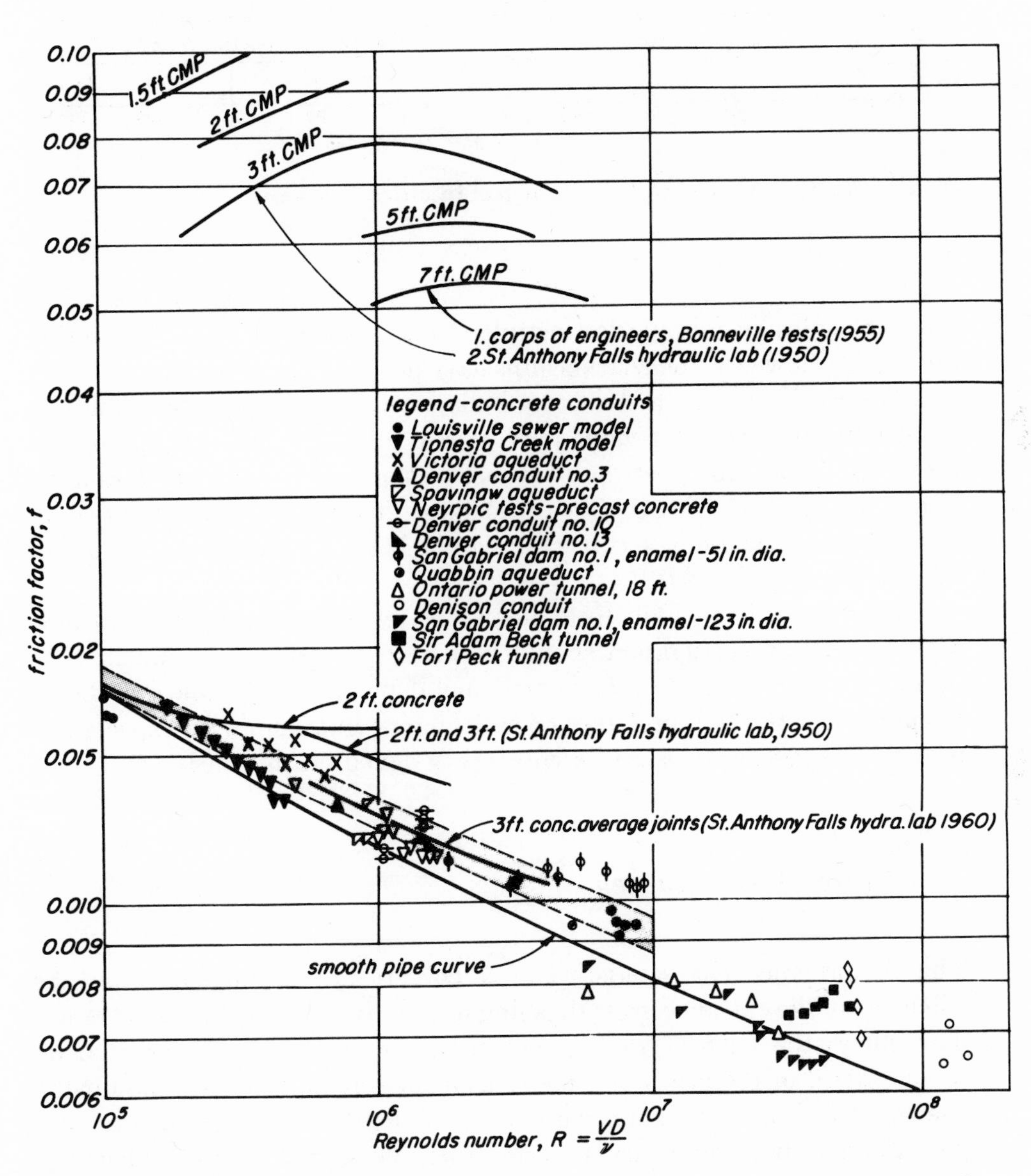

Fig. 27. Comparison of friction factor* f *for concrete and corrugated metal culverts.

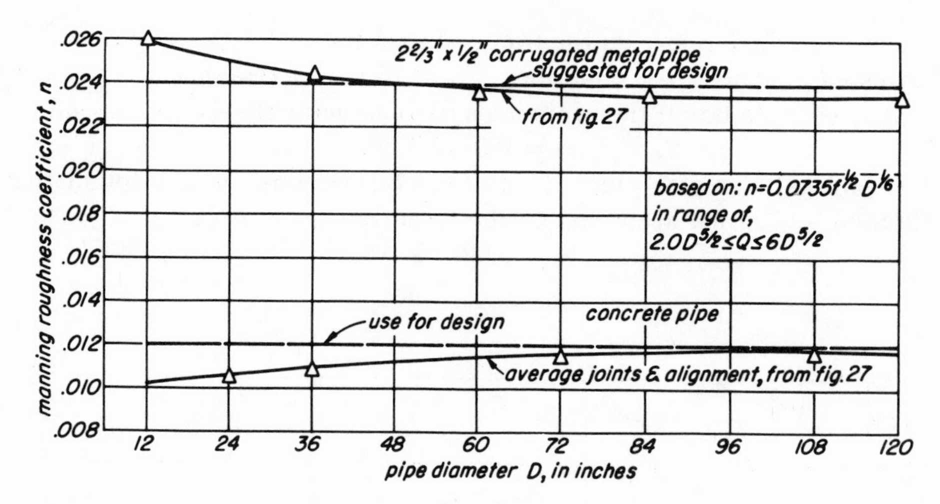

Fig. 28. Resistance coefficient for use in culvert design.

These formulas are for pipe flowing full. Other research indicates a variation with depth; however, the relationships have not yet been clearly established.

The work of the St. Anthony Falls Hydraulic Laboratory indicates $n = 0.010$ is a reasonable value for cast and vibrated concrete pipe placed with good alignment. Tests on field installations show values of n ranging from 0.009 to 0.011. To provide a reasonable margin of safety, it is recommended that concrete pipe culvert design be based on roughness factors for concrete pipe of $n = 0.012$.

The St. Anthony Falls tests also indicate that corrugated metal pipe with ½-in.-deep corrugation should be designed with an $n = 0.025$. The commonly used value for corrugated metal pipe, however, is $n = 0.024$. In most cases this will probably be satisfactory but cannot be expected to provide any reserve capacity in culverts designed on this basis.

Flow at Entrances

The performance characteristics of a culvert are dependent upon the efficiency of the entrance in establishing flow in the system. At the entrance, flow enters the culvert from a pool in which the energy represented by the elevation of the headwater pool surface is transformed into the kinetic energy of flow and the potential energy of depth and pressure. For best performance, it is necessary to establish flow smoothly and efficiently, keeping entrance velocities to a minimum. The extent to which this is accomplished is greatly influenced by the geometry of the entrance.

The characteristics of most entrances commonly used in culvert installations are such that the entrance acts as a restriction and prevents full use of the culvert pipe at the entrance section. The behavior of an orifice may be used to explain the mechanics of flow that occur. Orifice flow has long been recognized as a problem greatly influenced by geometry and has recently been found to be unquestionably related to flow in culvert entrances.

ORIFICE FLOW

Water flowing freely through an orifice forms a characteristic jet which constricts to a minimum diameter at a distance of one-half to one diameter from the orifice, as shown in Fig. 29a. Beyond this point the flow begins to expand and entrain a large amount of air. The point at which the jet has constricted to the minimum cross-section is known as the *vena contracta*. The dimension of the *vena contracta* is related to the size and geometry of the orifice through the contraction coefficient C_c. Thus the cross-sectional area of the *vena contracta* is given by

$$A_c = C_c A_o.$$

From the continuity equation, velocities of the *vena contracta* are given by

$$V_c = \frac{V_o}{C_c}.$$

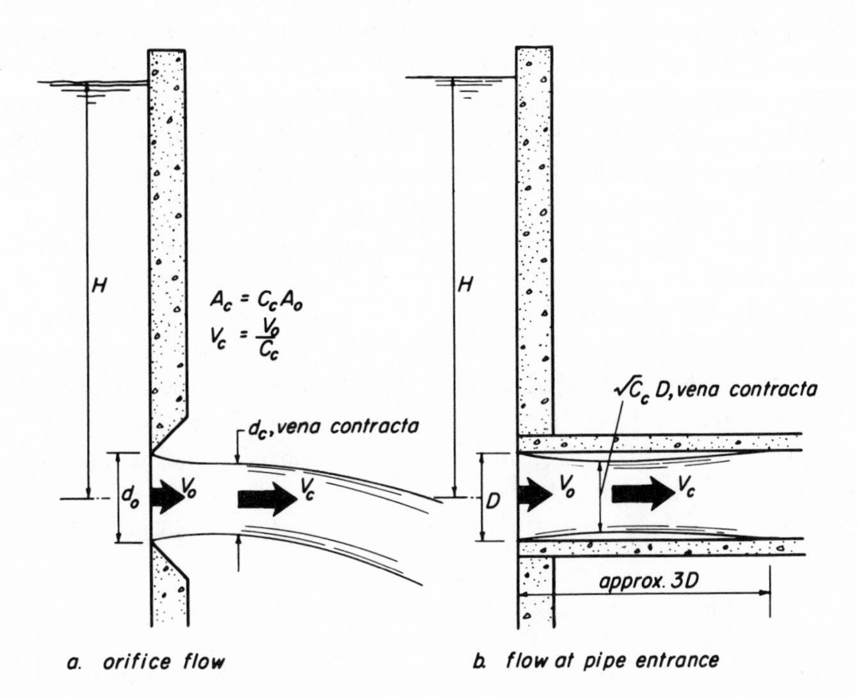

Fig. 29. Flow contraction.

The short distance from the orifice to the *vena contracta* provides little opportunity for realization of losses; therefore, the discharge may be obtained by application of the principle of velocity head to the continuity equation, giving

$$Q = C_c A_o \sqrt{2gH}.$$

The discharge that can flow through any given opening is thereby directly dependent upon the contraction coefficient that is associated with the geometric configuration of the opening. Examples of various-shaped openings and the corresponding contraction coefficient are given in Table 7.

TABLE 7. Contraction Coefficients for Various Orifice Rim Configurations

Type	C_c (King's Handbook)
Bell mouth	1.00
Well-rounded opening	0.98
Square-edge opening	0.82
Sharp edge	0.61
Sharp edge projecting	0.52

Although there are differences in geometry, it has been found that culvert entrances operate similarly to orifices illustrated in Fig. 29b. Culverts forming a square-edge opening in a headwall exhibit characteristics very similar to the sharp-edge orifice. With these types of opening, operating completely submerged, the entrance will admit approximately 61 per cent as much water as entrances with well-rounded inlets, such as the bell-mouth orifice. The discharge is thereby reduced 39 per cent below the maximum capability of the opening.

While the contraction coefficient may be used to express the relative efficiency of various entrances, actual discharges are more realistically expressed by use of a discharge coefficient C_d. Experiments have shown that due to slight frictional effects the actual velocities in orifice flow are somewhat less than that indicated by the foregoing (no energy loss) orifice equation. Discharges have been found to be 95 to 98 per cent of the expected rates. With this correction applied to the contraction coefficient, the orifice formula becomes $Q = C_d A_o \sqrt{2gH}$, where $0.98C_c \geq C_d \geq 0.95C_c$. Orifice-type flow exists when the downstream conditions do not affect the flow.

ENTRANCE LOSSES

Flow entering a pipe is constricted in accordance with the principles established for the operation of an orifice. Unlike the orifice, however, flow at the entrance is associated with high losses due to the effect of inlet geometry on downstream flow. It has been found, as a result of model tests conducted by the National Bureau of Standards, that entrance losses in a full pipe are due mainly to three factors. Most of the energy loss is due to the expansion of flow following the constriction caused by the entrance. In addition, frictional losses are experienced due to high velocities at the pipe walls which persist some distance downstream of the entrance. Thirdly, there are apparent losses that are ascribed to the entrance because of the nonuniform kinetic energy distribution of the established flow in the main part of the culvert barrel.

Expansion losses may be determined from Bernoulli's equation and the principles of conservation of momentum. If these losses H_L are applied to the energy available in the headwater pool, the expression is

$$H_L = \left(1 - \frac{1}{C_d}\right)^2 \frac{V^2}{2g}.$$

Low coefficient of contraction, C_c—hence low value of C_d—produces the larger expansion losses. In other words, as the flow is forced into greater degrees of constriction, the expansion losses become greater and cause the entrance to become less efficient.

Extra frictional losses are related to the roughness of the pipe wall and take place over a length of pipe, L_b, required to establish uniform flow in the pipe (length required for full boundary layer development). The friction factor ascribed to this type of flow is f_b and may be applied to the headwater elevation as extra frictional loss in the expression

$$H_b = (f - f_b)\frac{L_b}{D}\frac{V^2}{2g}$$

where H_b = energy loss due to boundary layer development
f = pipe friction factor
f_b = average friction factor for boundary layer development
L_b = length required for boundary layer development

This equation may be evaluated for concrete pipe or corrugated metal pipe by the factors established by Dr. Keulegan, National Bureau of Standards.

For concrete pipe, $(f - f_b)\frac{L_b}{D} = -0.06$.

For ½-in. corrugated metal pipe, $(f - f_b)\frac{L_b}{D} = -0.13$.

The equation of flow based on average velocity V must also be adjusted to account for nonuniform velocity distribution. The kinetic energy actually existing in the flow is given by

$$E_v = \alpha\frac{V^2}{2g}.$$

The energy grade line must, therefore, be adjusted downward by the amount

$$(\alpha - 1)\frac{V^2}{2g}.$$

Average value of α may be taken as 1.04 or 1.05 for concrete pipe and 1.15 for corrugated metal pipe.

A single entrance loss coefficient may be determined for each type of entrance and pipe combination by combining all of the factors discussed above. In order to account for all of the major effects of the entrance section, it will be necessary also to apply a correction for the unrealized friction in the short portion of the entrance occupied by the constricted jet. The length of this section may be estimated as three pipe diameters, with the correction given by the term

$$\frac{1.6f}{C_d}.$$

The entrance coefficient giving losses at the entrance is thus given by

$$K_e = \left(1 - \frac{1}{C_d}\right)^2 + (f_b - f)\frac{L_b}{D} + (\alpha - 1) - \frac{1.6f}{C_d}.$$

Values of K_e for most types of culvert entrances are given in Table 9, Chapter 5. If other types of entrances are used, the entrance loss coefficient may be obtained from the expression above. If losses are to be subtracted from the energy level represented by the headwater surface, the loss coefficient may be used as a positive number as given in Table 9. Entrance losses are then calculated by

$$H_L = K_e\frac{V^2}{2g}.$$

Entrance losses are important in culverts when the flow is controlled by downstream conditions.

Principles of Flow in Conduits Flowing Part Full

OPEN CHANNEL FLOW

The principles of open channel flow are the same as those that control flow in closed conduits; the only difference is in boundary conditions. In closed conduits the flow is totally enclosed, permitting pressures in the conduit to adjust to the flow. In open channels, the water surface is a flow boundary and is free and exposed to atmospheric pressure. The flow in this case must adjust itself so that the pressure at the water surface is equal to the pressure of the atmosphere. The major difference between hydraulics of open channels and closed conduits is due to different application of the predominant and independent controls. Examples of these controls are atmospheric pressure, constant-level reservoirs, water density, and confining flow boundaries.

Basic Hydraulic Relationships

Basic relationships for open channel flow are the same as for full-flowing conduits. Average velocities are determined according to the law of continuity of flow,

$$Q = VA$$

where Q = discharge, cfs
V = average velocity, fps
A = cross-sectional flow area, sq.ft.

Kinetic energy of flow is expressed in terms of head by the velocity head equation

$$H_v = \frac{V^2}{2g}$$

where H_v = velocity head, ft. of water
V = average velocity, fps
g = acceleration of gravity, 32.16 ft./sec.^{2}

Energy losses are computed in the same manner as for closed conduits. However, the loss coefficient in the equation

$$H_L = K\frac{V^2}{2g}$$

will be different due to different flow geometry.

Most important, the universal law of conservation of energy applies to flow in open channels as well as in closed conduits.

Energy Concept of Flow in Open Channels

The equations for flow in open channels are based on the principles expressed by Bernoulli's equation. The equation for flow with a free surface, as normally used, is slightly different in appearance from that for closed conduits. The term for pressure is eliminated since the surface pressure is assumed to be constant and equal to the atmosphere for all parts of the free water surface at all times. The term for elevation is divided into terms for relative elevation of the bottom of the channel and the depth of water in the channel. Bernoulli's equation for open channel flow is thus written

$$d + z + \frac{V^2}{2g} = \text{constant}$$

in which d = depth above bottom of channel
z = elevation of bottom of channel above horizontal datum
$\frac{V^2}{2g}$ = velocity head

If the elevation of the headwater surface defines the total energy

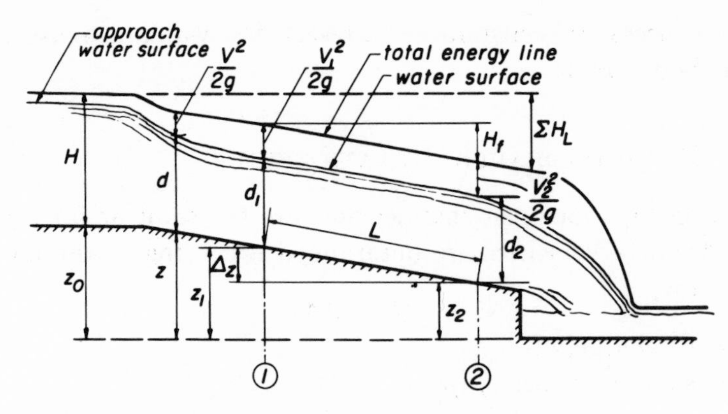

Fig. 30. Definition sketch for open channel flow.

available to the flow system, a more specific form of Bernoulli's equation may be written which accounts for losses and relates flow at any point in the system to the headwater elevation

$$H + (Z_o - Z) = d + \frac{V^2}{2g} + \sum H_L$$

in which H_L = energy loss

Headwater elevation is properly expressed by the sum of H and Z_o as illustrated in Fig. 30.

Of primary concern in open channel problems is the location of the free water surface. Although the Bernoulli equation establishes basic relationships, it does not permit direct solution of the various factors. Additional relationships are required to establish the depth at specific locations, after which the surface profile may be defined according to Bernoulli's equation.

Relationship of Free Surface to Flow

The principles of flow in open channels are illustrated in Fig. 30. The total energy line defines the available energy at any point in the channel. Changes in elevation of this line reflect losses and the manner in which they take place. In the example, an initial loss is experienced at the entrance and is shown as occurring over a short reach of channel near the entrance. Flow at the entrance is nonuniform as the transition is made from the comparatively still headwater to equilibrium flow in the channel. The velocity continually increases in this region as is indicated by increasing velocity head, measured between the total energy line and the hydraulic grade line. Note that in open channel flow the hydraulic grade line corresponds to the free water surface. Near the entrance the slope of the total energy line continues to increase with increasing velocity. Eventually, equilibrium is established at a velocity sufficient to cause a rate of friction loss equal to the slope of the channel bottom. At this condition, the slope of the total energy line, the water surface, and the channel bottom are parallel. This condition will continue to exist as long as the channel continues without change in shape, slope, or roughness.

Friction in Open Channel Flow

When equilibrium is established in an open channel the discharge is governed by a control section. According to the law of continuity of flow, the same rate of flow passes each section of the channel and will be equal to the flow at the controlling section. Several types of control are possible, the most common type being friction control. It is usually the dominant factor in long channels.

The average velocity established by channel friction may be determined by use of Manning's equation

$$V = \frac{1.486}{n} R^{2/3} S_o^{1/2}$$

where V = average velocity
n = channel friction factor
R = hydraulic radius
S_o = channel slope

This equation may also be used for conduits flowing full, as previously discussed, when the proper evaluations of the hydraulic radius and slope are made. The hydraulic radius for an open channel is defined by

$$R = \frac{A}{P}$$

where A = cross-sectional area of flow
P = wetted channel perimeter

In a closed conduit the slope is considered as the slope of the energy grade line, which is parallel to the water surface in open channel flow.

Discharge in an open channel is determined from Manning's equation by applying the flow area to the expression for velocity:

$$Q = \frac{1.486}{n} A R^{2/3} S_o^{1/2}.$$

The depth of flow resulting from friction control is the "normal" depth. Flow at depths either greater or less than normal is a condition of non-uniform flow.

Open Channel Flow Relationships

Problems in open channel flow usually require evaluation of depth and velocity of flow from one section of the channel to another. Useful simplified relationships can be derived from consideration of the sketch in Fig. 30. It may be seen that the elevation of any point on the total energy line is always determined by adding the sum of the depth and velocity head to the elevation of the channel invert, thus

$$E = Z + \left(d + \frac{V^2}{2g}\right)$$

Inasmuch as the channel elevation is always known, flow relationships at any section can be expressed in terms of specific energy H_o where

$$H_o = d + \frac{V^2}{2g}.$$

Any change in specific energy can be added to H_o, using proper algebraic signs, to determine the conditions of flow at any other section.

As an example, applying the concept of specific energy to sections 1 and 2 in Fig. 30, the sections of channel where uniform flow exists, it is found that

$$(H_o)_1 + Z_1 = (H_o)_2 + Z_2 + H_f$$

or

$$(H_o)_1 + (Z_1 - Z_2) = (H_o)_2 + H_f$$

From the conditions of uniform flow (Manning's equation) it is known that

$$H_f = Z_1 - Z_2.$$

Thus, the specific energy at sections 1 and 2 is the same and the conditions of flow are unchanged. However, any unbalance between energy gain due to fall (change in elevation) and loss due to friction or other causes will require a change in depth and velocity.

The expression for specific energy may be further generalized by writing the term for velocity in terms of discharge and depth thus:

$$H_o = d + \frac{Q^2}{2gW^2d^2}$$

where W = channel width

Since both discharge and width are constant, these terms may be replaced by a single term for discharge per unit width, q, where

$$q = \frac{Q}{W}$$

which is also constant for a rectangular channel of uniform width. The factor q may be considered as the unit discharge or flow concentration. The expression for specific energy becomes

$$H_o = d + \frac{q^2}{2gd^2}.$$

From an examination of this expression it is evident that for a constant value of unit discharge q there are an infinite number of values for H_o. Furthermore, there are two depths, alternate depths, that result in the same specific energy H_o. At the lower depth, velocities will be high or "shooting" while at the greater depth, velocities will be slow or "tranquil." Solution of the specific energy equation for depth at a known energy content is somewhat laborious since it involves the solution of a cubic equation. It is more convenient and meaningful to represent the specific energy equation as a family of curves in a specific energy diagram for various values of unit discharge as illustrated in Fig. 31. It will be noted that for each value of q there is a minimum specific energy value corresponding to critical depth d_c. Conventional usage refers to all depths above critical depth as greater than critical and all depths below critical as less than critical. Conversely, velocity of flow is referred to as subcritical and supercritical, respectively.

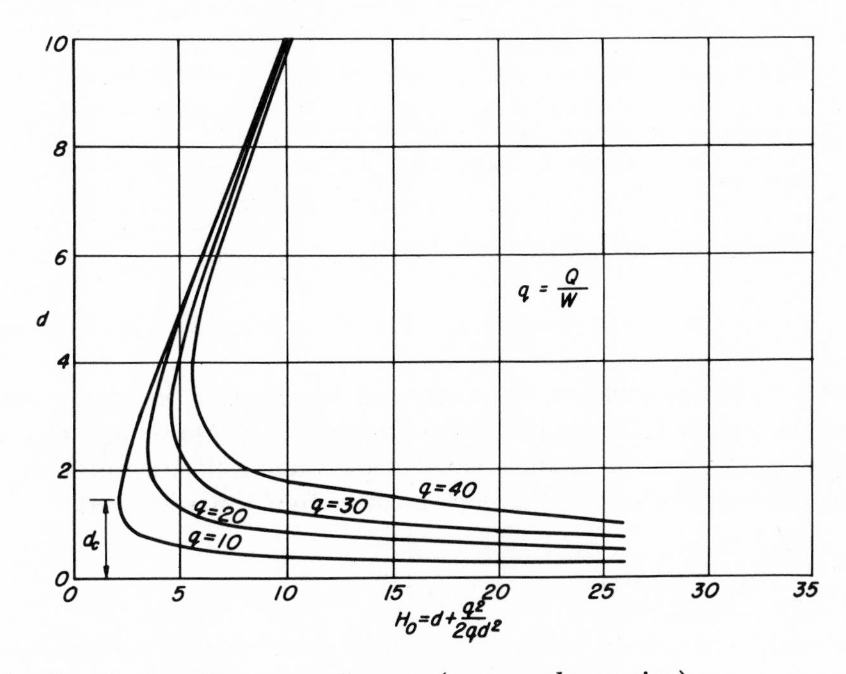

Fig. 31. Specific energy diagram (rectangular section).

Further examination of the specific energy equation shows that a similar family of curves can be constructed for constant values of H_o with depth and unit discharge as the variables. This type of curve, known as the discharge diagram, is illustrated schematically in Fig. 32 to show the location of the energy grade line for uniform flow in a sloping channel. It will be noted that this curve is similar to the curves in Fig. 31, showing that maximum discharge will occur at a particular depth for a given energy content. This is the critical depth and corresponds to the critical depth found from Fig. 31 for the indicated maximum unit discharge.

Curves of the type illustrated in Figs. 31 and 32 will be useful in establishing the operational characteristics of culvert barrels. It should be realized that these curves are completely general, indicating the necessary division of potential energy (depth) and kinetic energy (velocity head) for known discharges and total energy contents. The effect of friction and slope is considered by the effect these factors have on the total energy available at any given point in the channel. If constant depth and velocity over a length of channel are to be achieved, the losses due to

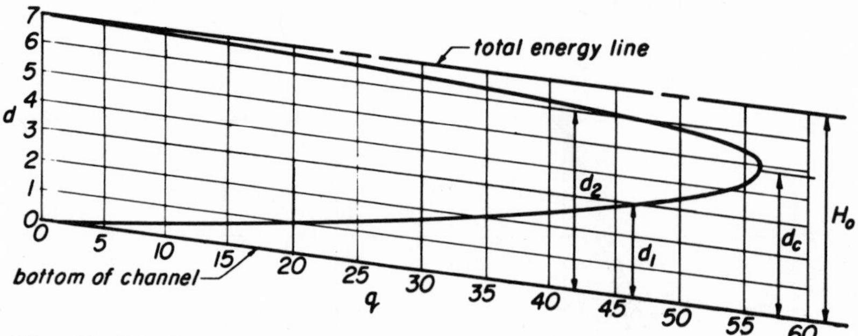

Fig. 32. Discharge diagram (rectangular section).

friction must be exactly counterbalanced by the gain in energy due to slope. Frictional losses may be determined from Manning's equation. Therefore, in order to produce equal depths and velocities in a channel twice as rough as another, the slope must be four times as great.

SPECIFIC HEAD DIAGRAM

It is often desirable to analyze flow in an open channel on the basis of changes in specific head due to channel changes. Specific head can be either increased or decreased. Decreases are due to losses caused by widening or narrowing the channel, channel obstructions, and roughness. Increases are caused by increasing the slope, dropping the bottom of the channel, or decreasing the friction effect. Analysis can be made, using the specific head concept, through use of the specific head diagram.

The specific head diagram was originally intended for use with rectangular channels. However, it is adaptable to channels with any cross-section by consideration of the average depth corresponding to the surface width. In reference to Fig. 33 (cross-section of a circular channel), the average depth is the flow area divided by the surface width,

$$d_{avg} = \frac{A}{W}.$$

The average velocity can be determined in the usual manner, according

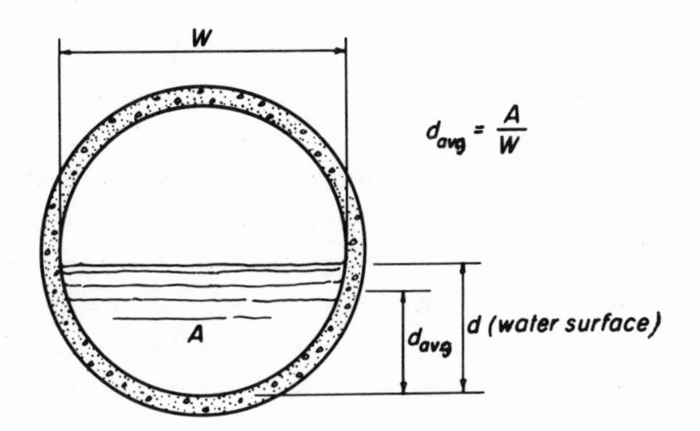

Fig. 33. Determination of average depth.

to the continuity equation

$$V = \frac{Q}{A} = \frac{Q}{Wd_{avg}}$$

which reduces to the form

$$V = \frac{q}{d_{avg}}$$

This form is identical with the original concept of unit discharge and may be used in the specific head relationships as the general case. However, the depth term representing potential energy must be used as actual depth and not average depth. The discharge diagram and the specific head diagram are, therefore, perfectly general and may be used for all channel shapes.

Use of Specific Head Diagram

Since the unit discharge acts as an independent variable, an analysis of open channel characteristics can best be made by use of the specific head diagram. The variability of the unit discharge is not inconsistent with the continuity theory since the unit discharge will change with a change in channel dimensions in accordance with the theory of continuity. Any change in the width of the channel will cause a corresponding change in the unit discharge. Consideration of an example will illustrate the effect and will reveal some surprising phenomena.

Consider a channel 2 ft. wide discharging at the rate of 20 cfs and flowing at a depth of 0.6 ft. The specific head is determined from the specific energy diagram, Fig. 31, for unit discharge of 10 cfs per foot. The specific head is determined to be 5.0 ft. If the channel were narrowed to 1 ft., unit discharge would be increased to 20 cfs per foot. If it is assumed that no loss in energy took place in the change, the depth of flow would be determined by a specific head of 5.0 ft. at a unit discharge of 20 cfs per foot. The resulting depth in this case would be 1.3 ft.

A different situation would exist if, for the same flow and initial channel width of 2 ft., the slope were adjusted so that the water was flowing at an initial depth of 4 ft. Narrowing the channel to 1 ft. would in this case cause the water surface to fall from 4 ft. to 3.6 ft. instead of rising as in the previous case. The difference in the two cases is due to the manner in which the energy was divided between kinetic and potential energy. In the former case, the energy existed principally as kinetic energy, which cannot increase without increasing the specific head. In order to conform to an increase in the unit discharge without increasing the specific head, the depth must necessarily increase. In the latter case, the energy exists principally as potential energy, which must decrease to cause an increase in velocity at no change in specific head.

EFFECT OF LOSSES IN OPEN CHANNEL FLOW

Losses in an open channel are experienced in the same manner as they are in full-flowing conduits. The effect of the various sources of the loss, such as bends, changes in sections, and expansions, is dependent upon the velocity head and is computed by the loss formula,

$$H_L = K_L \frac{V^2}{2g}.$$

The loss coefficient K_L for open channels will not necessarily be the same as for full conduits for the same source of energy loss. This is due to the influence of the free surface on the flow geometry. While flow contraction and expansion still occur, the effect will be attenuated to some degree.

The effect of losses on flow can be easily evaluated by use of the specific head diagram once the magnitude of the loss has been determined. Any uncompensated losses that occur will reduce the specific head and cause a corresponding adjustment in the depth of flow.

Consider the previous example of the channel 2 ft. wide flowing at a depth of 0.6 ft. and discharging at the rate of 20 cfs. The specific head in that case was determined to be 5.0 ft. If it is assumed that the transition from a channel 2 ft. wide to a channel 1 ft. wide caused a loss of 0.9 ft., the resulting depth after the transition would be determined from the specific head diagram for a specific head of 4.1 and a unit discharge of 20 cfs per foot. The resulting depth would be 1.6 ft. instead of 1.3 ft. as determined by consideration of no energy loss.

Similar analysis can be made for other situations involving either a net loss or gain in energy. It is merely necessary to determine the flow relationships at one point and to keep an account of the amount and location of energy changes. The specific head diagram may be used in either direction of flow to establish the flow relationship at any point in the channel.

Optimum Flow in Channels

Critical Depth and Critical Velocity

The flow established in a hydraulic system is dependent upon the total energy available between the inlet and the outlet. The naturally occurring discharge is that which will completely expend all of the available energy. Energy is thus expended in the flow system at entrances, in friction and other sources of loss, and in velocity head and depth. As may be seen from Fig. 31, it is possible to have many different discharges at the same energy level. However, the greatest attainable discharge at a given energy level occurs at critical depth d_c. The velocity associated with critical depth is critical velocity V_c and may be regarded as the optimum velocity for the available energy. An expression may be determined for critical depth from the specific energy equation, giving

$$d_c = \sqrt[3]{\frac{q^2}{g}}$$

This formula pertains specifically to rectangular channels but may be applied to channels of any shape by computing the equivalent average depth d_{avg}. In terms of the critical velocity V_c the relationship is

$$\frac{V_c^2}{2g} = \frac{(d_{avg})_c}{2} = \frac{A_c}{2W}$$

where A_c = cross-sectional area at critical flow
W = surface width

Curves for easy calculation of average depth d_{avg} and surface width W

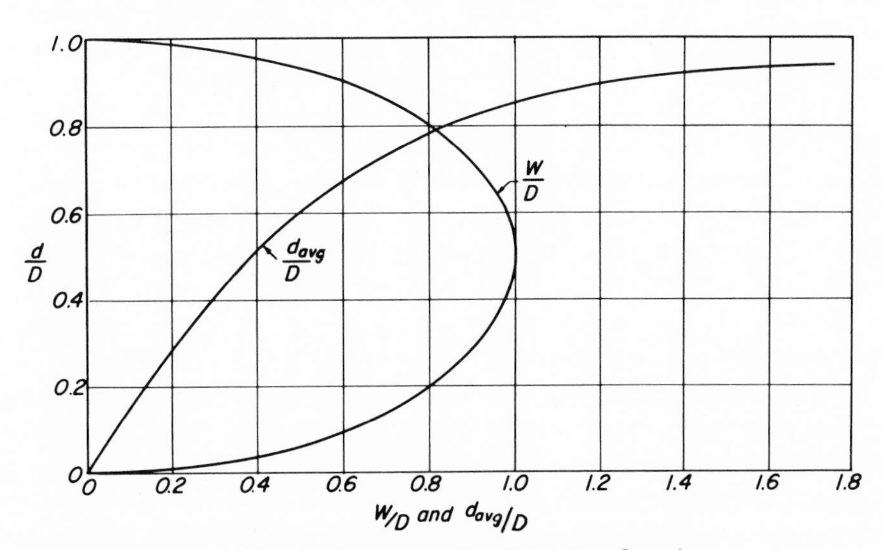

Fig. 34. Surface width and average depth in circular pipe.

for circular pipe are given in Fig. 34. Critical depth in circular pipe can then be computed by first determining the average depth at critical velocity, $(d_{avg})_c$, and then selecting the depth in a circular pipe corresponding to the average depth.

An understanding of the concept of critical depth is essential to understanding the mechanics of flow in pipe culverts. While theoretical considerations point to the desirability of achieving critical flow, this condition is almost never realized in operating hydraulics. However, it is desirable to approach critical conditions as an optimum to maximize the discharge for a given headwater. Therefore, critical flow is often used as a basis for establishing the conditions of optimum design as a goal to be approached.

CRITICAL DEPTH IN CIRCULAR SECTIONS

The complexity of the geometry of part-full circular sections discourages a direct mathematical solution for determining the critical depth in pipe. A general graphical solution is presented in Fig. 35 which is applicable to pipe of all sizes for all discharges. To make the curve generally applicable, ratios with dimensionless properties are used. Hence, the ratio of $Q/D^{5/2}$ will determine the critical depth in a pipe, d_c, in terms of d_c/D. The critical depth, measured from the pipe invert, is determined as follows:

$$d_c = \left(\frac{d_c}{D}\right) \times D.$$

This curve is intended to be used only to determine the critical depth

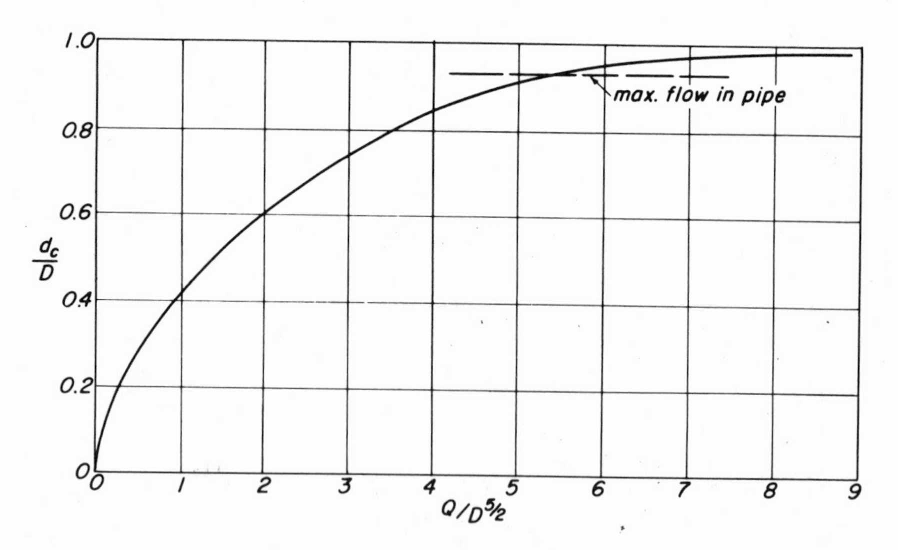

Fig. 35. Critical depth in circular pipe.

d_c corresponding to the total discharge Q in the pipe. Actual depth of flow must be established by means of the flow relationships involving entrance losses, resistance losses (Manning's equation), and specific energy relationships. If it is desired to base computations on critical flow, the slope of the channel must be adjusted in conjunction with the losses to make the design depth equal to the critical depth.

Hydraulic Features of Circular Conduits

Hydraulic Elements

Computations for flow in circular sections are often required and are difficult to make due to the complex relationship between depth and the other hydraulic factors. These computations are greatly simplified by use of the chart of hydraulic elements for circular pipe shown in Fig. 36. In this chart the hydraulic radius, area of flow, velocity, and discharge are shown in terms of depth for a full pipe. The values are based on Manning's

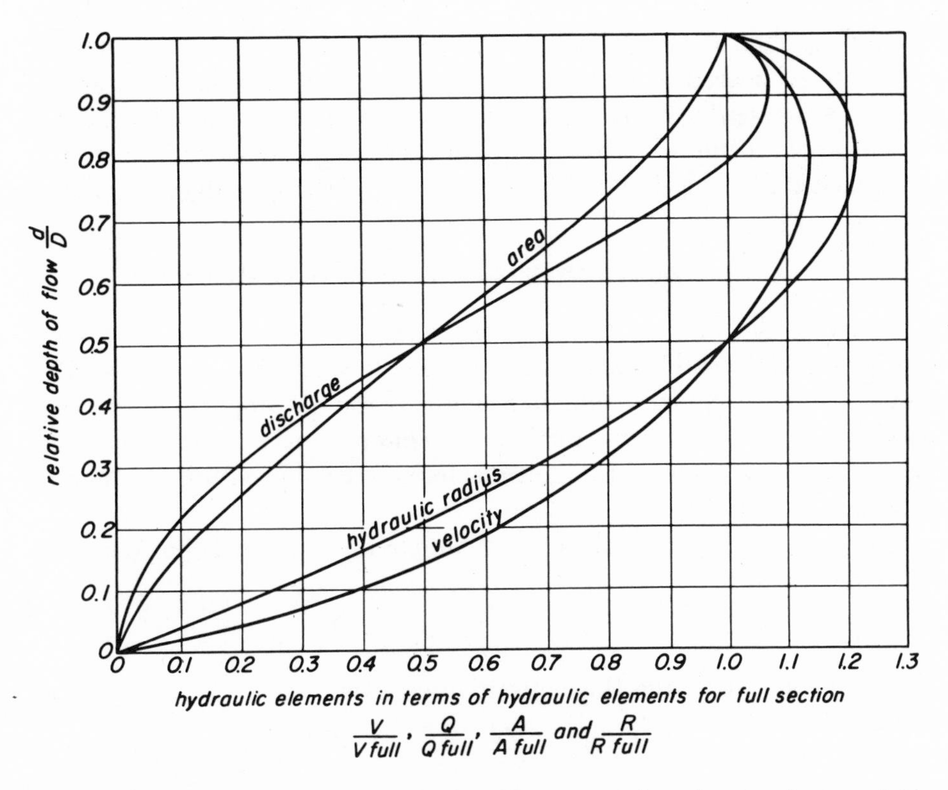

Fig. 36. Hydraulic elements—relative flow properties of a circular conduit.

formula in which the full section values are computed as follows:

$$A_f = \frac{\pi}{4}D^2$$

$$R_f = \frac{D}{4}$$

$$V_f = \frac{0.589}{n}D^{2/3}S_o^{1/2}$$

$$Q_f = \frac{0.462}{n}D^{8/3}S_o^{1/2}$$

The effect of friction as expressed by the coefficient n is assumed constant for all depths.

As an example of the use of the chart, consider a pipe flowing 0.6 full. Each element is computed from Fig. 36 as follows:

$$\text{Area} = 0.64A_f$$

$$\text{Hydraulic Radius} = 1.1R_f$$

$$\text{Velocity} = 1.06V_f$$

$$\text{Discharge} = 0.69Q_f$$

Final values depend on the internal diameter of the pipe, slope, and pipe roughness.

Fig. 36 illustrates an important property of circular pipe. Due to the effect of geometry on the hydraulic radius, the maximum open channel discharge capacity of a circular pipe will occur at a depth equal to 0.93 of the diameter. Theoretical maximum discharge occurs at this depth and is 1.075 times the discharge of a full pipe. A discharge rate equal to the full pipe discharge for unpressurized flow will then occur before the maximum rate is reached at a depth equal to 82 per cent of the pipe diameter.

ENERGY RELATIONSHIPS IN CIRCULAR SECTIONS

The discharge diagram and the specific energy diagram provide a convenient means of establishing the depth of flow in open channels. The diagrams established for rectangular channels are not applicable to other shapes. Comparable diagrams for circular channels may be used by making use of a modification of the unit discharge term q used for rectangular channels.

The equation for specific energy in circular channels in terms of velocity head and depth is

$$H_o = \frac{V^2}{2g} + d.$$

In terms of total discharge this equation becomes

$$H_o = \frac{Q^2}{2gA^2} + d$$

which can be rewritten in terms of pipe diameter and a ratio obtained from the chart of circular elements (Fig. 36) as

$$H_o = \frac{Q^2}{2ga^2A_f^2} + d$$

where a = area of flow divided by area of full pipe, A/A_f. In order to make the specific energy equation perfectly applicable to all circular channels without regard to size, it is necessary to divide both sides of the expression by the pipe diameter, thus

$$\frac{H_o}{D} = \frac{0.0252Q^2}{a^2D^5} + \frac{d}{D}.$$

In this form the specific energy equation is applicable to all circular channels in which H_o/D is a function of $Q/D^{5/2}$ and d/D, both of which are terms with dimensionless characteristics. This equation can be used to establish the specific energy diagram for circular channels similar to the corresponding diagram for rectangular channels in which the parameter for unit discharge q is replaced by a discharge factor $Q/D^{5/2}$. For simplicity, the term $Q/D^{5/2}$ will be called the discharge factor and will be indicated by a symbol denoting unit discharge in a circular channel, q_c. The equation for specific energy is then written

$$\frac{H_o}{D} = \frac{0.0252q_c^2}{a^2} + \frac{d}{D}.$$

The resulting specific energy diagram shown in Fig. 37 may be used to determine depth of flow in circular channels.

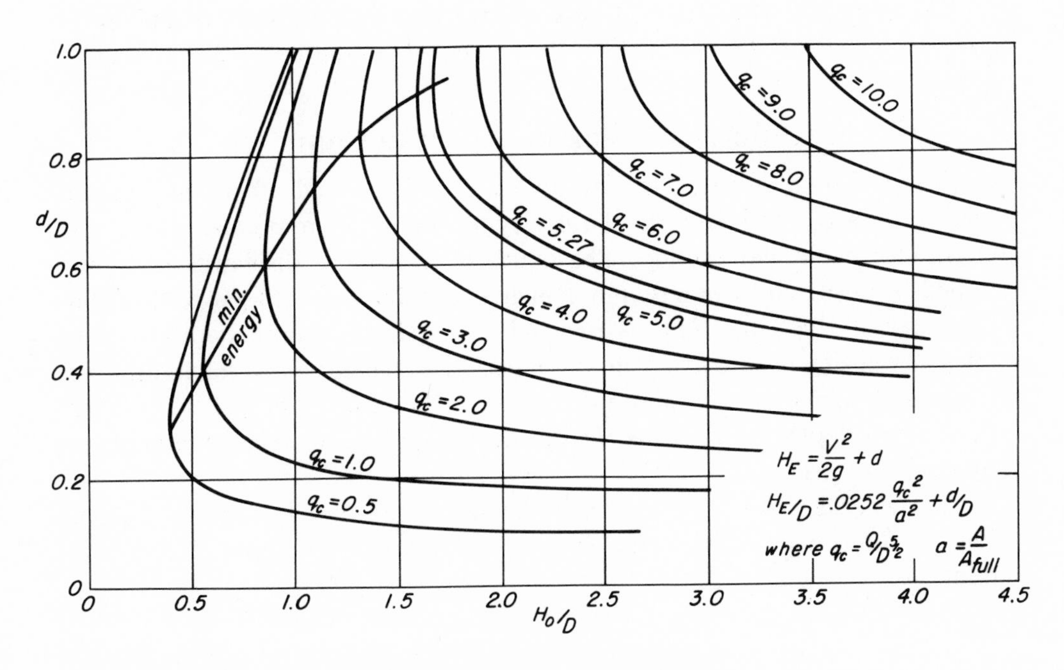

Fig. 37. Specific energy diagrams for circular channels.

APPLICATION OF PRINCIPLES OF CRITICAL DEPTH

The depth of flow in a channel is established by energy relationships. The energy existing at any point along the channel is largely determined by the initial headwater elevation, entrance losses, frictional losses, and channel slope. It can be seen from Figs. 32 and 37 that the depth of flow will be established by the discharge and the specific energy. It can also be seen that for each discharge rate there is a corresponding single value of critical depth. While the depth of flow may be at critical, the actual depth will usually be either greater or less than critical. When the actual depth of flow is less than the critical depth, the discharge in the channel is controlled by the entrance conditions of the channel. When the depth of flow is greater than the critical depth, the discharge is controlled by flow conditions in the barrel and at the outlet. Fig. 31 shows that the discharge will be a maximum for a given energy level when the actual depth corresponds to the critical depth. This condition can only be maintained in the laboratory and becomes a practical factor only in attempting to design for, or approach, the conditions of optimum discharge.

Because of its mathematical significance, critical depth will often be referred to as a guide or basis for design. As previously mentioned, Fig. 35 is a convenient chart to quickly determine critical depth in circular channels. The critical depth is determined from Fig. 35 by selecting the value of d_c/D corresponding to the ratio $Q/D^{5/2}$. The critical depth d_c is obtained by multiplying the ratio d_c/D by the actual diameter. Hence, for a discharge of 17 cfs in a 24-in.-diameter pipe, d_c/D is determined from Fig. 35 to be 0.74. The critical depth is then calculated to be $0.74 \times 2.0 = 1.48$ ft.

OPTIMUM DISCHARGE IN CIRCULAR CONDUITS

Optimum discharge in a circular pipe will be achieved when the pipe is placed so as to produce critical velocity at the depth maximizing the discharge for a circular section. The depth of maximum discharge is determined from the chart of circular elements, Fig. 36, to be 93 per cent of the diameter of the pipe. This is referred to as the optimum depth. When critical velocity occurs at optimum depth, the discharge is a maximum for the available energy. Optimum discharge is therefore obtained by making the critical depth the same as the optimum depth. This condition is given by $d_c/D = 0.93$.

A general expression for optimum discharge can be obtained from Fig. 35 for the foregoing relationship. Optimum discharge is thus determined to be

$$Q_{op} = 5.27D^{5/2}.$$

It is established that a long culvert designed to operate at optimum conditions will flow part full at discharges less than optimum and will flow full at discharges greater than optimum. Optimum discharge values are useful as a guide in establishing the operating characteristics for culvert design.

Critical Slope

In the foregoing sections it has been pointed out that there exists one depth of flow, known as the critical depth, for every discharge in a given channel. Flow at this depth represents the minimum possible energy level for the particular discharge. In the usual case of uniform flow the energy level is greater than that indicated by critical depth. Correspondingly, the depth of flow is greater or less than critical depth. Inasmuch as the relative value of the actual depth of flow to the critical depth is indicative of the type of flow in an open channel, the value for critical depth is an important consideration. From Manning's equation, the slope necessary to produce uniform flow at critical depth for a particular discharge can be computed and is identified as the critical slope. The value of the critical slope relative to actual slope is indicative of the operational characteristics of pipe culverts.

If the actual slope of a culvert exceeds the critical slope, there is no likelihood that the pipe will flow full at the particular discharge as long as the outlet remains unsubmerged. On the other hand, if the actual slope is less than the critical slope, the character of the flow must be further investigated.

The critical slope is not a unique value for a given size pipe. It varies with the discharge rate, wall roughness, and pipe size. The designer should be cautious in assuming that the design slope of a culvert installation exceeds the critical slope.

Due to the variable nature of the critical slope, it is desirable to establish a single number with significance for pipe culvert design. By making use of the concept of optimum discharge, a number that may be defined as optimum critical slope $(S_c)_{op}$ is established. Optimum critical slope defines the slope associated with the optimum discharge in a pipe of given size. Expressed in terms more readily comprehended, this is the minimum slope that will produce the maximum discharge without filling the pipe.

The optimum discharge given in the preceding section is

$$Q_{op} = 5.27D^{5/2}$$

Inserting the expression for optimum discharge in Manning's equation, it is established that

$$(S_c)_{op} = 111 \frac{n^2}{D^{1/3}}.$$

This number is also significant in establishing the combined effect of roughness and pipe diameter. For comparative purposes, it is applicable to any discharge for the same size pipe. Thus for a given discharge, comparable hydraulic characteristics will exist in two pipes of the same size in which one is twice as rough as the other as long as the rougher pipe is placed on a slope four times as great as the smoother pipe.

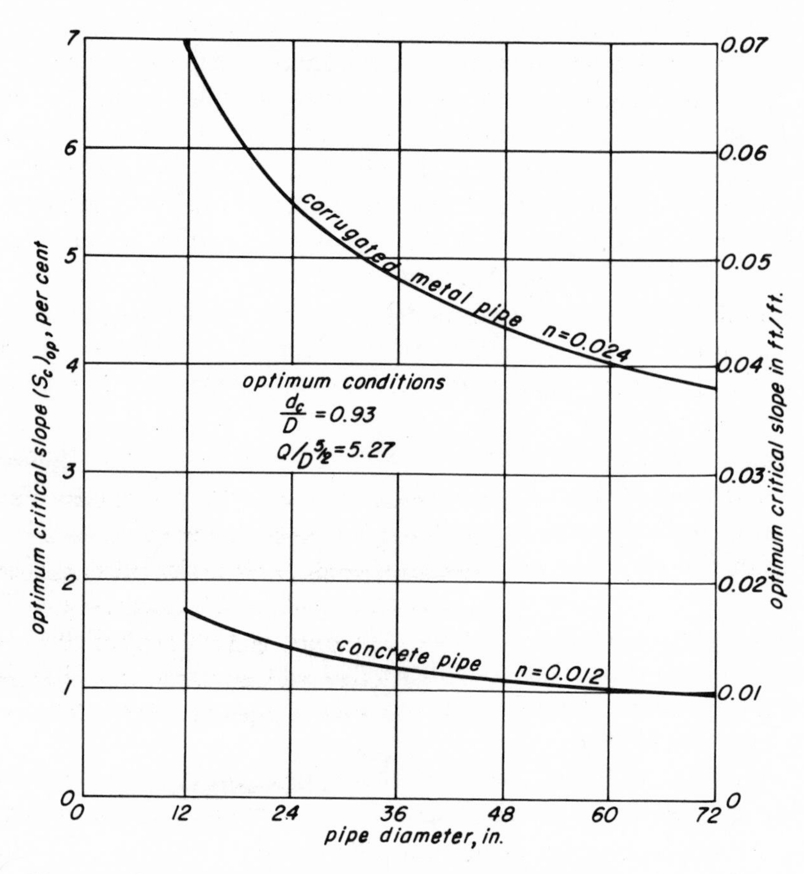

Fig. 38. Optimum critical slope for circular pipe.

Optimum critical slopes $(S_c)_{op}$ can be obtained directly from the curves of Fig. 38 for two of the most common pipe culvert materials. The curve given for concrete pipe is based on a Manning n of 0.012 and that for corrugated metal pipe is based on a Manning n of 0.024. Curves for other values of n can be constructed from the equation for optimum critical slope.

References

1. Bossy, H. G., "Hydraulics of Conventional Highway Culverts," unpublished paper presented at the Tenth National Conference, Hydraulic Division, American Society of Civil Engineers, Urbana, Ill., August 1961. (Copies available from Division of Hydraulic Research, Bureau of Public Roads, Washington, D.C.)
2. Bradley, J. N., and Thompson, L. R., *Friction Factors for Large Conduits Flowing Full*, Monograph No. 7, U.S. Bureau of Reclamation, Denver, Colo., 1951.
3. Linsley, Ray H., and Franzini, Joseph B., *Elements of Hydraulic Engineering*, New York, McGraw-Hill Book Co., 1955.
4. Neil, Charles R., "Hydraulic Roughness of Corrugated Pipes," ASCE, *Hydraulics Journal*, Vol. 88, No. Hy. 3, May 1962, p. 23.
5. Rouse, Hunter, *Elementary Mechanics of Fluids*, New York, John Wiley & Sons, 1957.
6. Straub, Loring G., and Morris, Henry, "Hydraulic Data Comparison of Concrete and Corrugated Metal Culvert Pipes," Technical Paper No. 3, Series B, University of Minnesota, Hydraulic Laboratory, St. Anthony Falls, 1951.
7. Straub, Loring G.; Bowers, Charles E.; and Pilch, Meir, "Resistance to Flow in Two Types of Concrete Pipe," Technical Paper No. 22, Series B, University of Minnesota, Hydraulic Laboratory, St. Anthony Falls, 1960.
8. *Friction Losses in Corrugated Metal Pipe*, Portland District Report No. 40-1, U.S. Army Corps of Engineers, Bonneville Hydraulic Laboratory, Portland, Ore., 1955.
9. *Hydraulic Design Criteria*, tenth issue of *Charts*, U.S. Army Corps of Engineers, Vicksburg, Miss., 1960.
10. King, Horace W., *Handbook of Hydraulics*, New York, McGraw-Hill Book Co., fourth edition, 1954.

4

Culvert Operation

THE HYDRAULIC OPERATION OF PIPE CULVERTS IS COMPLEX and often difficult to predict. However, once the type of operation is established, the analysis may proceed according to well-defined principles. It is well known that the discharge in a culvert is controlled by one of three means:

1. The geometry of the inlet
2. The combined effect of entrance, length, slope, and roughness of the pipe barrel
3. The elevation of the tailwater at the outlet

Furthermore, these conditions are identifiable by the characteristics of the resulting flow.

In the first case, the barrel of the culvert pipe will flow part full. The discharge is not affected by changes in slope or roughness of the pipe barrel.

In the second case, the characteristics of the flow do not always identify the type of flow. It is possible, particularly at low flows, for length, slope, and roughness to control the discharge without causing the pipe to flow full. However, this is not a common occurrence at design discharges which consider high flows. The usual condition for this type of flow at design discharges is one in which the pipe cross-section flows full for a major portion of the length of the culvert. The discharge in this case is controlled by the combined effect of all hydraulic factors.

The third type of control is similar in all respects to the second except that the downstream depth submerges the outlet and forces the culvert to flow full.

Hydraulic Factors of Culvert Design

The objective of the hydraulic design of pipe culverts is to establish the most economical size of pipe to operate at a predetermined discharge without exceeding an allowable headwater depth. It may be necessary to consider several different designs to establish the best choice. The different designs may operate similarly or entirely differently depending upon the interacting influences of the several important hydraulic factors involved in the mechanics of flow.

The fundamental principles contributing to the hydraulic operation of pipe culverts are discussed in the preceding sections. Figs. 39 and 40 indicate the application of the principles and the area of influence. Orifice effects occur at the entrance and are important factors in culvert operation. These effects are expressed by efficiency factor K_e or discharge factor C_d. The necessary energy for establishment of flow results in a headwater depth HW. Within the culvert the energy of the headwater is divided into depth, d; velocity of flow, V; and head loss, H_L. Head loss is the accumu-

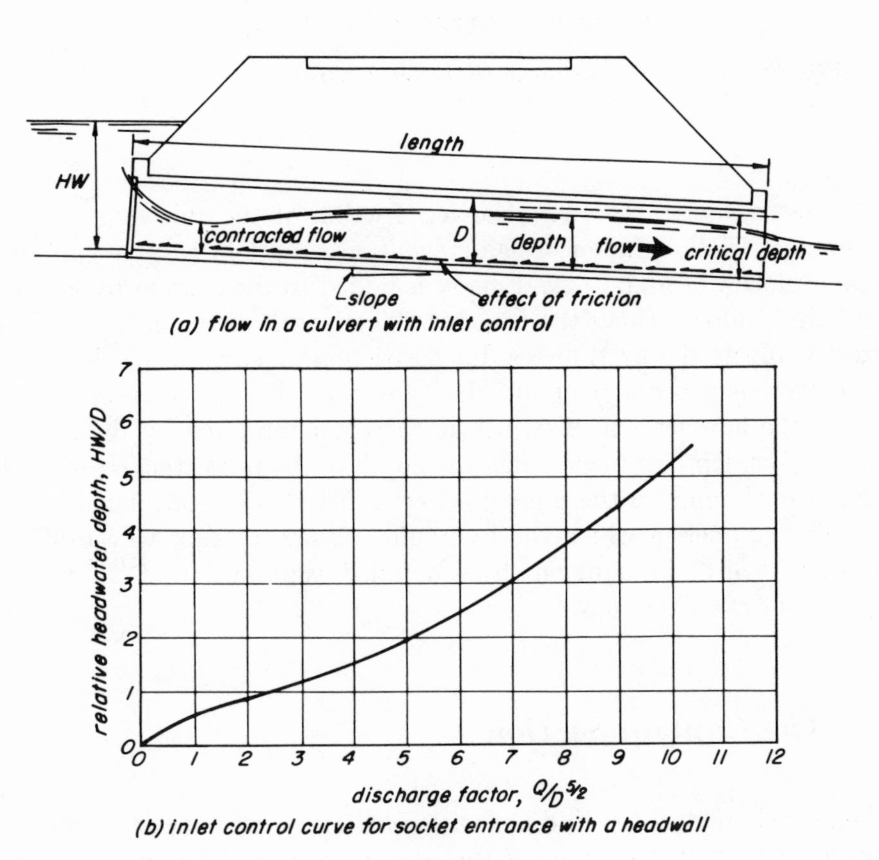

Fig. 39. Culvert operation with inlet control.

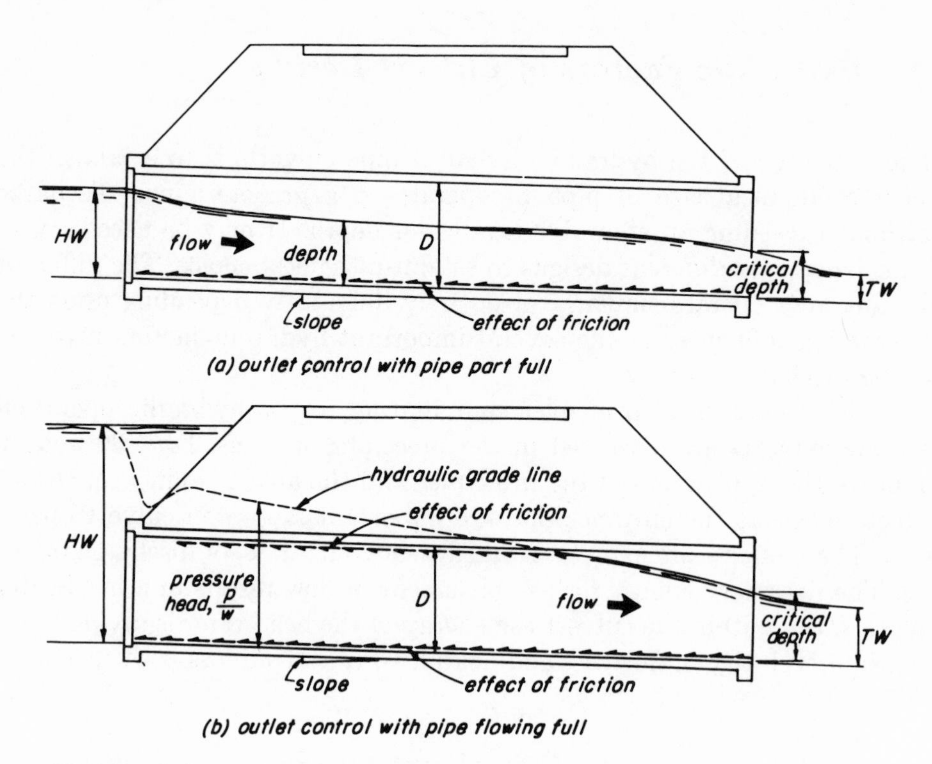

Fig. 40. Culvert operation with outlet control.

lated losses due to the entrance, K_e; friction of the sidewalls related to Manning's friction factor n; and eventually outlet losses equal to the actual velocity head, $\alpha V^2/2g$. Energy is added to the system by the fall of the barrel, slope S times the length L. The length of the culvert pipe also directly affects the head losses due to friction. The resulting discharge in the culvert is dependent upon velocity of flow, V, and the cross-sectional area of the flow section, A, which in turn is determined by the geometric effect of the depth of flow. When the depth of the tailwater, H_T, is greater than critical depth in the pipe, its effect must also be considered.

The manner in which the hydraulic factors interact to establish the discharge will be brought out by a detailed examination of the two principal types of culvert flow.

The Control Section

The flow characteristics and hence the discharge capacity of a culvert are determined by the location of the control section. The principle of the control section may be illustrated by a control valve in a pipeline. Adjustment of the valve will regulate the rate of flow. This being the case, the rest of the system must obviously have a greater capacity than is actually used. The control section may be envisioned as the section of the culvert pipe which operates at maximum capacity. Only rarely, in an extremely simple hydraulic system, do all parts of the system have equal discharge capacity.

Flow in culverts is also controlled by the hydraulic capacity of one section of the installation. As previously mentioned, the discharge is either controlled at the culvert entrance or at the outlet and is designated inlet control and outlet control, respectively. In general, inlet control will exist as long as the ability of the culvert pipe barrel to carry the flow exceeds the ability of water to enter the culvert through the inlet. Outlet control will exist when the ability of the pipe barrel to carry water away from the entrance is less than the flow that can enter the inlet. The location of the control section will shift as the relative capacities of the entrance and barrel sections change with increasing or decreasing discharge.

Inlet Control

With inlet control operation the discharge rate is independent of the length of the pipe, the slope, or the roughness of the pipe wall. The discharge will be dependent only upon the headwater elevation above the invert at the entrance, the pipe size, and the entrance geometry. Variation in factors affecting the culvert barrel will affect the flow characteristics within the culvert barrel but will have no effect on the total discharge. Total discharge can only be affected, in this case, by variations in barrel design that would cause the control section to shift to the outlet. When this occurs, the depth of flow in the barrel exceeds the critical depth and consequently causes the inlet and the barrel to operate collectively instead of separately.

The culvert will always flow part full when it is operating with inlet control. The factors that control the discharge capacity are the shape, entrance edge, and the pipe size. In many cases, particularly at higher discharges, the headwater will submerge the entrance of a culvert operating with inlet control. In these cases, flow contractions occurring at the entrance limit the flow. Fig. 39 illustrates the manner in which culverts operate when the control is located at the entrance. The depth of water in the barrel is determined by the depth of flow at the entrance, pipe size, roughness, slope, and length of the barrel. Roughness, slope, and length are not influential in determining the discharge capacity of a culvert operating with inlet control. They are important, however, in determining outlet velocities and the discharge at which the operation of the culvert changes from inlet control to outlet control.

Fig. 39b illustrates the characteristic operational relationship between discharge and headwater depth with inlet control. For a given entrance geometry, it has been found that the discharge and headwater depth can be generalized for all pipe sizes by use of the ratios $Q/D^{5/2}$ and HW/D. Thus, the discharge and headwater depth can be firmly established for a given pipe size and entrance condition. Similar curves for each common entrance shape can be used for comparative analysis of inlet control flow.

Outlet Control

In outlet control operation, the total discharge is affected by all hydraulic factors upstream of the outlet. These factors are headwater elevation, entrance geometry, pipe size, wall roughness, barrel length, and slope. The tailwater elevation is not a factor for culverts flowing full as long as it is below the critical depth of flow at the pipe outlet.

Culverts flowing full must operate with outlet control. However, for flows that do not submerge the entrance, a culvert flowing part full may operate with either inlet control or outlet control. Tailwater depth will be important only in cases where the tailwater submerges critical depth at the pipe outlet. If the tailwater depth is greater than critical depth in the pipe, it may cause the control to shift from the inlet to the outlet. The effect of tailwater may be projected all the way upstream to the inlet or it may result in the formation of a hydraulic jump at the outlet.

The two cases of outlet control operation not affected by tailwater are illustrated in Fig. 40. Fig. 40a illustrates outlet control in which the entrance is not submerged. Outlet control exists in this case due to the effect of excessive friction in the barrel not compensated by slope. Fig. 40b illustrates outlet control with the inlet submerged. This is the most common situation when outlet control exists at the design discharge. In this case the pipe flows full.

The term "flows full" has been used by engineers to mean two different types of behavior in describing outlet control culvert flow. One condition of flow, as shown in Fig. 40b, is full for only part of the barrel length. In this case "flows full" refers to the upstream full pipe sections that are flowing under pressure, with the hydraulic grade line above the crown of the pipe. The length of backwater profile (free water surface) depends on barrel slope and friction losses. The other condition of flow often referred to as "flows full" is a result of a high tailwater submerging the culvert outlet. With the entrance and the outlet submerged, the culvert barrel will be full. Although the differences may appear to be minor, design aids based on the different conditions of flow result in different operating headwater. When used properly, the different design aids give compatible results in many cases.

Influence of Slope on Location of Control Section

The slope of the culvert barrel has a decided influence on the operating characteristics of pipe culvert installations. By means of the slope, energy is added to the flow within the pipe barrel to compensate in part or overcome the effect of friction. The effect of slope operates to a greater or lesser degree, depending on the length of the culvert. It is always necessary to ascertain the effect of slope to determine the location of the control section.

Often a cursory analysis of the effect of slope will suffice for design purposes. Such an analysis can be made for long culverts in which it can be assumed that the flow will approach or stabilize at normal depth. In this case a comparison of normal depth to the critical depth for the particular discharge will establish the type of control. If the normal depth is less than the critical depth, the control for the particular discharge will be at the entrance and the culvert will operate with inlet control. Conversely, if the normal depth is greater than the critical depth, the culvert, except in very few cases, essentially operates with outlet control.

The computations for determining the effect of slope on the location of the control section in long culverts can be greatly simplified by generalizing the factors that are involved. This has been done in Fig. 41. In this diagram relative depths are used in which the normal depth d and critical depth d_c are expressed in terms of diameter of the pipe, D. These functions are shown on the vertical scale. Discharge Q is expressed in terms of the discharge factor $Q/D^{5/2}$ and is shown on the horizontal scale. The combined effect of roughness, pipe size, and barrel slope may be expressed as a ratio of actual barrel slope S_o to the optimum critical slope $(S_c)_{op}$. The ratio of $S_o/(S_c)_{op}$ is referred to as the relative slope s_o and may be used to establish the relative depth d/D at various values of the discharge factor. Further, relative critical depth d_c/D may be plotted on the same chart to obtain an immediate comparison of normal depth and critical depth for any discharge.

Slope and discharge at a given depth are related by the Manning equation so that $Q \propto S^{1/2}$. Therefore, discharges in culverts with slopes relative to the optimum critical slope are also proportional at equal values of d/D. Thus the curves for relative slope in Fig. 41 are also represented

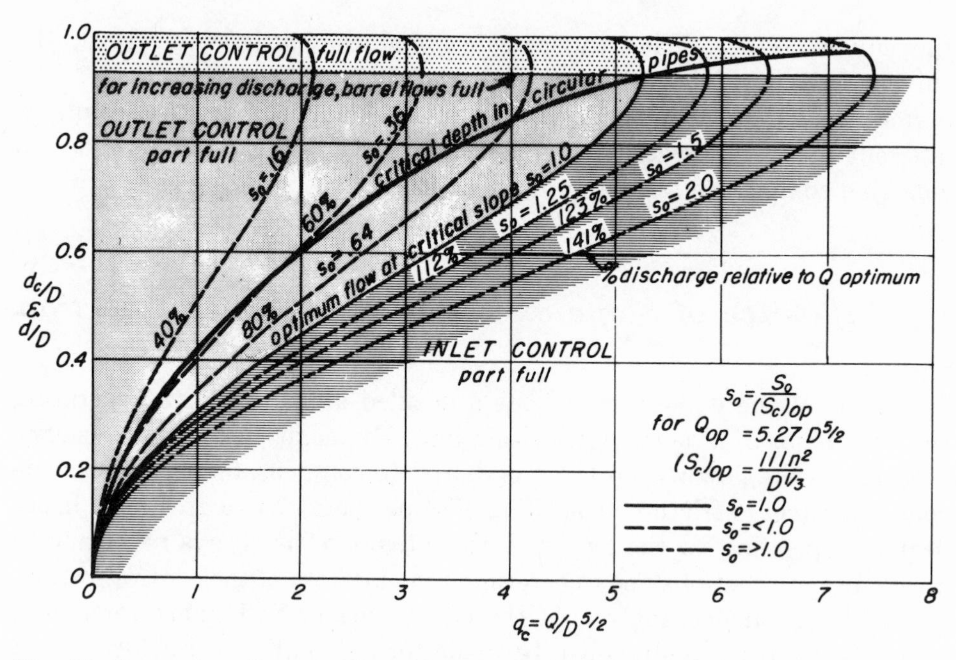

Fig. 41. Operation diagram for long circular culvert barrels flowing part full.

by values of relative discharge expressed in terms of per cent of the discharge in a pipe placed at a slope equal to the optimum critical slope.

Several important characteristics of flow in pipes are illustrated by the operations curves in the diagram of Fig. 41. First, it will be noted that major portions of the operations curve for relative slopes greater than 0.64 lie below the critical depth curve. This means that the normal depths for a large range of discharges are less than the critical depth. The control will be at the entrance whenever the normal depth is less than the critical depth. This establishes an area on the diagram in which the culvert will flow part full with inlet control.

Second, it will be noted that at low values of relative slope, major portions of the operations diagram lie above the critical depth curve. In this area the normal depth is greater than critical depth and the flow will be controlled by friction and conditions at the outlet. This establishes an area of part-full flow with outlet control. It should be recognized, however, that this diagram is based on flow in long culverts in which the depth of flow is constant. An attempt to apply this to short culverts would be overconservative inasmuch as actual depths in short culverts are somewhat less than normal depth.

A third important point illustrated in Fig. 41 will be noted in the shape of the operations curves. It will be observed that the maximum discharge that can be carried by a pipe with a free water surface at any slope is at a relative depth of 0.93. Any increase in discharge from this maximum point can only be carried by a pipe flowing full. A third area is thus established in which the culvert will flow full with outlet control. Any discharge in excess of the maximum indicated by the appropriate operations curve will fall into this area and will cause a long culvert to flow full.

The curves of Fig. 41 will be most useful for making a quick check of the probable type of culvert operation. Flow in a pipe culvert approaches normal depth from depths less than normal. Therefore, depths of flow in culverts of moderate or short length will be less than indicated by the operations curve. Because of this characteristic it is not necessary to check the type of operation further if the operations curve indicates that the culvert will flow part full with inlet control. The effect of length is discussed in more detail in the section "Culvert Control Length" beginning on page 105.

Submerged Outlets

In some cases the tailwater of the natural channel will submerge the outlet. The culvert in these cases will flow full with outlet control. The total discharge will be dependent on all the hydraulic factors of culvert design. The hydraulic grade line will terminate at the tailwater surface and the flow will be determined by the difference in the headwater and tailwater elevation.

Operating Characteristics

The operating characteristics of culverts are illustrated in Fig. 42. This figure uses the two common entrances for concrete pipe: namely, the square-edged entrance and the socket entrance. The inlet control performance curve of each of these two entrance conditions is designated. In addition, flowing-full conditions are illustrated for a 500-ft., 36-in.-diameter concrete pipe culvert with a square-edged inlet for three different barrel slopes. In this illustration the downstream pipe outlet flow condition is not affected by the tailwater for either the inlet or outlet control conditions.

Flow in entrance control is essentially in two parts—nonsubmerged inlet flow and submerged inlet flow. At the beginning of flow, the entrance edge contracts the flow to a depth below critical depth; therefore, the pool elevation is slightly greater than minimum specific energy. As flow increases, the flow is contracted a greater amount. The degree of flow contraction determines the depth just downstream of the entrance face and therefore controls the discharge. A socket entrance does not contract the flow as severely as a square-edged inlet; therefore, a socket inlet has greater flow capacity.

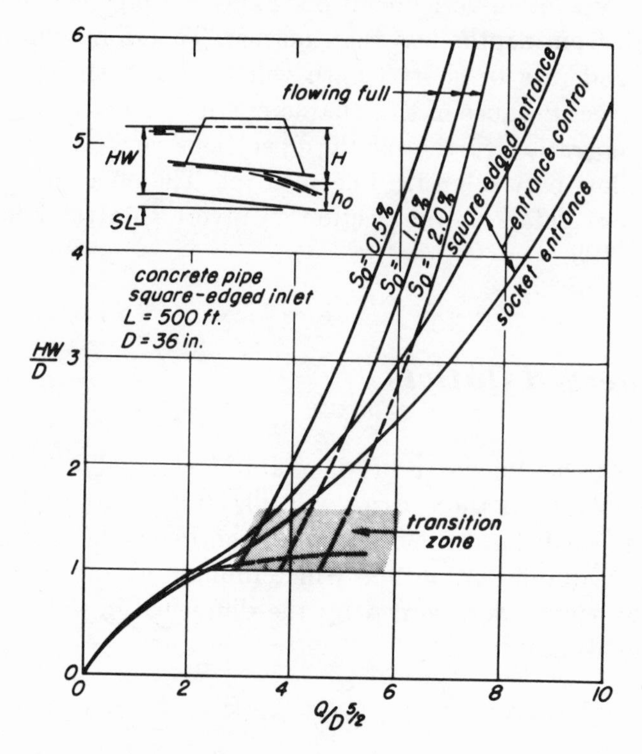

Fig. 42. Operational characteristics of culvert flow.

As discharge continues to increase, the entrance becomes submerged and a change in the flow occurs. The flow becomes fully contracted with only a small amount of ponding over the inlet face. A transition zone is defined between $1.0 < HW/D < 1.5$ for nonsubmerged and submerged inlet flow for the development of the contracted flow. For further increase in discharge, the flow is essentially in fully contracted entrance control.

In the transition zone (Fig. 42) culvert models have been observed to commence flowing full. For instance, at $HW/D = 1.0$ the flow will either continue on the entrance control curve with an increase in discharge or follow the lower dashed line to the right and flow full. The point at which the lower dashed curve intercepts the slope curve for flowing full at the particular installation would determine the maximum benefit from flowing full. However, this benefit is unreliable, and dashed lines are used to depict this type of operation. Only under very special conditions can the predictability of flowing full in this zone be ascertained.

The tendency to full flow is aided by improvement of the inlet. Inlets that have less contraction (greater flow depths inside the barrel entrance) tend to flow full. Also, ideal conditions of flow approaching the culvert are essential to this type of full flow. However, most approach flows in field installations are not conducive to this filling operation. In fact, the nonuniform approach flow conditions cause random eddies and vortices to develop which prevent the predictability of full flow on steep slopes, as previously described.

Instead of flowing full on steep slopes, the culvert can be predicted to operate on the entrance control curve as defined in Fig. 42. As the discharge is further increased, there will be a point at which the depth of flow in a long barrel will approach that of full flow. Depth of flow is determined by roughness (Manning n), barrel slope, hydraulic radius, and discharge. At this point, the barrel will fill and operate as a flowing-full conduit. This is illustrated in Fig. 42 by the intercepts of the flowing-full curves and the entrance control curve for square-edged entrances only. Socket inlets will have slightly different intercepts due to entrance effects. This type of filling is predictable and the culvert operation is stable.

Transfer of control in a long culvert can be illustrated by use of Fig. 42 for a pipe on a 2 per cent slope and with a square-edged entrance. From the appropriate curves, it can be predicted that the headwater will increase on the entrance control curve with increasing discharge to the point of intercept with the 2 per cent flowing-full curve; with further increase in discharge, the barrel will fill and operate on the 2 per cent flowing-full curve. Under ideal conditions, the culvert might commence flowing full in the transition range, following the dashed line to the point of intercept with the dashed portion of the 2 per cent flowing-full curve, and continue upwards on this curve. However, this flow condition is unreliable until the headwater for outlet control becomes greater than the headwater for entrance control.

Both slope and length of the culvert barrel are important factors in determining the discharge capacity of the culvert. For entrance control, the culvert must either be very short or on a steep slope. As long as the capacity of the culvert barrel exceeds that of the inlet, the culvert will operate with inlet control. The effect of slope on outlet control is also illustrated in Fig. 42. The 2 per cent slope curve has a greater capacity for a given headwater than the milder slopes. Also, the greater slope extends the entrance control flow operation over a larger discharge range than for the milder slopes. Similar effects occur with culvert lengths. Short culverts tend to remain in entrance control over a larger discharge range than long culverts.

In short culverts it is doubtful that the culvert will operate with outlet control. Flow changes normally occur because of an increase in resistance losses which are affected by the length and slope of the culvert barrel. In short conduits the resistance losses do not have an opportunity to change the depth of flow appreciably before the culvert outlet is reached. Since resistance head loss over a short barrel length is small compared to the total energy necessary for flow, short culverts will normally operate with inlet control. The point at which friction losses become an appreciable factor in the total energy requirements for flow signifies the change from a short culvert to a long culvert.

Operating Sequence of Pipe Culverts

Within the practical range of discharges and headwater depths, the operational characteristics of pipe culverts can be expected to vary. However, similarities of operation do exist and can be classified qualitatively rather than quantitatively. Submergence or partial submergence of the outlet will modify the flow conditions described. The various classes of operation may be generalized as follows:

Case 1—Actual culvert slope exceeding the optimum critical slope with headwater depth below the culvert crown.

Case 2—Actual culvert slope exceeding the optimum critical slope with headwater depth submerging the culvert entrance.
- (A) Culvert flowing part full.
- (B) Culvert flowing completely full.

Case 3—Actual culvert slope less than optimum critical slope with headwater depth below the culvert crown.

Case 4—Actual culvert slope less than optimum critical slope with headwater depth submerging the culvert entrance.
- (A) Culvert flowing part full.
- (B) Culvert flowing completely full.

CASE 1

Culverts operating in the manner described by Case 1 will flow through critical depth at the entrance for all discharges less than the optimum discharge given by the equation $Q_{op} = 5.27D^{5/2}$. Tests have shown that the headwater will exceed the height of pipe long before optimum discharge

The smooth interior wall of this 84-in. concrete culvert pipe will provide efficient discharge operation.

is reached. Therefore, discharges greater than optimum are typified by the Case 2 description of flow. Case 1 flow is illustrated in Fig. 43.

Case 2

Culverts operating in the manner described by Case 2 will operate with inlet control at discharges exceeding the optimum discharge by an amount determined by the length of the culvert and the ratio of the actual slope to the optimum critical slope. Initially, Case 2 (A) flow passes through critical depth to a minimum contracted depth controlled by the inlet geometry. If the normal depth of flow as determined by Manning's formula is greater than the contracted depth, the actual depth of flow in the culvert barrel will increase throughout the length of the culvert. Normal depth of flow may be determined from Fig. 41. If the depth within the culvert barrel does not reach a depth of $0.93D$, the culvert operation will continue in accordance with Case 2 (A), inlet control.

As the discharge increases, both the headwater depth and the depth of flow in the culvert will increase. At a sufficiently large discharge, the depth of flow in the culvert barrel will exceed the depth $0.93D$ before the end of the culvert barrel is reached. This will cause the barrel to flow full and the operation will change from Case 2 (A) to Case 2 (B), outlet control.

Fig. 43 illustrates the operational characteristics of a culvert which operates successively with Case 1, Case 2 (A), and Case 2 (B) operation. Case 1, inlet control operation, exists until the entrance becomes submerged. When submerged, the entrance operates as a Case 2 (A) type and continues until the depth of flow in the culvert causes the pipe to fill and operate as Case 2 (B), outlet control. At the point at which the control transfers from Case 2 (A) to Case 2 (B), the culvert may operate more

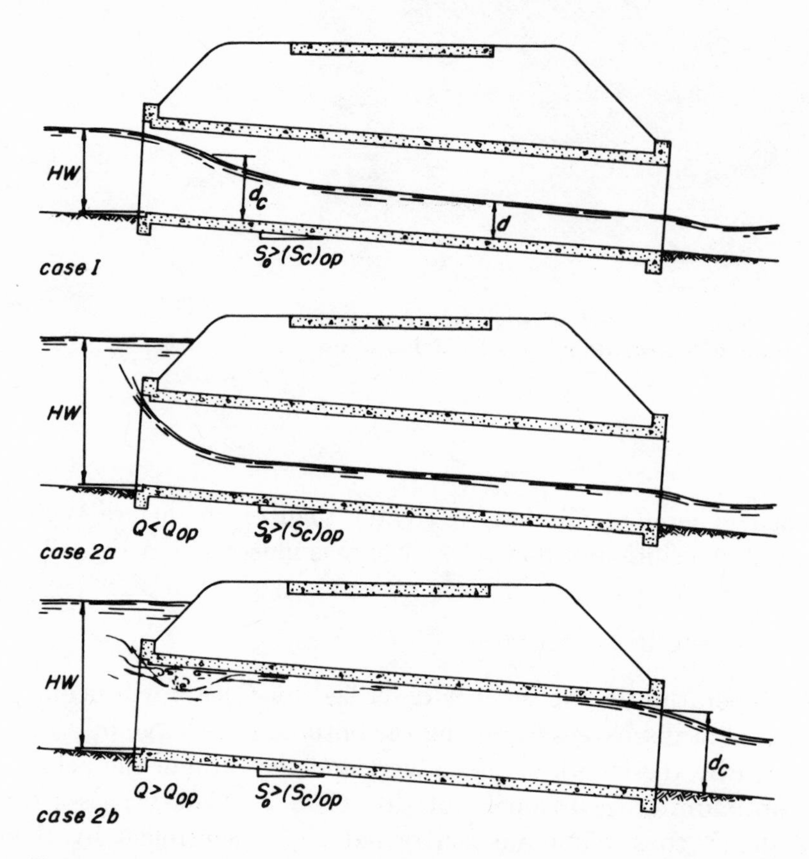

Fig. 43. Operational characteristics of pipe culvert flow.

efficiently with outlet control than with inlet control. However, the difference is slight and does not always exist. Where it is desired to be conservative, the design is based on the greater headwater depth according to either the inlet control or outlet control calculation without regard to whether or not the greater headwater depth will actually occur. At even greater discharges, the outlet control will exist and will require the greater operating headwater.

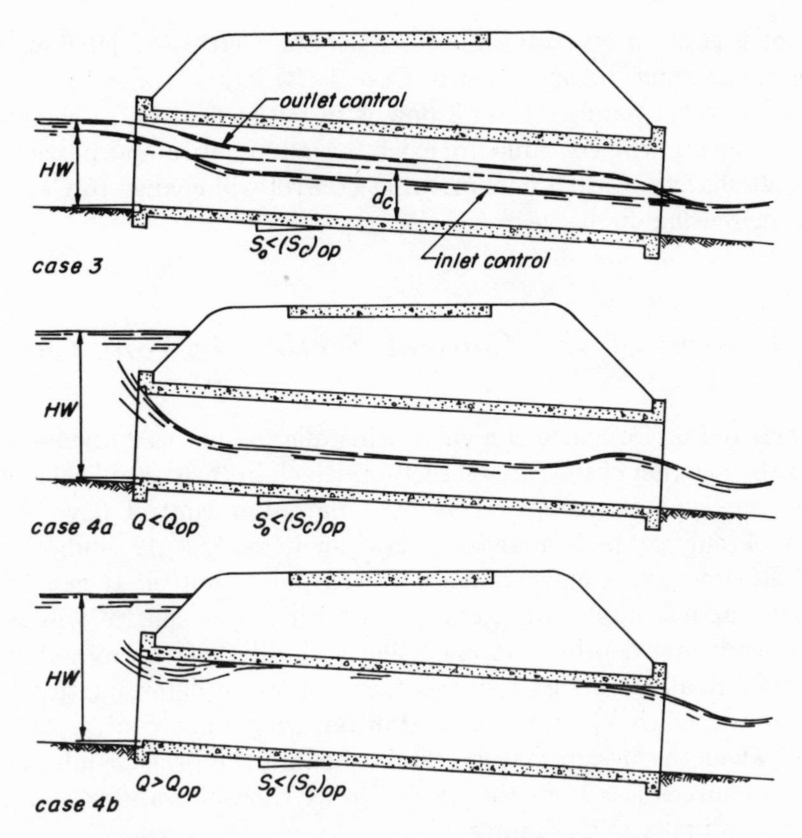

Fig. 44. Operational characteristics of pipe culvert flow.

Case 3

Culverts operating in the manner described by Case 3 may operate with inlet control or outlet control (Fig. 44). If the slope of the culvert is insufficient to overcome friction, the culvert will operate with outlet control, with the flow passing through critical depth at the outlet. If the slope is sufficiently large, the flow will pass through critical depth at the entrance and the culvert will operate with inlet control. The difference in headwater elevation is not large for either operation in small culverts, but can be an appreciable amount as culvert size increases.

Case 4

Culverts operating in the manner described by Case 4 develop from Case 3 flow (Fig. 44). If the Case 3 flow is in inlet control, the flow will continue to operate in inlet control at the greater discharges. Inlet control, Case 4 (A), will continue to exist until the resistance forces in the barrel become sufficiently large to overcome the forces of the contracted jet flow at the entrance, changing the operation to Case 4 (B), outlet control flow.

On the other hand, if Case 3 flow is in outlet control, as shown, this type of control will continue to exist for all practical purposes for all greater discharges. Case 3 flow in outlet control will change to Case 4 (B) flow at increasing discharges.

Location of the Control Section in Long Culverts

The predicted performance of a culvert installation is based upon a knowledge of the location of the control section, which in turn establishes culvert flow as the type characterized as inlet or outlet control flow. A comparison of culvert performance curves, such as Fig. 42, indicates the desirability of having culverts operate with inlet control. It can be seen that, in practical application, operation with outlet control will require greater headwater depths than operation with inlet control at comparable discharges. Realistic design requires fairly accurate determination of the discharge at which operation will transfer from inlet control to outlet control. Then the design may be established on the basis of inlet control for all discharges less than the discharge at time of transfer and outlet control for all greater discharges.

In many cases it is only necessary to establish a general idea of the operating characteristics. In these cases the Manning equation will be adequate, although this technique is only strictly applicable to long culverts where equilibrium flow conditions will be established. The operation diagram for long circular culvert barrels flowing part full (Fig. 41) shows the depth of flow and discharge characteristics for circular sections at various slopes. Also shown is the relationship for critical depth at various discharges. All values are given in dimensionless terms. Using optimum discharge and optimum critical slope as a basis for comparison, depth-discharge relationships are given for slopes producing discharges of 40 per cent, 60 per cent, etc., at the same depth. Operation with inlet control or outlet control may be determined by comparing the operation curve to the curve for critical depth. When the actual depth in the pipe is less than critical depth for the same discharge, the culvert will operate with inlet control.

When the actual depth as given by the operation curve is greater than the critical depth for the same discharge, the pipe will operate with outlet control. This type of operation is described in the preceding section as Case 3 with outlet control. Operation as Case 3 with inlet control (Fig. 41) falls in the area bounded by the curve for critical depth and the pipe operation curve for a slope equal to the optimum critical slope, $s_o = 1.0$.

Fig. 41 also indicates the point at which the culvert pipes will flow full with outlet control. This condition exists for discharges exceeding the maximum open channel discharge which occurs at a depth of $0.93D$.

An example will illustrate the use of Fig. 41: Determine the discharge at which the operation will change from inlet control to outlet control for a 60-in. concrete pipe on a 0.64 per cent slope. From Fig. 38, Chapter 3, the optimum critical slope is found to be about 1.0 per cent. Therefore, the curve for a relative slope s_o of 0.64 per cent is selected. It is found that the pipe operation curve crosses the critical depth curve at a discharge factor of 4.0. The transfer in control would then take place at a discharge of approximately

$$Q = 4 \times 5^{5/2} = 224 \text{ cfs.}$$

The transfer of control would occur somewhat differently if the culvert was installed with a slope of 2.0 per cent rather than 0.64 per cent. In this case the flow in the pipe is expressed by the curve for a relative slope s_o of 2.0. The transfer of control is determined by the optimum depth of $0.93D$ and occurs at a discharge factor of approximately 7.43. This corresponds to a discharge in a 60-in. pipe of

$$Q = 7.43 \times 5^{5/2} = 416 \text{ cfs.}$$

It should be remembered that these curves can only be expected to be approximate in their intended application to long circular pipes. They can be used for other lengths to provide a general indication of the operational characteristics. In many cases these curves will be sufficient since the range of practical operation will lie well within one type of control or the other. The pipe operation curves are of value in determining which type of control should be used in predicting the operational characteristics for culvert design, and they also indicate the depth of flow at or near the outlet.

Culvert Control Length

The geometry of culvert entrances causes the flow entering the culvert to contract in a manner similar to the operation of an orifice. As with the orifice, the degree of contraction is governed by the edge details of the opening and its placement. The contractions at culvert inlets in pipes flowing part full always result in water surfaces well below the critical depth of flow and usually below the normal depth of flow. The effect of the contraction is projected well downstream of the opening and may reach the outlet without the flow becoming uniform. For this reason short culverts seldom flow full and may be designed for inlet control operation. Also, steep culverts extend the influence of the entrance flow conditions and, therefore, they must be designed for inlet control operation.

Various combinations of entrance geometry, length, slope, roughness, and discharge combine to produce the effect of long or short culverts. The pipe operation curves (Fig. 41) are specifically for long culverts.

High flows and low fill heights require multiple culverts as in this installation.

Backwater computations are used to establish the controlling length in determining whether or not a culvert installation is effectively long or short. The results of this type of computation are plotted in a general form in Figs. 45 through 49 and are applicable to circular pipes of any material for selected entrance geometries. A family of curves has been prepared for various relative slopes (actual culvert slope to optimum critical slope) in terms of a dimensionless relationship including optimum critical slope, length, and diameter, $(S_c)_{op}L/D$, versus the discharge factor $Q/D^{5/2}$. The control length curves are presented for four different entrance shapes.

Uniform-flow conditions are indicated on each figure with a dashed line showing the extent of flow at a depth of $0.93D$. At discharges less than that defined by the intercept of the dashed curve with the curves for s_o, the culvert is part full and operates independently of length. At greater discharges the culvert operation is influenced by the length. The culvert will be part full for $(S_c)_{op}L/D$ and $Q/D^{5/2}$ intercepts falling below the

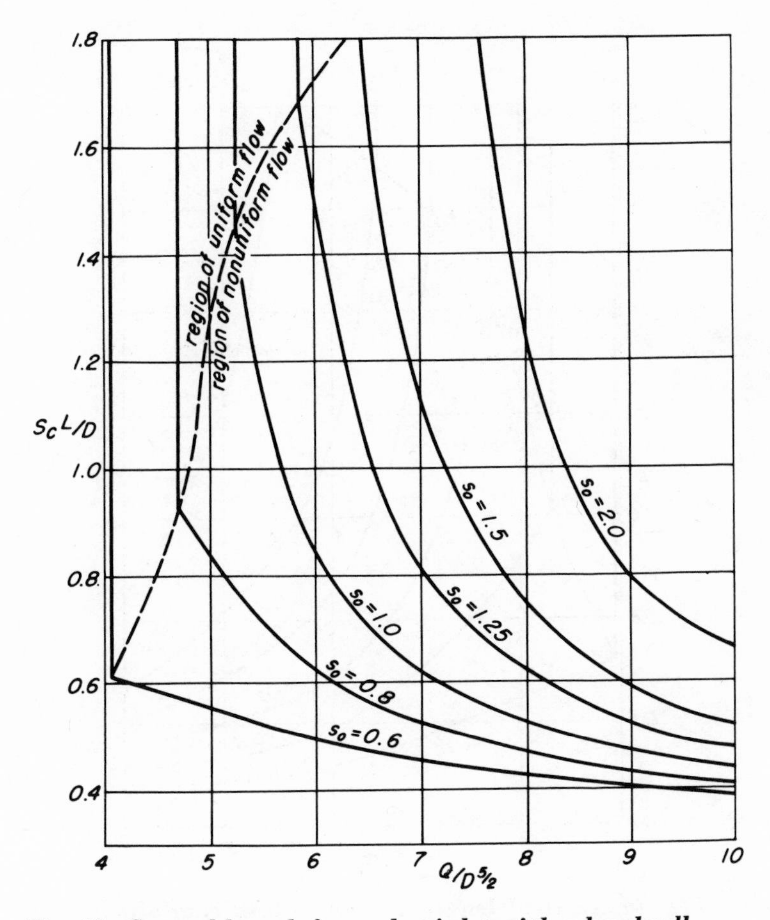

Fig. 45. Control length for socket inlet with a headwall.

appropriate relative slope curve. Similar points lying above the appropriate relative slope curve indicate that the culvert will flow full. Culverts thus defined as flowing full are long culverts and the pipe operation curves of Fig. 41 are applicable.

The control length curves are intended to be used as a means of making a close estimate of the length of culvert pipe required to force the pipe to flow full as a result of friction. Thus, knowing the discharge factor and relative slope, the value of $(S_c)_{op}L/D$ can be selected. The length required to cause the culvert to flow full can then be determined. Culverts shorter than the computed length would be expected to operate with inlet control; culverts longer than the computed length would be expected to operate with outlet control at the design discharge. These curves, therefore, are useful in establishing the criteria for long or short culverts.

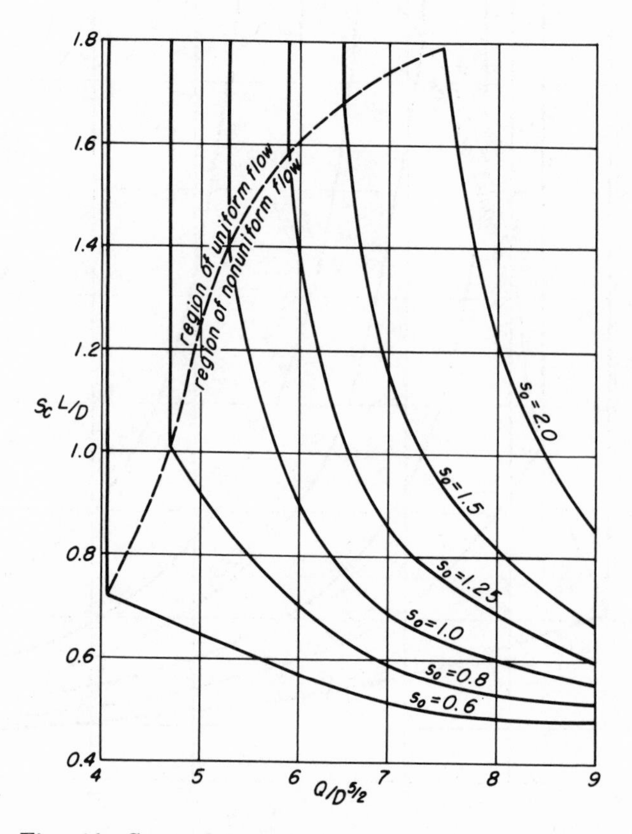

Fig. 46. Control length for projecting conduits with socket-shaped inlet.

The control length curves can also be used to establish the approximate discharge rate at which a culvert of given size, length, and slope can be expected to flow full. At discharges exceeding the computed amount, the culvert will operate with outlet control, while for lesser discharges it will operate with inlet control. Exact operational characteristics are uncertain along the curve. Design should be conservative when a clear case of inlet or outlet control cannot be established.

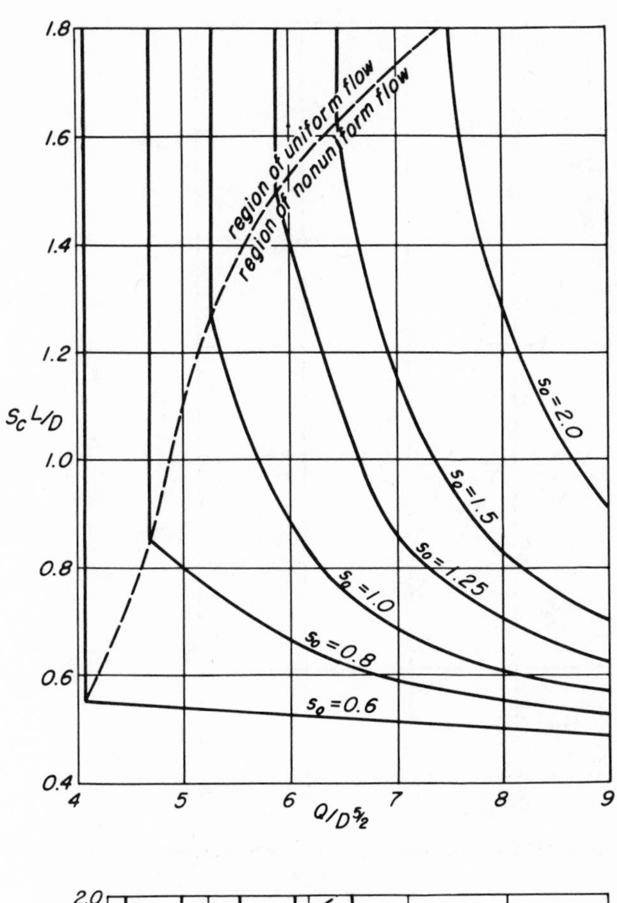

Fig. 47. Control length for square-edge entrance with a headwall.

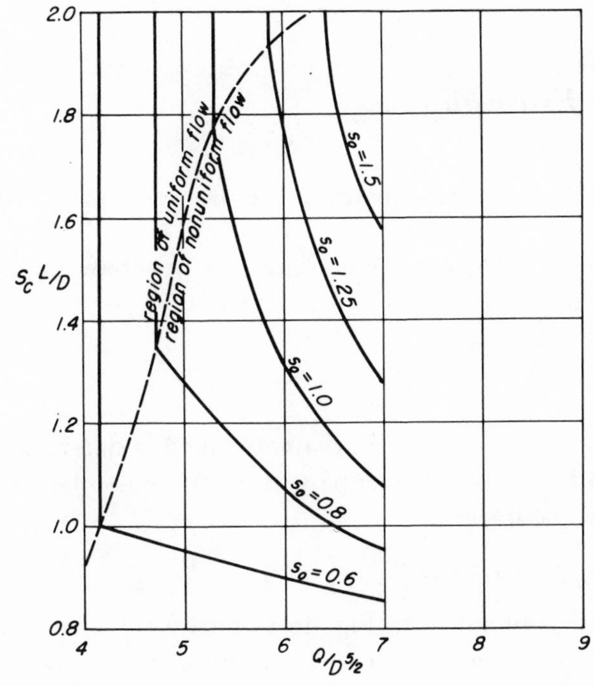

Fig. 48. Control length for projecting thin-edge inlet.

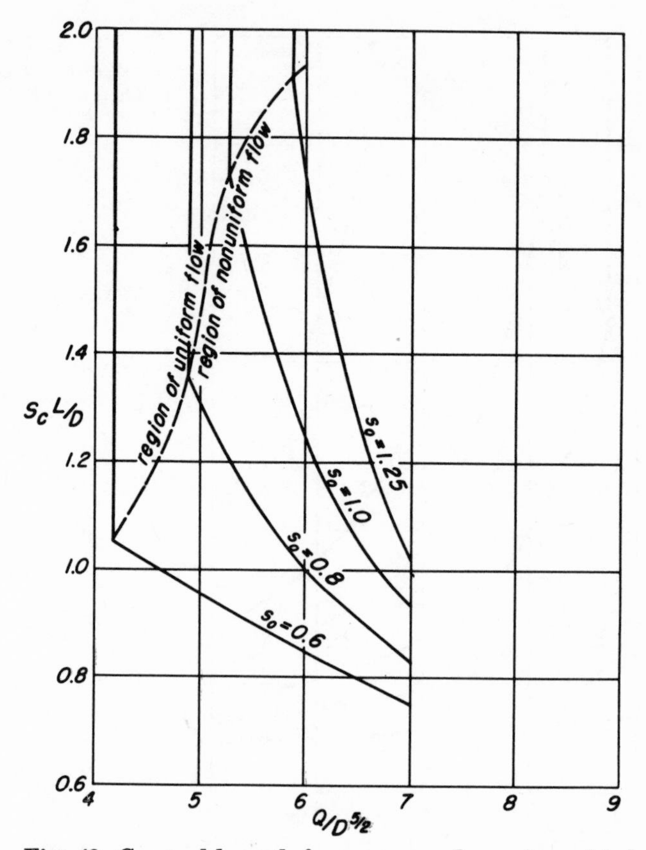

Fig. 49. Control length for square-edge mitered inlet.

Control Length Example

The following example will serve to illustrate the use of the control length curves.

Estimate the discharge at which a 60-in.-diameter concrete culvert 500 ft. long with a socket inlet in a headwall on a slope of 0.64 per cent can be expected to start to flow full.

Solution:

Optimum critical slope $(S_c)_{op}$ of a 60-in.-diameter pipe is determined from Fig. 38 as 1.0 per cent. The relative slope s_o is computed to be 0.64. The value of the control length ratio is

$$(S_c)_{op}L/D = 0.01 \times \frac{500}{5} = 1.00$$

The discharge factor $Q/D^{5/2}$ is found from Fig. 45 to be 4.2 for a value of $(S_c)_{op}L/D = 1.00$. The discharge at which full conduit flow can be expected is then computed as

$$Q = 4.2 \times 5^{5/2} = 235 \text{ cfs.}$$

From the limiting condition, it will be noted that the culvert will operate in a similar manner at a minimum length given by $(S_c)_{op}L/D = 0.67$, from which the minimum length may be calculated to be

$$L = 0.67 \times \frac{5}{0.01} = 335 \text{ ft.}$$

Placing this culvert at a slope of 2 per cent will change the operating conditions. From Fig. 45 the discharge factor for a relative slope of 2.0 is found to be 8.47. The culvert, then, will not flow full until a discharge of

$$Q = 8.47 \times 5^{5/2} = 474 \text{ cfs}$$

is reached. It will be noted that longer lengths will flow full at lower discharges, while the converse is true for shorter lengths.

Culvert Backwater Computations

In most cases, backwater computations for culvert design are not necessary. However, an understanding of the procedure will contribute to an understanding of the overall operation of a culvert. By means of a backwater analysis, it is possible to account for the effects of shape, friction, and other losses in determining the depth of flow at any point in the flow channel.

It has been shown that depth of flow in a part-full culvert is determined by:

1. Contraction at the entrance
2. Wall friction along the pipe
3. Slope

It has already been pointed out that the initial contraction at the entrance occurs without a loss in energy. Bossy[1] has shown that the minimum contraction occurs within a distance of approximately $3D$ downstream of the entrance opening. Following this, expansion losses in the flow take place to cause a rather rapid change in depth. The major portion of the losses occurs in a distance of $3D$ to $6D$. However, the full effect of the entrance losses may be extended a considerable distance downstream depending on the roughness of the pipe wall. Smooth pipe requires greater distances to fully realize entrance losses. A good approximation of the depth within a distance of $5D$ of the entrance can be obtained by applying the entrance loss coefficient to the inlet control curve. This establishes the energy level which is entered into the specific energy curve (Fig. 37, Chapter 3) to establish the depth of flow. An example of this relationship

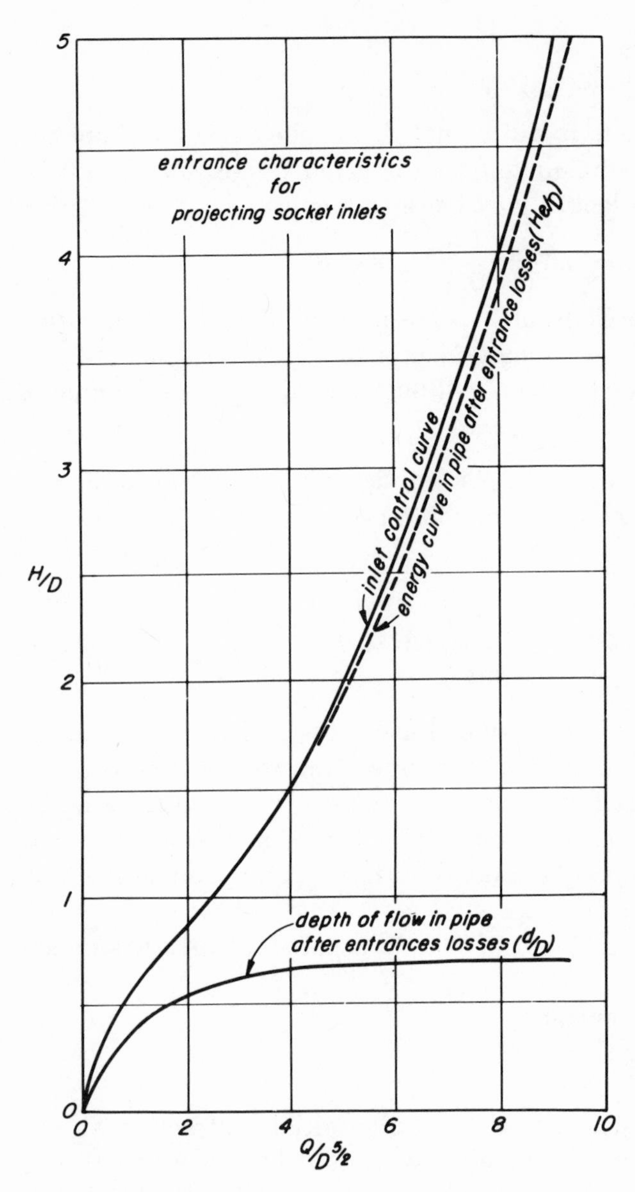

Fig. 50. Performance curve for a projecting socket inlet.

for a projecting concrete pipe with a socket entrance is given in Fig. 50. The depth thus obtained is the initial depth for the channel reach. Depth will change throughout the reach due to the combined effects of friction and slope.

The depth of flow at any location downstream of the initial depth starting point may be obtained from the specific energy curves (Fig. 37) by determining the specific energy at the particular location. In terms of energy head this is

$$H_e + S_oL - S_fL = H_E$$

where H_e = energy head at starting point
S_oL = energy gain due to slope
S_fL = energy loss due to friction
H_E = specific energy, $\frac{V^2}{2g} + d$

The friction slope S_f may be obtained from the Darcy-Weisbach equation in which

$$S_f = 185 \frac{n^2}{rD^{4/3}} \frac{V^2}{2g}.$$

Since the expression for optimum critical slope includes the effect of n and D, a substitution may be made in which

$$S_f = \frac{1.66(S_c)_{op}}{rD} \frac{V^2}{2g}.$$

The actual slope S_o may also be expressed in terms of the optimum critical slope, so that

$$S_o = s_o(S_c)_{op}$$

where s_o is the aforementioned relative slope. The energy equation for backwater computations in dimensionless terms then becomes

$$\frac{H_e}{D} + \left(s_o - \frac{1.66}{rD} \frac{V^2}{2g}\right)(S_c)_{op} \frac{L}{D} = \frac{V^2}{2gD} + \frac{d}{D}.$$

By introducing the discharge factor in the left-hand side of the equation, a more usable form of the equation results:

$$\frac{H_e}{D} + \left(s_o - \frac{0.0418}{ra^2} q_c^2\right)(S_c)_{op} \frac{L}{D} = \frac{V^2}{2gD} + \frac{d}{D}.$$

The factors r and a are obtained from the chart of hydraulic elements and are the relative terms for hydraulic radius and area, respectively—in other words, the ratio of part-full flow to full flow.

The curves of Figs. 45-49 were computed by means of the above equation for various entrance geometries to determine the length required to reach a depth of $0.93D$. A general set of curves was then drawn in terms of discharge factors, q_c, and $(S_c)_{op}L/D$ for various relative slopes. The values of $(S_c)_{op}L/D$ in Figs. 45-49 are not exact since the roughness factor was taken as equal to that for a full pipe. The values of $(S_c)_{op}L/D$ are therefore slightly conservative.

Culvert Design Aids

Design aids have been developed by the Bureau of Public Roads to simplify the computations of the hydraulic analysis for specific culvert installations. These are computational aids only and do not replace good judgment and a thorough understanding of the principles of culvert operation. The aids have been prepared in three forms:

1. Culvert capacity charts
2. Inlet control nomograph
3. Outlet control nomograph

Design aids for circular pipe are reproduced in appendices. Instructions and discussions of each set of aids are also included to facilitate design of common culvert installations. For special designs and difficult installations, the designer must use the principles of hydraulics previously discussed for design solutions.

Bureau of Public Roads Culvert Capacity Charts

Within the indicated applicable range, the culvert capacity charts reproduced in Appendix A will give sufficiently accurate values for culvert design. Curves are given for inlet control operation (solid line) and a limiting outlet control condition (dashed line). The applicability of each curve is given by the index number, the numerical value of a ratio of length and slope: $L/100S_o$, where L = length, ft., and S_o = slope, ft. per ft. For values of $L/100S_o$ falling between the two curves, the headwater depth or discharge may be interpolated. For values of $L/100S_o$ less than given for the inlet control operation curve (solid line), headwater and discharge are obtained from the inlet control curve. For values of $L/100S_o$ greater than those given on the dashed curve, it will be necessary to analyze the operation by other means, although the charts provide a guide to the type of operation. If it is established that the culvert will flow full, the outlet control nomograph should be used. If, on the other hand, the culvert will not flow full, even though it operates with outlet control, it will be necessary to analyze culvert operation by backwater computations. In this case, calculations should proceed upstream from the outlet. The depth at the outlet will be the critical depth, provided the tailwater depth is not higher than the critical depth in the pipe culvert. If the tailwater depth exceeds the critical depth at the outlet, the backwater computations should be based on the actual tailwater at the outlet.

The horizontal dotted line on the culvert capacity charts indicates the upper limit with which these charts can be used with satisfactory accuracy. For operating conditions exceeding this limit, accuracy decreases and either the outlet control nomograph or the inlet control nomograph should be used for accurate operating conditions. The proper nomograph to be used can be determined from the culvert control length curves.

An example is given on each chart showing the selection of culvert pipe size on the basis of permissible values. The operating conditions for the selected pipe are also indicated.

Inlet Control Relationships

Relationships describing inlet control operation in the original pipe culvert investigations were confined to graphical representations. The introduction of the generalized relationships involving H/D and $Q/D^{5/2}$ was a significant contribution. This still provides an expedient method of establishing the design of pipe culverts operating with inlet control. Further investigation by French[3] established mathematical relationships explaining inlet control operation and permitting the construction of inlet control curves for various entrance shapes without recourse to experimental investigation.

Experimental work has revealed that the operating characteristics of culverts with inlet control change when the entrance becomes submerged. With the entrance unsubmerged, flow can be assumed to be controlled by the requirements of minimum energy; that is, flow will pass through critical depth. French[3] found that this assumption is generally correct but requires the addition of correction factors. There is a correction also for the effect of slope and an experimental head increment related to the discharge factor. The equation for inlet control flow for unsubmerged inlets is given as

$$\frac{H}{D} + 0.5S_o = \frac{H_c}{D} + \frac{H_e}{D}$$

where in addition to previously defined symbols

H_c = specific energy

H_e = head increment

The above relationship is valid until a limiting upper value of H_e, corresponding to a discharge factor of about 3.25, is reached. This value has been experimentally determined and is given in Table 8 in this chapter. The empirical relationship between the head increment H_e and the discharge factor $Q/D^{5/2}$ is given by

$$\frac{H_e}{D} = k\left(1.273\,\frac{Q}{D^{5/2}}\right)^m$$

The values of k and m have been experimentally determined and are given in Table 8 for the various entrance shapes.

With the entrance submerged, the operating characteristics of pipe culverts flowing with inlet control are defined by the expression $H/D + 0.5S_o = h_1/D + k_1(Q/D^{5/2})^2$ for values of the discharge factor $Q/D^{5/2}$ exceeding an experimentally determined minimum given in Table 8. The

*TABLE 8. Inlet Control Performance Coefficients**

Entrance shape	Submerged inlet flow			Nonsubmerged inlet flow		
	h_1/D	k_1	$Q/D^{5/2}$**	k	m	H_e/D†
With headwall						
Groove edge, .05Dx.07D	0.74	0.0468	3.3	0.0018	2.5	0.035
Rounded edge, .15D radius	0.74	0.0419	2.58	0.00065	2.67	0.016
Square edge	0.67	0.0645	2.58	0.0098	2.0	0.105
Headwall and 45° wingwalls						
Groove edge, .05Dx.07D	0.73	0.0472	3.0	0.0018	2.50	0.035
Square edge	0.70	0.0594	3.5	0.0030	2.67	0.072
Headwall and parallel wingwalls						
Groove edge, .05Dx.07D	0.74	0.0528	4.0	0.0020	2.67	0.048
Miter (square edge)						
2:1 embankment slope	0.74	0.0750	4.0	0.0210	1.33	0.091
Projecting entrance						
Groove edge, .05Dx.07D	0.70	0.0514	2.58	0.0045	2.0	0.049
Square edge (thick wall)	0.64	0.0668	3.5	0.0145	1.75	0.116
Thin edge	0.53	0.0924	4.0	0.0420	1.33	0.205

*Taken from Reference 1.

**The equation for inlet control with submerged inlet only applies when $Q/D^{5/2}$ is larger than the listed values.

†The equation for inlet control with nonsubmerged inlet only applies when H_e/D is less than the listed values.

factor k_1 and the quantity h_1/D are also empirical and are given in Table 8 for various entrance shapes.

The inlet control operation curve can be constructed for each entrance shape from the above relationship. In several cases, an undefined region will exist which is not described by either equation. This transition region will not be extensive and may be defined by a smooth connecting curve tangent to the mathematical curves for the unsubmerged and submerged entrances.

Inlet Control Nomographs

The inlet control operation curve may be placed in the form of a nomograph. This has been done for several entrance shapes and the resulting nomographs have been included in Appendix B. The nomographs will give the same results as the inlet control curves developed from the above relationships. The inlet control curves in the BPR Culvert Capacity

Charts will be found to correspond to the inlet control nomographs. In general, it is more convenient to use the culvert capacity charts within the applicable range. When discharges exceed the chart limits, it is necessary to use the nomographs.

The use of the inlet control nomographs is discussed in more detail in Chapter 5, "Entrances and Headwalls."

Outlet Control Relationships and Nomographs

The outlet control nomographs given in Appendix C have been constructed to solve the equation for flow in pipe culverts flowing with outlet control. This equation is

$$H = \left[\frac{2.5204(1 + K_e)}{D^4} + \frac{466.18n^2L}{D^{16/3}}\right]\left(\frac{Q}{10}\right)^2.$$

The terms are the same as those that have been used previously in this book, except that H is the combined effect of all head terms and is evaluated by the relationship

$$H = HW + LS_o - h.$$

The term h is introduced to account for tailwater depth or the elevation at the outlet of a depth equivalent to the location of the hydraulic grade line. If the tailwater submerges the outlet, the proper value of h is the actual depth. If the tailwater does not submerge the outlet, the value of h is provided by the curves of Fig. C-3, Appendix C. It will be noted that this value is a variable depending on the discharge factor and somewhat on the slope of the pipe. Two curves are given for each type of pipe (concrete pipe and corrugated metal pipe). The upper curves are for culverts at zero slope, while the lower curves are for culverts on a mild slope. Mild slopes exist when the normal depth is greater than the critical depth.

The outlet control nomograph may be used for any entrance condition by using the length scale given for the appropriate entrance loss coefficient K_e. For entrances with entrance loss coefficients other than those given, the nomograph may be solved by interpolating for the proper entrance loss coefficient. Entrance loss coefficients for various entrances in outlet control are given in Table 9 of Chapter 5.

Hydraulic Design Procedure for Pipe Culverts

Sufficient information now exists to satisfactorily predict the hydraulic performance of pipe culverts. The hydraulic design is based on the discharge determined from the hydrologic study of the culvert drainage area. Hydraulics permits the proper culvert selection to carry the design storm without excessive damage.

Culvert design aids have been prepared to expedite the design procedure. For most culvert installations, the design can be obtained by use of the culvert capacity charts. In using the charts, it is not essential to determine inlet or outlet control flow. However, for cases of design outside the limits of this aid, it is necessary to know the type of flow that exists at the culvert. Nomographs for inlet and outlet flow conditions are aids for determining the respective flow conditions. Even so, many problems will arise in which the basic understanding of culvert hydraulics as presented in this chapter will be of invaluable assistance. The information in this chapter aids in determining the type of flow control that exists, and provides the basic understanding of hydraulics necessary for culvert design.

The culvert hydraulic design procedure outlined below is based on the premises that the design storm or storms has previously been selected and that the majority of the problems can be satisfactorily solved by use of the design aids in Appendix A.

The following procedure is a suggested systematic method for pipe culvert selection:

1.0—Define controlling (design) conditions.
- 1.1—Maximum expected or design discharge Q.
- 1.2—Maximum permissible headwater depth HW *max*.
- 1.3—Entrance shape.
- 1.4—Culvert length L.
- 1.5—Culvert slope S_o.

2.0—Try culvert selection by culvert capacity charts, Appendix A.
- 2.1—Plot maximum design condition, Q vs. HW *max.*, on appropriate chart.
- 2.2—Compute $L/100S_o$.
- 2.3—Select trial pipe size D.
- 2.4—Interpolate for $L/100S_o$ ratio where necessary.
- 2.5—Determine actual HW.
- 2.6—Evaluate results.
  - 2.61—If actual HW is satisfactory, repeat calculations for other types of pipe.
  - 2.62—If actual HW is too high, repeat calculations for larger pipe.
  - 2.63—If area of culvert operation falls outside the scope of the culvert capacity charts, select applicable nomograph and proceed to next step.

2.7—Solution by use of design nomograph.
  2.71—Compare index number $L/100S_o$ with curve values on culvert capacity chart.
  2.72—If value of index number exceeds maximum curve values, proceed to outlet control nomograph.
  2.73—If value of index number is less than minimum curve value, proceed to step 3.0.

3.0—Culvert selection outside the range of design aids.
  3.1—Compute optimum critical slope $(S_c)_{op}$.
  3.2—Compute control length ratio $(S_c)_{op}L/D$.
  3.3—Compute relative slope s_o.
  3.4—Compute discharge factor $Q/D^{5/2}$.
  3.5—Determine discharge factor at which culvert will flow full.
  3.6—Calculate headwater depth for design discharge.
    3.61—If $Q/D^{5/2}$ is less than discharge factor for full flow, check pipe operation curve, Fig. 41.
      3.611—If normal depth d_n is greater than critical depth d_c, compute for outlet control by backwater calculation.
      3.612—If normal depth d_n is less than critical depth, use inlet control nomograph.
    3.62—If $Q/D^{5/2}$ is greater than discharge factor for full flow, use outlet control nomograph.
  3.7—If resulting headwater depth HW is considerably lower than allowable, repeat calculations for smaller pipe.
  3.8—If resulting headwater depth HW is greater than allowable, repeat calculations for larger size pipe.
  3.9—Once satisfactory size is established, recompute for other types of material if necessary.

4.0—Culvert selection for submerged outlet.
  4.1—Culvert crown submerged.
    4.11—Determine head H from outlet control nomograph.
    4.12—Determine headwater depth HW from head H.
  4.2—Outlet crown not submerged.
    4.21—Compare tailwater depth with critical depth.
    4.22—If tailwater depth is less than critical depth, proceed according to step 3.611.
    4.23—If tailwater depth is greater than critical depth, compute backwater using tailwater depth as control.
    4.24—Repeat calculations for various pipe sizes until resulting headwater depth HW is satisfactory.
    4.25—Repeat for other pipe materials if necessary.

This procedure need not be followed rigorously in order to arrive at satisfactory results. It is intended to serve as a guide until such time as the designer develops his own procedures.

In some cases, special design problems will occur and the designer can arrive at satisfactory design solutions by using the hydraulic principles presented in this chapter.

References

1. Bossy, H. G., "Hydraulics of Conventional Highway Culverts," unpublished paper presented at the Tenth National Conference, Hydraulic Division, ASCE, August 1961. (Copies available from Division of Hydraulic Research, Bureau of Public Roads, Washington, D.C.)
2. Chow, Ven Te, *Open-Channel Hydraulics*, New York, McGraw-Hill Book Co., 1959.
3. French, John L., *First Progress Report on Hydraulics of Short Pipes—Hydraulic Characteristics of Commonly Used Pipe Entrances*, National Bureau of Standards Report 4444, Washington, D.C., 1955.
4. French, John L., *Second Progress Report on Hydraulics of Culverts—Pressure and Resistance Characteristics of a Model Pipe Culvert*, National Bureau of Standards Report 4911, 1956.
5. French, John L., *Third Progress Report on Hydraulics of Culverts—Effect of Approach Channel Characteristics on Model Pipe Culvert Operation*, National Bureau of Standards Report 5306, 1957.
6. French, John L., *Fourth Progress Report on Hydraulics of Culverts—Hydraulics of Improved Inlet Structures for Pipe Culverts*, National Bureau of Standards Report 7178, 1961.
7. Rouse, Hunter, *Engineering Hydraulics*, New York, John Wiley & Sons, 1949.
8. *Design of Small Dams*, Washington, D.C., U.S. Bureau of Reclamation, 1960.
9. *Culvert Design Aids: An Application of the U.S. Bureau of Public Roads Culvert Capacity Charts*, Portland Cement Association, 1962.

5

Entrances and Headwalls

EFFICIENT CULVERT OPERATION IS GREATLY AFFECTED BY THE design of the entrance. As shown in Chapter 4, a culvert operates with the flow control at either the entrance or the outlet. If the control is at the entrance, the operational characteristics are completely dependent upon the entrance design and are independent of all other features of the culvert. If the control is at the outlet, the operational characteristics are modified by the culvert barrel, but are nevertheless greatly affected by entrance characteristics.

The purpose of this chapter is to provide information on the hydraulic design of the entrance. Design aids in the form of charts and nomographs are included in the appendices. Inasmuch as entrance design implies the use of headwalls and wingwalls, they are discussed in conjunction with the entrance geometry that results.

Scour Protection by Use of Headwalls and Wingwalls

Headwalls and wingwalls are often used for bank protection. In many cases their use for this purpose may be justified. Usually bank scour at entrances is seldom a problem since there is little opportunity for generation of concentrated currents of bank-eroding velocities. Of course, exceptions to the rule do occur and can only be anticipated from considerable experience. In such cases, headwalls or wingwalls may be necessary to protect the embankment. Often riprap is used in conjunction with end structures.

The most frequent potential danger to an embankment is due to the generation of vortices at the crown of the culvert. However, even this danger is minimal since the vortices are usually concentrated directly above the entrance. The largest vortex encountered in culvert flow will occur when the headwater has just submerged the entrance. Surface velocities associated with this condition are low. The greatest potential erosive danger from vortices occurs at a headwater depth of $1.2D$ to $1.5D$. Even here most of the high velocities in the flow are contained within a lateral radius approximately equal to $0.1D$ of the pipe. Normal embankment slopes will place the erosive action due to vortex circulation far from danger.

Another source of potential scour damage at the entrance is flow currents approaching the inlet at an angle. In such cases, severe damage often occurs because of the direct-flow jet impinging on the highway embankment. Use of training walls to turn or guide the flow into the culvert is necessary for this condition.

Headwalls often are used to stabilize the fill slopes at culvert entrances from rill erosion and bank sloughing. High embankment fills are capable of producing considerable downslope flow. This flow can create serious erosion at a culvert entrance by undermining and sloughing the bank into the stream flow with the material being ultimately carried downstream.

Characteristics of Common Entrances

It was shown in Chapter 4 that the geometry of an entrance is a controlling factor on the amount of water that can pass through equal-size openings. In fact, almost any improvement of the entrance edge will increase the flow capacity of a culvert. Another important fact is that improvement of the entrance not only gives better inlet control performance but also results in less entrance loss in outlet control flow. However, not all seeming improvements in entrance geometry result in hydraulic improvement to provide greater flow capacity.

To give better performance, an inlet must guide the flow into the culvert barrel with as little flow contraction as possible. An ideal entrance condition would be a large-radius bell mouth entrance in which no flow contraction occurred and the barrel just downstream of the entrance face flowed full. From a practical viewpoint this is rarely accomplished for culvert design because approach flow conditions are rarely of the type conducive to ideal performances. Nevertheless, inlets that approach the

TABLE 9. Entrance Loss Coefficients for Submerged Circular Pipe Culverts

Type of entrance	Entrance head loss coefficient, K_e
Pipe entrance with headwall	
Grooved edge	0.19
Rounded edge (0.15*D* radius)	0.15
Rounded edge (0.25*D* radius)	0.10
Square edge (corrugated metal pipe)	0.43
Pipe entrance with headwall and 45° wingwall	
Grooved edge	0.20
Square edge (corrugated metal pipe)	0.35
Headwall with parallel wingwalls spaced 1.25*D* apart	
Grooved edge	0.30
Square edge (corrugated metal pipe)	0.40
Miter entrance for 2:1 embankment slope	0.62
Projecting entrance	
Grooved edge, thick wall	0.25
Square edge, thick wall	0.46
Sharp edge, thin wall (corrugated metal pipe)	0.92

ideal condition provide the greatest flow capacity. For long, expensive culverts, considerable economy can be achieved by special entrance design. The normal culvert installation can also achieve economy with an efficient entrance design.

Many entrance combinations are possible. While the qualitative effect may be predicted, the quantitative effect must be established by tests and experiment. The nomographs in Appendix B show the hydraulic characteristics of the most commonly used entrances as established by model tests at the National Bureau of Standards and reported by French.[2,3,4]

The nomographs shown for each type of entrance may be used in design for inlet control flow conditions only. Under certain conditions inlet control may exist for headwater depths of 6 or 10 pipe diameters. However, in the normal condition (flat slopes and long lengths), inlet control seldom exists beyond a depth of 3 pipe diameters above the invert.

After that, the control usually shifts to the outlet. Design for outlet control should be made by use of the nomographs in Appendix C, using the entrance loss coefficients for full pipe flow listed in Table 9.

The following is a description of each type of common entrance, its use, and possible limitations. The design nomographs for these inlets are in Appendices B and C for entrance and outlet control design.

Projecting Inlets

The projecting inlet is the simplest form of culvert entrance. The two common culvert types of projecting inlets are shown in Fig. 51. The flow contraction at these two inlets is also illustrated. The concrete socket entrance is more efficient because it does not contract the flow as severely as the corrugated metal pipe inlet.

The flow curvatures of the socket entrance in Fig. 51b are mild in comparison to those in Fig. 51a. More energy is required to turn the flow and put it through the thin corrugated metal pipe entrance. The energy requirements or headwater elevation are directly related to the entrance efficiency. The slightly rounded nature of the ends of corrugated metal pipe is not sufficient to cause an improvement in the flow characteristics. However, the thick wall provided by the concrete pipe acts as a guide to the flow and improves the flow capacity.

The nomographs for design apply to inlets constructed according to Figs. 51a and 51b. In each case the pipe is brought out to the toe of the sloping embankment with the pipe invert at the same elevation as the bottom of the approach channel. However, the nomographs may be used for inverts that are slightly raised. Tests have shown that these data apply equally well to various approach channels for submerged entrances. Considerable variation for nonsubmerged entrances will occur for other than in-line approach flow. In fact, projecting entrances should only be

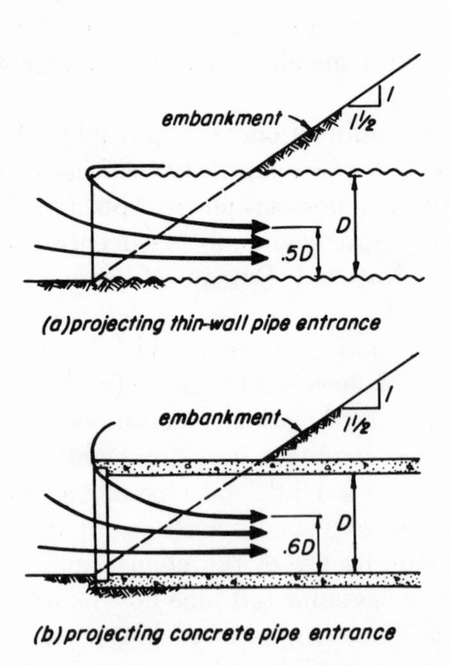

Fig. 51. Common projecting culvert inlets.

Good culvert entrance characteristics are provided by placing the grooved end of concrete pipe upstream.

used on culverts in which the approach flow is in line with the culvert axis. Serious scour problems at the entrance may result from other flow conditions.

Tests have been made at the St. Anthony Falls Hydraulic Laboratory, University of Minnesota, to establish the entrance loss coefficient for pipes flowing full. More recent tests at the National Bureau of Standards substantiate the earlier tests. The values for the entrance loss coefficient for various inlets for use with full-flowing culverts are listed in Table 9.

Flush Inlets

In flush inlets the pipe is brought to the face of the headwall, as shown in Fig. 52. This is a common type of construction and usually results in efficient hydraulic operation. It is not necessary to extend the headwall any higher than is necessary for embankment retention. The height of the headwall above the crown of the pipe should be a minimum of 12 in. or 0.2 pipe diameter, whichever is greater.

The additional thickness provided by the headwall provides a guide to the flow. In the case of a thin-wall corrugated pipe, the headwall makes the entrance as efficient as that of a square-edged concrete pipe in a headwall. However, a socket entrance in a headwall (Fig. 52) is the most efficient entrance of the simple headwall type.

The projecting square-edged concrete pipe is shown with the inlets in Fig. 52 because the hydraulic capacity has not been greatly modified by the headwall. This is because only a small thickness is necessary for improved hydraulic performance. In this case the thickness of concrete pipe suffices. However, a square-edged concrete pipe in a headwall will have the same capacity as a socket entrance if a bevel equivalent to the socket entrance is placed in the headwall.

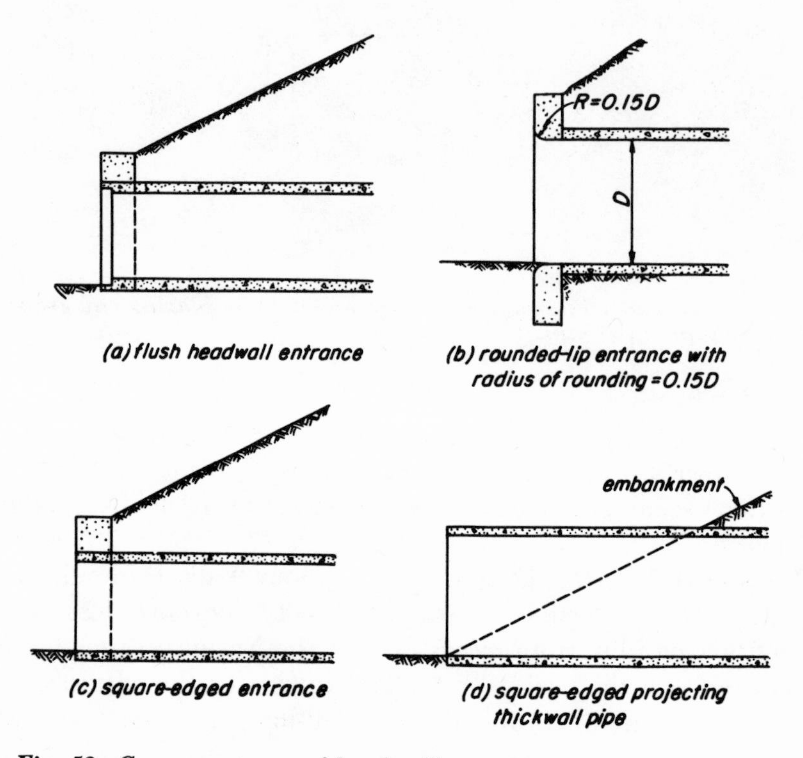

Fig. 52. Common types of headwall entrance.

A well-rounded inlet as shown in Fig. 52b results in the most efficient standard type of inlet. Slight additional capacity can be obtained with this inlet by use of training walls or wingwalls. In fact, special designs for entrance-flow-control structures use the hydraulic efficiency of the well-rounded edge and specially designed training walls.

Besides improving hydraulic performance, flush inlets provide stability to the embankment fill. The headwall provides stability against embankment erosion. Headwalls should be considered whenever the approach

The paved approach channel and the excellent entrance condition on this 84-in. concrete pipe provide an efficient culvert installation.

flow at low headwaters is not in direct alignment with the entrance and scouring eddies can develop.

In culverts flowing full, the entrance loss coefficients recommended for design are summarized in Table 9 and given here for ready comparison:

Concrete pipe in headwall	
Socket entrance	$K_e = 0.19$
Bevel (equivalent to socket)	$K_e = 0.19$
Rounded lip	$K_e = 0.10$
Square edge	$K_e = 0.43$
Concrete pipe projecting, square edge	$K_e = 0.46$
Corrugated metal pipe in headwall, square edge	$K_e = 0.43$

Flared Wingwalls

It is often desirable to modify headwall inlets with flared wingwalls to further retain and protect the embankment. Experiments have shown that very little hydraulic advantage is gained by the simple modification shown in Figs. 53a and 53b. In fact, wingwalls that are parallel or offset back

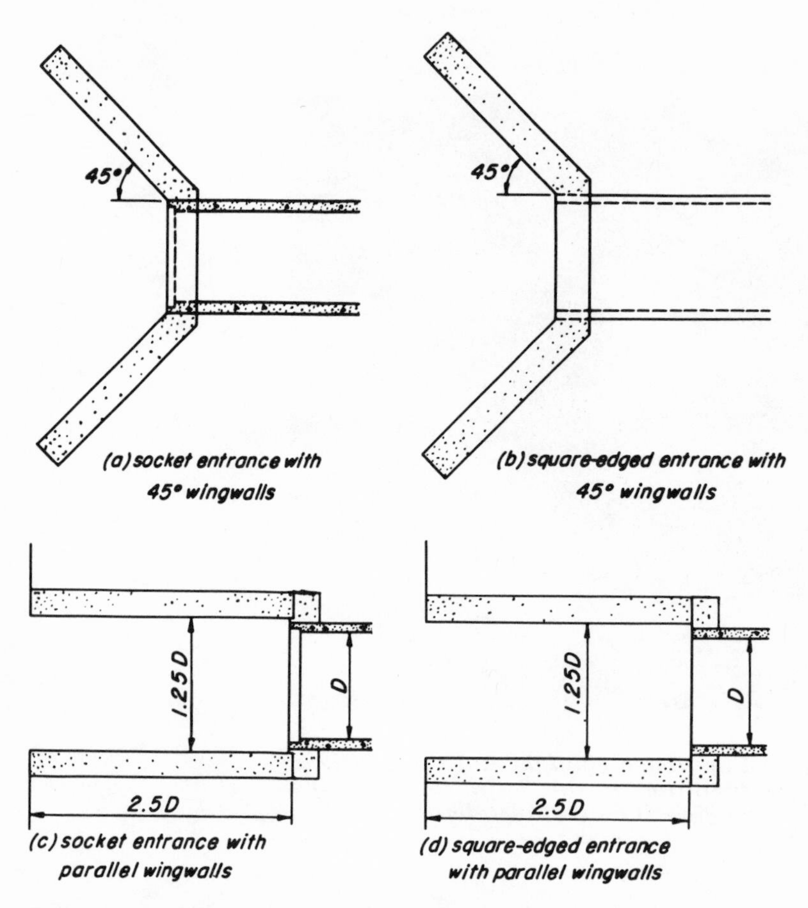

Fig. 53. Common types of wingwall entrance.

from the edge of the pipe reduce the effectiveness of an otherwise good entrance. The use of wingwalls must be justified under normal design conditions by their protection of the embankments.

Wingwalls protect the embankment by preventing scour. The walls act as a guide, keeping the flow from impinging on the embankment fill. Also, wingwalls tend to stabilize scouring eddies that may develop at the entrance. The wingwall is used as an embankment-retention structure more than as a hydraulic structure. In some cases, wingwalls can perform the dual function of a hydraulic transition structure (training wall) and an embankment-retention structure.

Experience has shown that the best hydraulic operation results when flared wingwalls are placed at the edge of the pipe. Detrimental results have been observed when the headwall ends of the wingwalls are offset from the sides of the pipe.

Tests at the National Bureau of Standards have shown that the entrance loss coefficients for culverts flowing full are the same as for culverts with submerged entrances operating with inlet control. These coefficients show no change for socket entrances with a headwall, while some

One means of adapting a skewed drainage channel to a right-angle crossing.

improvement is effected by the use of wingwalls for square-edged entrances. The following coefficients were determined from the NBS tests:

For pipe with socket end $K_e = 0.20$

For square-edged pipe $K_e = 0.35$

These coefficients can only be expected to apply for wingwalls that are brought to the edge of the pipe. Offset wingwalls will require higher coefficients reflecting higher entrance losses.

Parallel Wingwalls

In order to reduce the required wingwall length, wingwalls have been built parallel to the axis of the culvert. Experience has shown this to be poor practice except in cases where drainage is a minor factor, such as for cattle passes. Model studies have confirmed field experience and show that parallel wingwalls slightly offset, as shown in Figs. 53c and 53d, adversely affect the hydraulic operation of an otherwise good design. This is particularly true for the grooved or socket inlet configuration. The effect of parallel wingwalls on square-edged entrances is also significant.

While it is not recommended that parallel wingwalls be used, there are times when this type of design is desirable. Therefore, nomographs are included for design purposes and may be used for the entrance configurations shown in Figs. 53c and 53d. The geometry of the pipe opening continues to have considerable effect on the performance of the entrance. A significant difference exists between the square-edged openings and grooved inlets with parallel wingwalls. The desirable flow characteristics of the grooved inlet are partially destroyed by the geometry of the offset parallel walls.

The undesirable effects of parallel wingwalls for culvert operation with inlet control are also evident in outlet control operation. According to the test results of the NBS, the effect is severe on the socket-shaped entrance. The following entrance loss coefficients have been determined for each type of inlet:

Socket or grooved entrance, concrete pipe	$K_e = 0.30$
Square-edged inlet, corrugated metal pipe	$K_e = 0.40$

Mitered Inlets

Where projecting inlets are objectionable, mitered inlets are sometimes installed. A mitered inlet is the same as a projecting inlet in every feature except that the projecting end is cut off flush with the embankment slope. In usual practice no embankment protection is provided.

The only advantage of a mitered inlet is that it is inconspicuous and facilitates maintenance mowing. Structurally there is no advantage either in strength of the culvert section or in embankment protection. The added cost of cutting actually makes this type of culvert expensive, and when combined with impaired hydraulic operation it becomes economically undesirable.

The hydraulic characteristics of mitered inlets are very similar to those of square-edged inlets; therefore, a square-edged entrance chart will provide hydraulic solutions. In the case of mitered inlets, the grooved inlet characteristic of concrete pipe is destroyed, resulting in a more or less square edge at the entrance. In this respect, all types of pipe with this entrance operating with inlet control perform in the same manner.

If a mitered inlet must be used, improved hydraulic operation will result by rounding the entrance. This will not completely restore the flow efficiency of concrete pipe grooved entrances but should result in a significant improvement. The nomograph for mitered inlets in Appendix B is for a lip with a radius of curvature equal to $0.125D$. Greater curvatures will likely provide some further improvement to a maximum radius of $0.15D$.

There are little experimental data pertaining to hydraulic characteristics of mitered inlets for culverts flowing completely full. A coefficient has been calculated by the Bureau of Public Roads in which $K_e = 0.62$. If the entrance is rounded, a slightly lower coefficient can be used for better performance. If it is desired to be conservative, for a square miter a coefficient slightly less than for a sharp-edged projecting inlet can be used with safety.

The practice of mitering should be avoided if possible. No degree of rounding will restore the hydraulic efficiency of a socket and projecting concrete pipe. A projecting culvert entrance is not unsightly and does not greatly interfere with mowing.

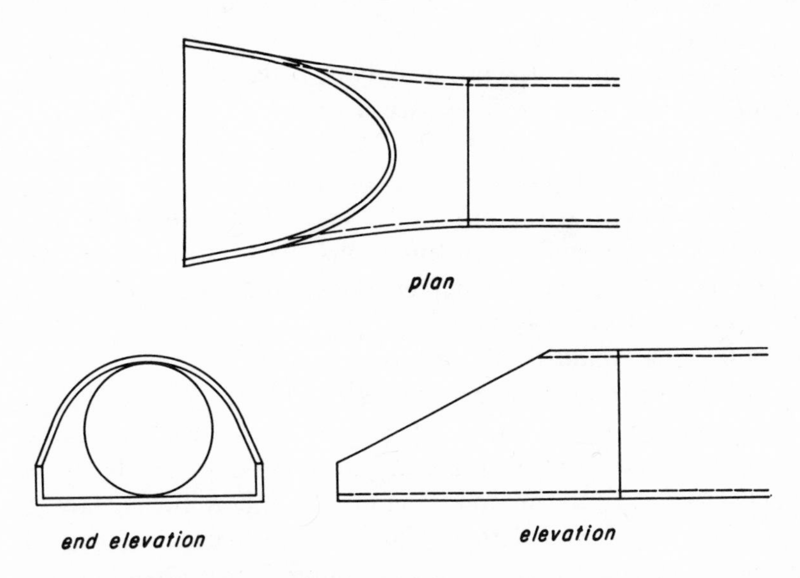

Fig. 54. Typical concrete transition entrance.

Other Types of Entrances

Entrances of types other than those discussed have been used in some areas. One that is particularly worthy of mention is the mitered tapered inlet illustrated in Fig. 54. This is a precast concrete section tapering from a relatively large opening to a circular pipe inlet. The top is open, with the section forming a mitered entrance. Actual proportions vary with different manufacturers. The hydraulic characteristics of this type of entrance have not been determined. However, due to use of a smooth-transition section to provide good guidance and uniform acceleration of flow, it is expected that this type of entrance will be at least as efficient as a grooved pipe entrance with a headwall.

Rounded entrances are a distinct improvement over square-edged entrances or sharp-edged entrances. Almost any degree of rounding results in some improvement in flow characteristics. Experimental tests have shown that the optimum radius of curvature is $0.25D$. The precise effect of rounding is dependent upon conditions both outside and inside the entrance. Exterior conditions are typically the proximity of embankments, guidewalls and headwalls, and the turbulence of the water. Some of the interior conditions affecting the entrance characteristics are pipe roughness, obstructions, and change in geometry.

As an example, it would do no good to round the outside edge of a grooved socket inlet since the flow would merely strike the inside of the groove. It has been found that the improvement in the discharge characteristics of moderately rounded inlets from those of grooved concrete pipe inlets is small. Therefore, it is not usually considered economical to modify the grooved end of concrete pipe with a rounded lip. The reason for this similarity has been discussed in Chapter 4. Use of rounded instead of square-edged entrances in headwalls is preferable.

The flow characteristics for round-edged flush inlets with inlet control are presented in Appendix B nomographs. The radii of curvatures are $0.25D$ and $0.15D$. When the culvert flows full, the entrance loss coefficients have been found to be:

$K_e = 0.15$ for rounded inlet where $R = 0.15D$

$K_e = 0.10$ for rounded inlet where $R = 0.25D$

Other rounded-entrance modifications have been investigated. It has been shown that surface roughening at the entrance is beneficial. This has the effect of causing the flow to cling and follow the surface, thus reducing the degree of contraction. However, no method of evaluating or correlating the cause and effect has been found. There are, of course, many geometrical shapes that may be developed for a culvert entrance. Most of the common ones have been discussed herein. A good indication of the performance of other shapes may be deduced from similarity with the common shapes for which data are available. For the purpose of this handbook, only one other entrance need be considered. This is a square-edged projecting thick-wall pipe which may be used occasionally when a concrete pipe is cut off or reversed. A square-edged projecting thick-wall pipe operates with flow characteristics roughly halfway between those for a projecting socket entrance and a projecting thin-wall entrance.

Entrance Loss Coefficients for Culverts Flowing Completely Full

Table 9 lists the entrance loss coefficients recommended for the design of culverts flowing completely full. The general equation describing flow in a full-flowing culvert, hence with outlet control, is

$$\frac{H}{D} - 1 + \frac{SL}{D} = 0.0252\left(1 + K_e + \frac{fL}{D}\right)\left(\frac{Q}{D^{5/2}}\right)^2$$

The value K_e is selected on the basis of experimental data and presented in Table 9.

Headwall Construction

Headwalls are a minor structural problem and do not usually require structural analysis. A wall with nearly parallel faces in most cases will be quite adequate inasmuch as the major portion of the wall surface consists of the culvert opening. The embedment of the culvert pipe in the embankment can be expected to provide sufficient anchorage to preclude the necessity for a retaining-wall analysis. Minimum reinforcement is sufficient in the majority of cases to prevent uncontrolled cracking. In order to provide adequate cover for the reinforcement and space for proper placement of the concrete, a minimum headwall thickness of 9 in. is recommended. In order to safeguard against movement due to freezing, it is recommended that a 1-to-12 batter be provided on the embankment side of the headwall. Furthermore, it is recommended that the bottom of the headwall be placed below the frost line.

If high headwater depths are likely, a short apron is often desirable to prevent bottom scour at the toe of the wall. In general, if entrance velocities are likely to cause scour, an entrance apron should be provided with headwall construction. The apron should extend at least one pipe diameter upstream of the entrance and the top of the apron should not protrude above the normal stream elevation. Culverts with wingwalls should be designed with a concrete apron extending between the walls.

Wingwall-Headwall Configuration

The most important hydraulic purpose of wingwalls at entrances is to guide the channel flow to the culvert inlet in a manner so as to ensure maximum hydraulic efficiency. As discussed in Chapter 1, the culvert

A 90-deg. wingwall provides cross-drainage from a parallel ditch.

should be aligned with the natural channel wherever possible. Where this is undesirable and where channel realignment is impractical, wingwalls or training walls should be used to change the direction of flow. For this reason, wingwalls should be constructed relative to channel alignment rather than relative to the culvert alignment. This is recommended practice in some states and will usually result in improved overall performance. Some typical configurations and their applications are given in Fig. 55.

In order to avoid gravity-wall construction, the wingwall may be doweled to the apron. The other structural details are similar to headwall construction. Aprons should be reinforced with wire-mesh reinforcing to control cracking.

The joint between the headwall and wingwall should be constructed so that movement in the wingwall will not impose a load on the headwall. On the other hand, any movement in the wingwall should not open the

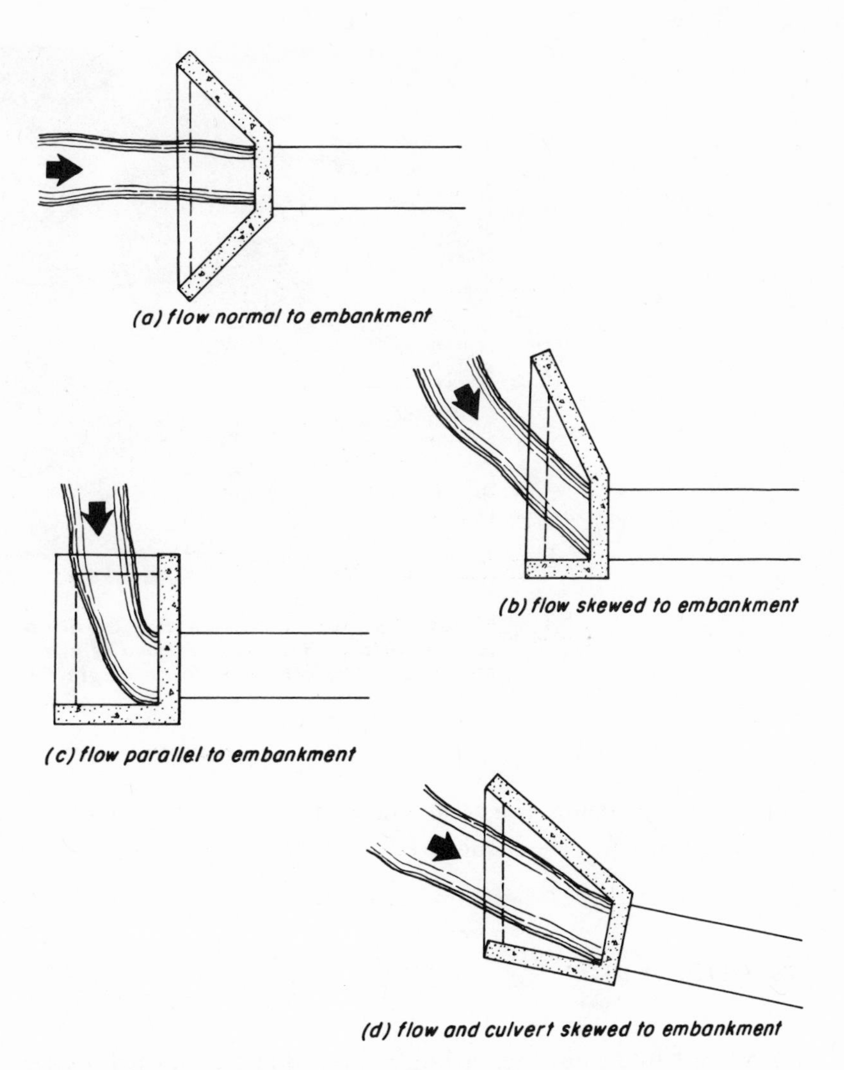

Fig. 55. Examples of wingwall aligned with respect to the approach flow.

joint so that earth or water can pass through. The joint in the headwall should be shaped with the ends of the headwall parallel to and aligned with the wingwall.

A toewall is often desirable on apron construction. For conditions of adverse approach flow currents, a toewall ensures stability against undermining scour. Not all locations will need toewalls; however, culverts in alluvial soils and constant-flowing streams often require additional protection against scour and uplift (buoyancy) forces at culvert entrances. This protection can be achieved by toewalls and aprons. For cases in which the headwall is built without an apron, the headwall should ex-

Wingwalls and headwalls may be adapted to any situation. This is a skewed channel with the end of the pipe cut on an angle.

tend into the ground below the frost line or to sufficient depth that some scouring will not destroy the structure.

Training Walls

Optimum overall hydraulic operation is provided by the use of training walls. Training walls, as opposed to wingwalls, are shaped to guide the flow smoothly from the channel to the entrance of the culvert. Wingwalls may be thought of as a collector structure that contains the flow as it finds its way to the culvert. The use of training walls tends to decrease hydraulic losses at the culvert entrance as exemplified by vortices and large eddies. If high flow velocities are to be encountered, training walls should always be considered. No one training wall configuration will be applicable for every situation. The design should attempt to make the transition from channel flow to culvert flow as smooth as possible. Ideally, the training walls will become flow boundaries, with the flow accelerating gradually and uniformly from the natural conditions in the channel through the inlet into the culvert barrel. Obviously, many configurations are possible. The only reliable method of selecting the best configuration is by laboratory testing of hydraulic models for which much information is already available. The next best method is to make the selection on the basis of judgment and experience. Some examples of typical training wall configurations are shown in Fig. 56.

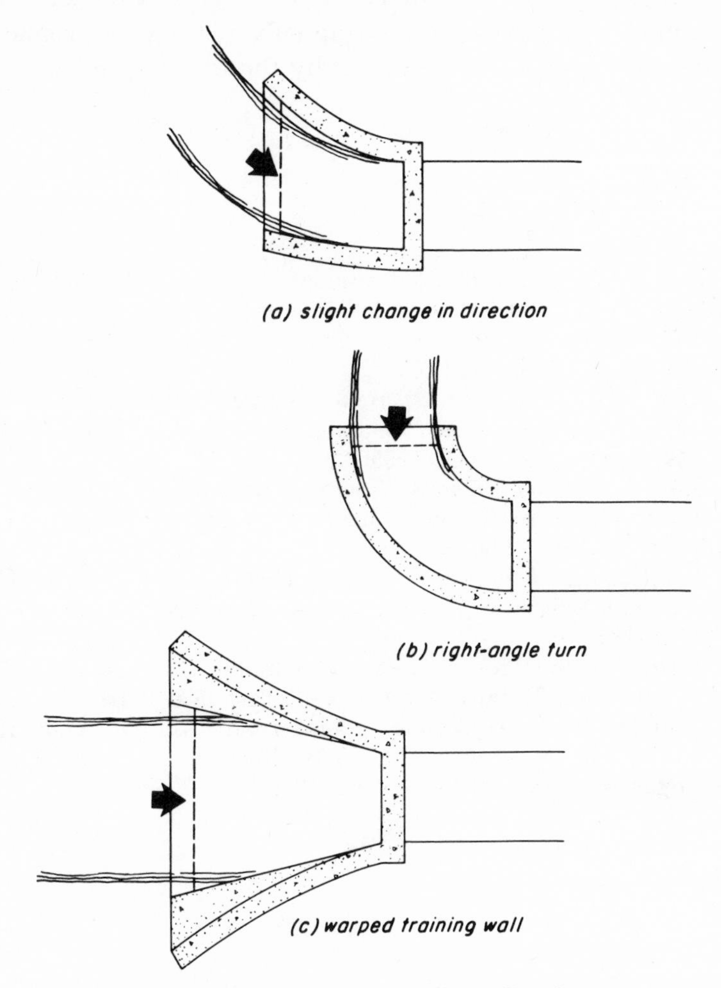

Fig. 56. Examples of training wall applications.

The following basic principles will be helpful in making the layout for a training wall installation:

1. All sections should be smooth without abrupt breaks or interruptions.
2. Flow on a converging boundary will follow a shorter radius of curvature than on a diverging boundary.
3. Flow should enter the transition section parallel to the training wall.
4. Flow should not be permitted to diverge more than 10 deg. from the diverging wall.

5. The radius of curvature of the diverging wall should not be less than one times the surface width of the natural stream at the design flow, and preferably should be greater than two times the surface width.
6. Training walls should terminate at the edge of the inlet to the pipe.
7. The pipe entrance should have an enlarged bevel or rounded lip to maintain the efficiency provided by the training walls.

References

1. Bossy, H. G., "Hydraulics of Conventional Highway Culverts," unpublished paper presented at Tenth National Conference, Hydraulic Division, ASCE, August 1961. (Copies available from Division of Hydraulic Research, Bureau of Public Roads, Washington, D.C.)
2. French, John L., *First Progress Report on Hydraulics of Short Pipes—Hydraulic Characteristics of Commonly Used Pipe Entrances*, National Bureau of Standards Report 4444, Washington, D.C., 1955.
3. French, John L., *Second Progress Report on Hydraulics of Culverts—Pressure and Resistance Characteristics of a Model Pipe Culvert*, National Bureau of Standards Report 4911, 1956.
4. French, John L., *Fourth Progress Report on Hydraulics of Culverts—Hydraulics of Improved Inlet Structures for Pipe Culverts*, National Bureau of Standards Report 7178, 1961.
5. Straub, Loring G., and Morris, Henry, "Hydraulic Data Comparison of Concrete and Corrugated Metal Culvert Pipes," Technical Paper No. 3, Series B, University of Minnesota, Hydraulic Laboratory, St. Anthony Falls, 1951.
6. Mavis, F. T., *The Hydraulics of Culverts*, Bulletin 56, Pennsylvania State College, Engineering Experiment Station, 1942.

6

Endwalls and Outlet Structures

In usual practice, culvert outlets have little to do with efficient culvert flow operation. However, outlet structures are required for two practical purposes: (1) to retain the embankment and support the end of the culvert, and (2) to prevent damage by scour to the culvert, embankment, stream bed, or adjacent property. Although it is common practice to make inlet and outlet structures identical, the two structures serve different purposes and, therefore, logically should be treated separately. For this reason, a distinction is made between headwalls (used at entrances) and endwalls (used at outlets).

In those cases where headwalls and endwalls are used to support the ends of the pipe or retain the embankment, the two structures may be treated the same. This holds true also for projecting culverts when no outlet problem exists. The only difference is in end shape. The socket end of a concrete pipe provides no useful purpose at the outlet end of the pipe and should be placed in accordance with Chapter 5; i.e., the socket end should be placed at the entrance.

Culvert Outlet

In those cases in which high outlet velocities present a problem, special outlet structures are required. This problem arises from steeply sloped culverts or from culverts operating with high headwater depths producing erosive velocities. Structures for moderate velocities may also be required in those areas where erosion problems have been experienced for culverts of similar design.

Scour at culvert outlets occurs primarily because of (1) concentrated flow issuing from the culvert pipe, and (2) eddies and waves along the banks at the sides of the culvert. Flow concentrations cause scour of the stream bed at the outlet; scour may progress to undercut the end of an unprotected culvert. Eddies generated between the flow stream and the banks of the channel provide a scour hazard to the channel banks and to the toe of the embankment fill.

Control of flow at culvert outlets is required in some cases to prevent erosion of the downstream drainage channel.

Another form of scour at culvert outlets is channel degradation, which is the process of erosion over a considerable length of channel. A culvert is a control on channel degradation. The general erosion of the stream bed is magnified at the culvert outlet because the culvert is not eroded and lowered. Many scour problems are a result of channel degradation rather than of culvert outlet velocities being excessively high. A good outlet design will anticipate channel erosion and set a lower elevation at the culvert outlet structure to provide a margin of safety. Other means of protection would be the inclusion of special riprap or armorplating in design to allow for channel degradation and maintain the integrity of the outlet structure.

The process of erosion causes the excavated material to be redeposited in the channel some distance downstream from the point of scour. It is entirely possible that eventually a shoal will be formed capable of causing excessively high tailwater depths during periods of high flow. High tailwater depths may work either to the advantage or disadvantage of the culvert operation. Usually any advantage in this respect is offset by the undesirability of upsetting the natural channel balance. If deeper tailwater is required, it should be provided with a properly designed outlet structure.

Wherever potential scour exists, steps should be taken either to protect the culvert and embankments or to control the flow so as to eliminate the hazard. Elaborate structures are not usually required. In most cases, discharge velocities will be less than those that will cause serious scour. In cases where additional attention is required, simple structures such as wingwalls and an apron, a small weir, or a break in grade in the culvert pipe may be quite adequate. Where serious problems exist, more refined structures such as the impact basin and hydraulic jump basin have been found to serve satisfactorily.

Erosive Velocities

Erosive velocities vary widely, depending upon the characteristics of the channel material, the depth of flow in the channel, and the velocity distribution. To date, no one method can be used to determine when erosion in a channel is imminent. However, over a period of years, experience and experiments have established erosive velocity limits for various types of soil. A considerable area of uncertainty between the erosive and nonerosive velocities remains to be resolved.

Available information can be used to recognize the existence of a potential culvert outlet problem. Table 10 shows the maximum permissible mean velocities in straight, well-seasoned channels of small slope flowing less than 3 ft. deep. Table 11 shows permissible velocities in various types of cohesive soils, based on data published in Russia in 1936. These data are for straight channels flowing at an average depth of 3 ft. A correction should be made for average depths other than 3 ft. in accordance with the correction factors listed in Table 12.

TABLE 10. Maximum Permissible Mean Velocities Recommended by Fortier and Scobey* for Straight, Aged Channels on Small Slope

Material	Mean velocity, clear water, fps	Mean velocity, silty water, fps
Fine sand, colloidal	1.50	2.50
Sandy loam, noncolloidal	1.75	2.50
Silt loam, noncolloidal	2.00	3.00
Alluvial silts, noncolloidal	2.00	3.50
Ordinary firm loam	2.50	3.50
Volcanic ash	2.50	3.50
Stiff clay, very colloidal	3.75	5.00
Alluvial silts, colloidal	3.75	5.00
Shales and hardpans	6.00	6.00
Fine gravel	2.50	5.00
Graded loam to cobbles, noncolloidal	3.75	5.00
Graded silts to cobbles, colloidal	4.00	5.50
Coarse gravel, noncolloidal	4.00	6.00
Cobbles and shingles	5.00	5.50

*1926 Special Committee on Irrigation, ASCE.

TABLE 11. Permissible Velocities in Cohesive Soils

Material	Loose, fps	Fairly compact, fps	Compact, fps	Very compact, fps
Lean clayey soils	1.2	2.5	3.4	4.4
Clays	1.3	2.8	3.9	5.4
Heavy clayey soils	1.5	3.0	4.1	5.8
Sandy clays (sand <50%)	1.7	3.2	4.3	6.0

TABLE 12. Correction Factors* to Be Applied to Permissible Velocity

Average depth, ft.	Correction factor	Average depth, ft.	Correction factor
1	0.81	6	1.14
2	0.91	7	1.18
3	0.99	8	1.21
4	1.04	9	1.24
5	1.11	10	1.26

*For cohesive and noncohesive soils.

Rocky channels such as this can withstand high flow velocities without scour.

Example:

Permissible velocity for fine gravel, clear water = 2.5 fps (Table 10).

Permissible velocity for depth of 9 ft.:

$V = 2.5 \times 1.24 = 3.1$ fps.

While the permissible velocities listed in these tables are helpful, they are neither inclusive nor infallible. The most reliable indicator, a local experience, should always be used where possible. Where experience is inconsistent with the listed values of permissible velocity, experience should govern.

Control of Outlet Flow

Various types of outlet structures have been used to control erosion below culverts. No one type of structure meets all requirements. In the case of moderate velocities, a simple endwall and apron can provide ample protection. However, this structure is less effective for high velocities.

Channel erosion below culverts is due to the kinetic energy of the water. If the kinetic energy can be transformed to potential energy or dissipated, the erosion potential will be either eliminated or substantially reduced. Either of two methods is used:

1. Flow distribution
2. Energy dissipation

Flow distribution is the spreading of the concentrated jet flow across

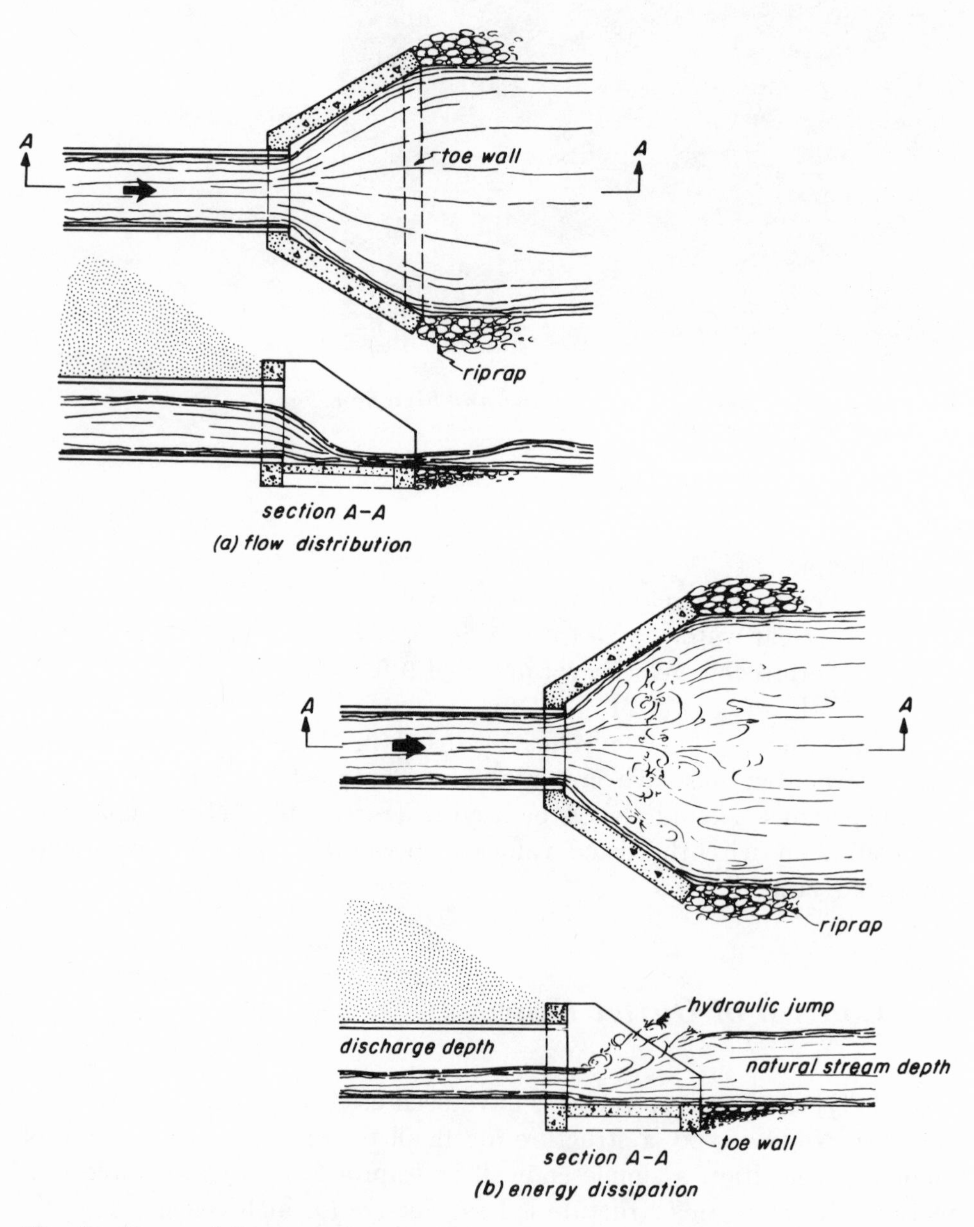

Fig. 57. Types of flow at culvert outlets.

the entire flow channel. As shown in Fig. 57a, a wingwall and apron provide a basin to contain the flow while it accelerates during the spreading process. The effect of spreading the flow is to decrease the flow concentration. The energy in the flow is then more readily absorbed in the tailwater pool or transformed into potential energy. By distribution of flow across the channel, bank-eroding eddies are either prevented or minimized.

Energy dissipation is the destruction of a large part of the kinetic energy. As a result of the large energy losses that occur in energy dissipation structures, the erosive potential of the culvert discharge is substantially reduced. A characteristic but not a necessary feature of energy dissipation is the transition from shallow to deep flow. This transition is usually characterized by a sudden and violent churning action that must be contained at least in part on a concrete apron.

Examples of each type of outlet flow control are shown in Figs. 57a and 57b. Fig. 57a shows the principal features of a "flow distribution" type of control and Fig. 57b shows an "energy dissipation" type of control. Note that flow distribution is accomplished in the plan section, while energy dissipation is accomplished in elevation. These techniques are often combined for maximum effect.

Channel Effect

The design of outlet structures for erosion control is directly affected by the natural water level elevation in the channel. Table 12 shows that higher mean velocities are permissible in deep uniform flow than can be tolerated for rather shallow flow. It is apparent that high velocities discharged into shallow channels will be far more destructive than flows discharged into the cushion afforded by deep water.

Every channel exhibits flow and stage characteristics that are peculiar to it. Thus it is possible to establish the tailwater elevations for a known discharge. The Manning formula is used by many engineers for this type of calculation. All channels exhibit a rising stage characteristic for increasing discharges, as shown in Fig. 58. As a general rule, the depth of flow for the same discharge will be greater in mildly sloping channels than in steeply sloping channels. Also, from well-known channel relationships it can be shown that the velocity will be less in mildly sloping channels than in steep channels.

While slope is a dominating and controlling factor of flow in channels, other factors can alter normal channel characteristics. As in culvert flow, roughness has a retarding effect and in certain cases causes water to flow deeper. Obstructions have the same effect as roughness. By introducing

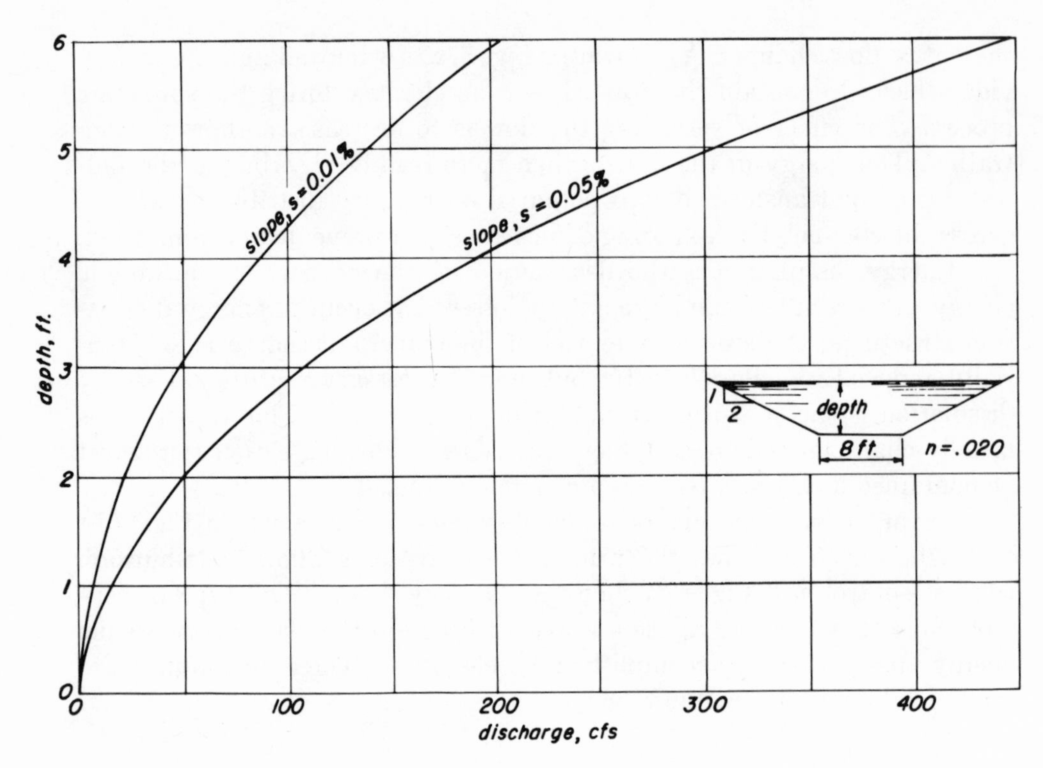

Fig. 58. Channel discharge characteristics (example).

obstructions such as large rocks, it is possible to change the discharge-stage relationships over a short reach of channel. This device can often be used to advantage to cause deeper flow at culvert outlets and thereby achieve more satisfactory culvert operation. It is sometimes desirable to construct a permanent structure such as a small weir for tailwater control.

High tailwater-discharge relationships are desirable for outlet structures of either the flow distribution or energy dissipation type. In the former case, the water serves as an excellent energy absorber and efficiently transforms the high-velocity culvert flow to stream flow. In the latter case, high tailwater elevations are necessary to cause a hydraulic jump and to prevent the high-velocity jet from projecting itself onto the erodible stream bed.

Endwalls

Endwalls (see Fig. 59) are the counterpart of culvert headwalls. Although the two structures look alike, they are used for different purposes. Each is

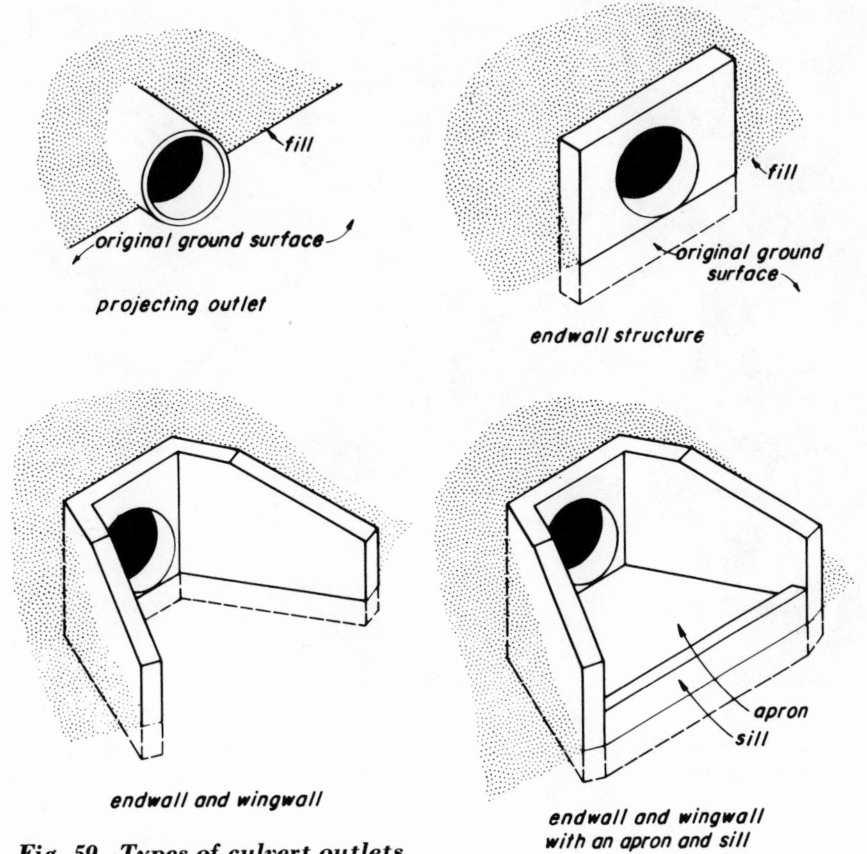

Fig. 59. Types of culvert outlets.

a separate problem and should be considered separately. It is entirely possible that an endwall should be used on some culverts that do not require a headwall.

The purpose of an endwall (header, without any attached structure) is to support the end of the culvert and to act as a retaining wall for the embankment. Any additional structure attached to it is primarily for the purpose of protecting the endwall so that it may continue to function in its original capacity.

When the tailwater submerges the culvert outlet, the endwall should be as high as the expected tailwater depth. Endwalls of insufficient height encourage eddies that can erode the embankment and eventually endanger the culvert and endwall. If the tailwater is not expected to submerge the outlet, the endwall should merely enclose the pipe.

The face width of a free standing endwall is not readily determinable and cannot be expressed in a simple statement of fact. However, a good rule of thumb is to provide a face width at least equal to or preferably

Outlet scour from this 12-in. culvert is controlled with low parallel wingwalls and a paved apron.

slightly wider than the low-water downstream channel. Since the potential formation of surface eddies at culvert outlets is ever present, endwalls should be wide enough to prevent any part of the eddy from coming in contact with the embankment. If the tailwater is such that eddies are unlikely, any convenient width will be satisfactory. In areas of doubt, wingwalls are definitely required, and the endwall-wingwall structure should enclose the flow.

In some cases it may be permissible to avoid the use of wingwalls by lining the embankment adjacent to the endwall with riprap or concrete. This protection should extend at least two pipe diameters on either side of the outlet.

Outlet Aprons

Concrete aprons at outlet structures afford excellent protection to endwall structures. Erosion potential is the greatest at the invert and erosion can quickly cause the endwall to collapse. Concrete aprons remove the point of potential erosion far from the endwall foundation and thereby ensure the stability of the structure.

When wingwalls are used to contain surface eddies formed in the tailwater, a concrete apron should always be provided. Aprons in this case should extend between the wingwalls and from the endwall to the end of the wingwalls. The absence of an apron encourages channeling and undercutting along the wingwall.

It should be noted that many installations do not require aprons at the outlet. Discharge velocities less than the maximum permissible do not cause erosion and therefore the protection provided by an apron is not required. In some cases wingwalls are merely used as retaining walls and are not intended to serve for bank erosion protection. In these cases an apron is not required. However, if the tailwater is expected to partially submerge the outlet where wingwalls have been used, an apron is required to reduce the hazard of undermining the walls.

Outlet Design to Control Erosion

Bank and stream bed erosion can be controlled by means of properly designed outlet structures. Much experimental work has been done on the design of outlet structures for dams in which the flow is uniformly distributed across the flow section. However, relatively little has been done on the design of outlets for circular culverts in which the flow is discharged as a highly concentrated jet. Nevertheless, in most cases the same principles can be used to design reasonably satisfactory culvert outlets. In some cases model studies may be necessary to determine the most satisfactory design. In the absence of such studies, attention to the principles outlined here will minimize erosion problems.

Culvert outlet structures take several forms, such as:

1. Projecting pipe, free-springing jet
2. Endwall, free-springing jet
3. Endwall, supported jet
4. Endwall and wingwall, free-springing jet
5. Endwall and wingwall, supported jet
6. Apron-supported hydraulic jump
7. Stream-bed-supported hydraulic jump
8. Pipe-contained hydraulic jump
9. Plunging pools
10. Submerged outlets
11. Impact structures

SPRINGING JETS

Free-springing jets occur when the culvert outlet is greater than the tail-water depth. The operation is the same for projecting outlets, endwalls, or endwalls with wingwalls.

This type of operation is common in steeply sloped terrain. The erosive potential is quite high, particularly if the depth of flow in the discharge channel is shallow as in steeply sloped streams. However, this type of outlet can provide satisfactory operation when the depth of flow in the channel is approximately equal to the diameter of the pipe.

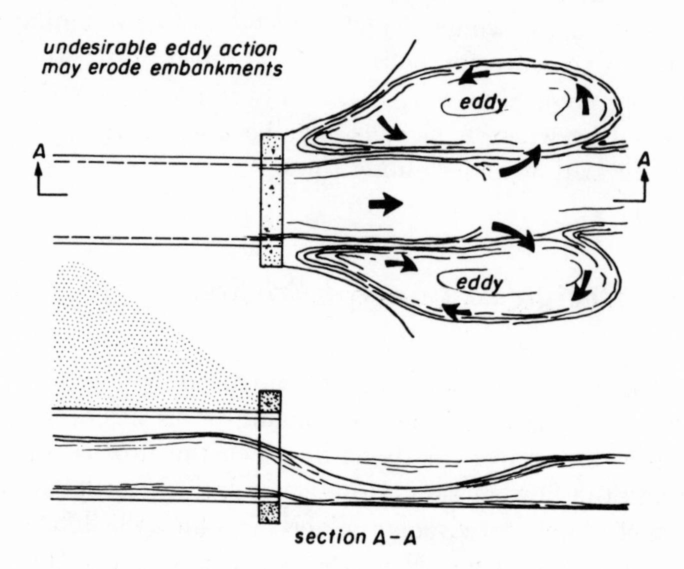

Fig. 60. Characteristic flow at outlet of partially submerged culvert.

In some cases the natural depth in the flow channel will cause partial submergence (Fig. 60). Energy dissipation and flow distribution are not well developed in the vicinity of the outlet of the free-springing jet. Unless the stream bed and banks are highly stable, serious erosion is likely. Bank scour is likely if the flow channel is narrow with respect to the outlet. Undercutting and embankment cutting are also likely unless protection is provided by endwalls, wingwalls, or riprap.

In general, free-springing jets or partially submerged jets are only satisfactory in highly stable channels or for infrequent high-discharge operation. For more or less continuous operation, such as in culverts on continuously flowing streams, a special outlet structure should be considered.

Supported Jets

Supported jet outlets are those in which the downward diffusion of the jet is prevented by either a natural or specially constructed floor or apron. If little or no tailwater is present, the spreading of the jet on the apron results in velocities higher than the discharge velocity from the culvert pipe. The advantage of this type of operation is in the tendency of the flow to spread and distribute itself across the width of the discharge channel. This spreading reduces the opportunity for strong bank-eroding eddies to form. The total flow energy is then better distributed and is more quickly dissipated by the natural stream.

The high velocities accompanying the supported jet make it advisable to provide an apron of sufficient length to fully distribute the flow before it reaches the natural channel. Little or no experimental work has been done to determine the rate at which the collapsing jet supported on an apron will expand. From consideration of kinetics of the free jet, the distance required for the jet to fall a distance equal to the diameter of the culvert pipe is given by

$$L = \sqrt{\frac{2D}{g}}\, V_o = 0.247\sqrt{D}V_o$$

where L = horizontal distance required to fall distance D, ft.
D = diameter of culvert pipe, ft.
V_o = discharge outlet velocity, fps.

The influence of the apron on the jet collapse and flow adjustment will require an apron approximately 50 per cent longer than distance given by the above expression. The approximate length of apron required to distribute the flow across the flow channel will then be given by

$$L_a = 0.37\,V_o\sqrt{D}$$

where L_a = length of apron.

Outlets with Endwalls and Wingwalls

In many cases the natural tailwater depth of the flow channel will cover the outlet apron and partially submerge the culvert outlet. The normal collapse of the jet will be modified in accordance with conditions imposed by the controlling influence of the stream. Inasmuch as it is difficult to control the expansion of flow for all possible discharges, it is often desirable to provide wingwalls to prevent bank erosion at the outlet transition for high discharges.

Outlet performance and hence the best outlet designs can be determined by means of the curves in Figs. 61 and 62a through 62d. These curves are based on the principle of constant momentum in which the force due to momentum and pressure at the pipe outlet must be exactly equaled by the force of momentum and pressure in the flow channel.

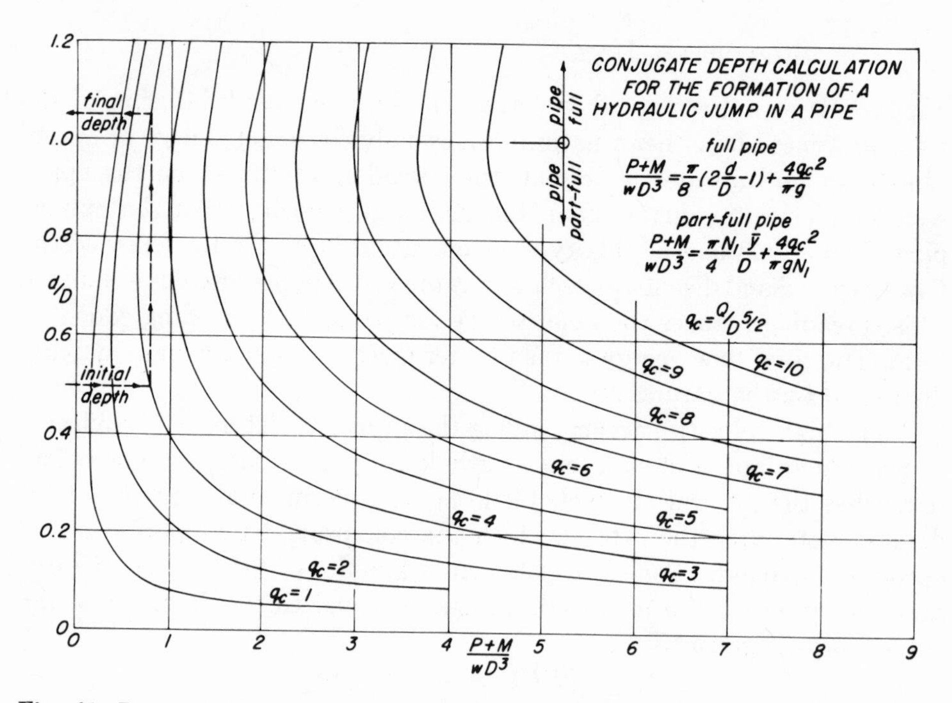

Fig. 61. Pressure plus momentum for various depths of flow in circular pipe.

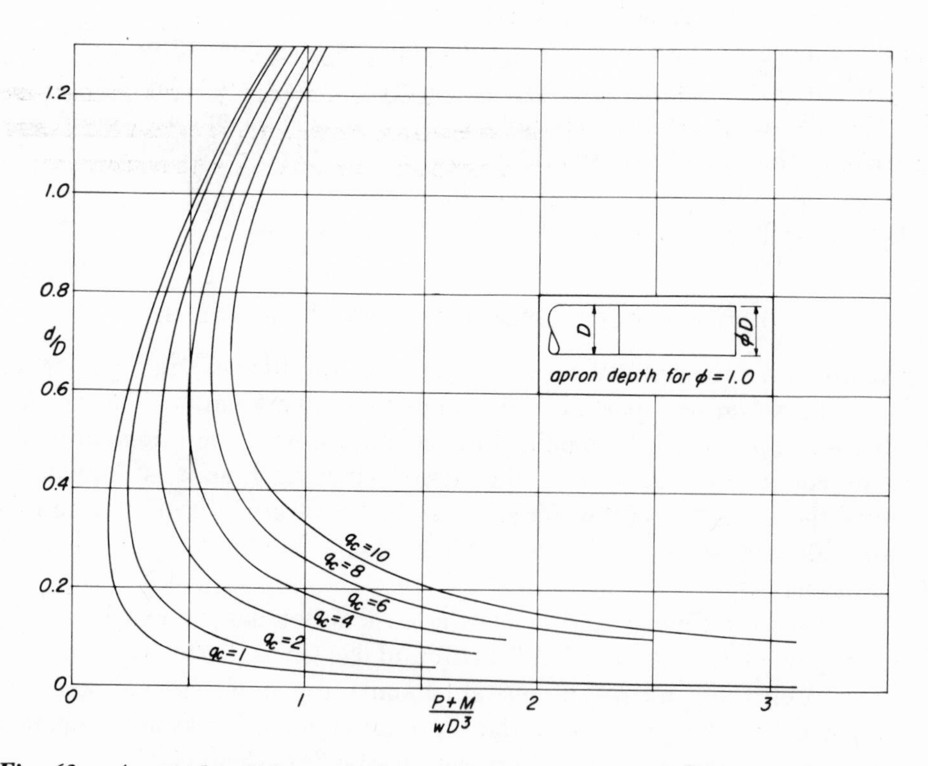

Fig. 62a. Apron depth for end of apron width equal to pipe diameter.

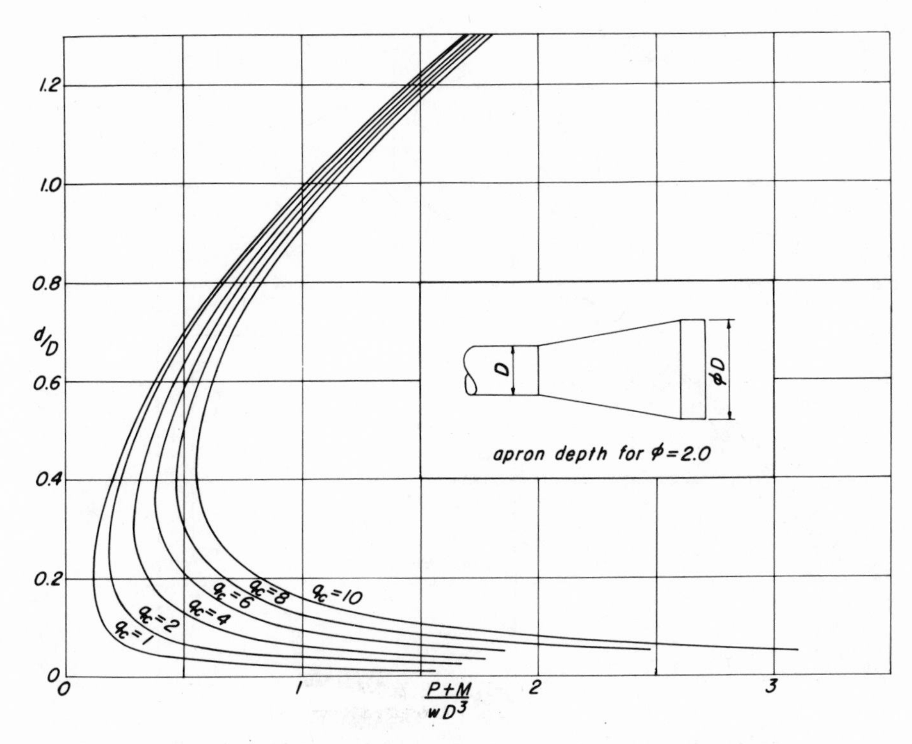

Fig. 62b. Apron depth for end of apron width equal to 2D.

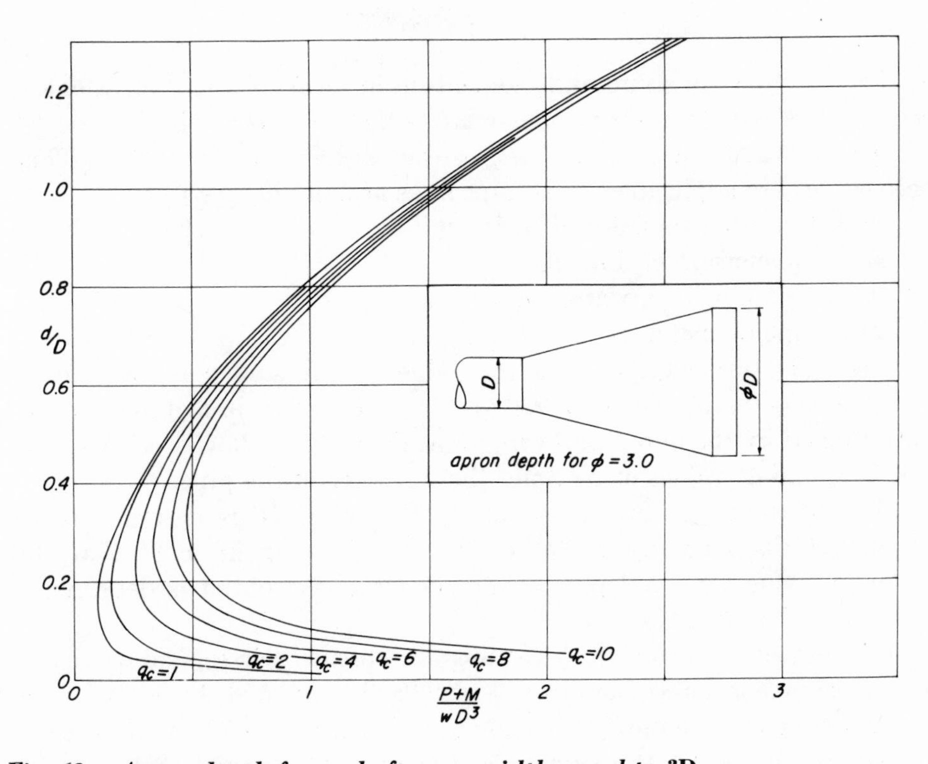

Fig. 62c. Apron depth for end of apron width equal to 3D.

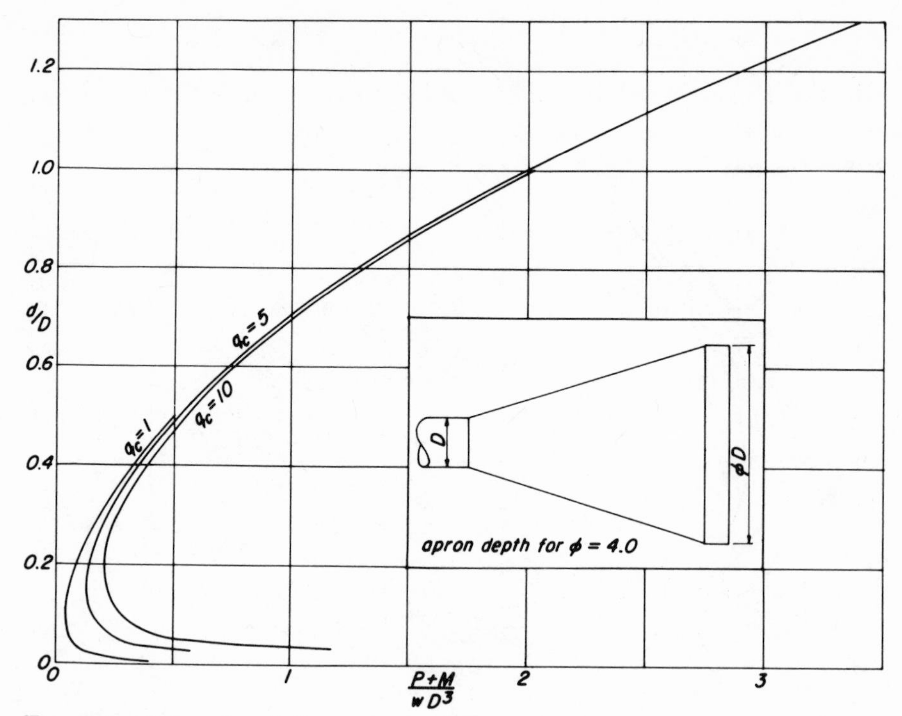

Fig. 62d. Apron depth for end of apron width equal to 4D.

Fig. 61 shows pressure and momentum in terms of the dimensionless term $(P + M)/wD^3$ versus various relative depths d/D at the pipe outlet for constant values of q_c, in which q_c is the discharge factor $Q/D^{5/2}$. Thus these curves are applicable for all pipe sizes and discharges where

P = force due to depth of water, lb.

M = momentum of flow, lb.

w = unit weight of water, 62.4 lb./ft.^{3}

D = pipe diameter, ft.

Figs. 62a through 62d show the values of pressure plus momentum in the same terms as Fig. 61. Fig. 62 is for uniform flow in rectangular sections, formed by the apron and wingwalls, for width of flow sections equal to 1, 2, 3, and 4 (values of ϕ) times the diameter of the pipe.

To use these curves, the value of $(P + M)/wD^3$ is determined for the culvert discharge by means of Fig. 61, keeping in mind that the maximum value for a full pipe unsubmerged at the outlet is determined by a value of d/D of 1.0.

The condition of flow in a rectangular channel corresponding to the flow in the pipe is determined from Figs. 62a through 62d. Basic hydraulic theory requires constancy of momentum unless some external force is applied. In the outlet transition area, it may be assumed that no such force exists. Consequently, the value of $(P + M)/wD^3$ existing at the pipe outlet must also exist on the rectangular outlet apron. The depth of flow on the apron is then determined from Figs. 62a through 62d for the value of $(P + M)/wD^3$ corresponding to the pipe outlet.

Whether or not the water will follow the wingwalls and establish depths according to Figs. 62a through 62d depends on the presence or absence of sufficient tailwater depth. If there is insufficient tailwater depth, the angle of divergence may be too great for the flow to follow the wingwall. The existing tailwater, however, may be used to establish proper operation by selecting a width at the end of the transition in which theoretical depth corresponds to natural stream depth. Natural tailwater depth is established in accordance with the stage-discharge characteristics of the particular stream. For a known discharge, the tailwater depth may be established and a transition width may be determined from Figs. 62a through 62d, which will establish the same depth within the transition section.

From a study of the curves of Fig. 62, it may be seen that depth of flow decreases with increasing width of transition. If the outlet width of the transition is too narrow, downstream depths greater than the natural tailwater depth will be required to balance the culvert outflow. In this case, the outlet flow will force the natural tailwater off the apron, possibly subjecting the channel to scour. On the other hand, if the outlet width of the transition is too great, depths less than the natural tailwater depth are required to balance the outflow. In this case, the tailwater will force itself on the apron and establish a position of equilibrium within the variable width portion of the transition. This latter case is to be preferred.

The curves of Figs. 61 and 62a through 62d show the relationship between mathematical quantities and do not include the effect of friction. At large values of d/D, the effect of friction on the short reaches involved in transitions is negligible. However, at the extremely low depths indicated by the curves of Figs. 62a through 62d, friction forces will be effective in counteracting a part of the force of pressure and momentum, thus reducing the value $(P + M)/wD^3$. It can be seen that as a result of friction the relative depth will be greater than indicated by the curve. The exact amount of friction will depend on the roughness of the apron material and the apron area. An approximation of the total friction force may be estimated from

$$F = AC_f \frac{wV^2}{2g}$$

in which F = total friction force
C_f = friction coefficient
V = average velocity on apron
w = unit weight of water, 62.4 lb./ft.^{3}

g = acceleration of gravity, 32.2 ft./sec.^{2}

For purposes of estimation, the value of C_f may be taken as 0.004. The value of $P + M$ should be reduced by the value of F to obtain d/D. This procedure must necessarily be accomplished by trial and error.

Hydraulic Jump on the Outlet Apron

The hydraulic jump provides an excellent means of controlling high-velocity culvert discharge. In the hydraulic jump, the flow changes from high-velocity flow at shallow depths to tranquil flow at much greater depths. This transition is usually accompanied by a violent and rapidly fluctuating water surface resulting from the loss of a great amount of kinetic energy in a very short distance.

To cause the formation of a hydraulic jump, two conditions must be present. The tailwater depth must be greater than the critical depth, and the depth of the approach flow must be less than critical. Furthermore, the two depths must occur in the relationship expressed by

$$\frac{d_2}{d_1} = \frac{1}{2}(\sqrt{1 + 8F_1^2} - 1)$$

This 72-in. concrete pipe outlet is provided with a hydraulic jump basin and warped wingwalls.

where d_2 = tailwater depth
d_1 = initial depth

$$F_1^2 = \frac{V_1^2}{gd_1}$$

V_1 = velocity of approach flow, fps.
g = acceleration of gravity, 32.2 ft./sec.^{2}

The depths of d_2 and d_1 are called sequent depths.

The curves of Figs. 62a through 62d may also be used to determine the sequent depths in a hydraulic jump. It will be noted that two values of d/D exist for every value of $(P + M)/wD^3$. These curves are similar to the specific head curves and exhibit the same properties except that the depths are related to force (pressure and momentum) instead of to energy. All values of d/D less than the value at minimum $(P + M)/wD^3$ represent depths less than critical and all greater d/D values are depths greater than critical. The two depths possible for each value of $(P + M)/wD^3$ are the sequent depths that will form a hydraulic jump.

In the design of a hydraulic jump outlet structure, consideration must be given to providing the conditions under which a jump will form with the natural tailwater. The stream's stage-discharge characteristics must be obtained for determining the tailwater depth d_2. The transition outlet width should be selected so that the proper initial depth will be established within the transition section for all conditions in which a hydraulic jump is desirable. From the curves of Figs. 62a through 62d it may be seen that as the tailwater depth increases, the initial depth must decrease in order to form a jump. This may be accomplished by increasing the outlet width of the transition. It follows that if the transition is sized for maximum flow, a jump will form for lower discharges at some point within the transition section.

Hydraulic Jump at Low Tailwater Depths

In some cases where the tailwater depth is too low to cause a hydraulic jump, it is desirable to make use of the hydraulic jump principle. The necessary depth can be provided in one of the following ways:

1. Depressing the outlet apron to establish the necessary depth of water.
2. Providing a broad-crested weir at the end of the apron to create a pool of sufficient depth to meet the tailwater requirements of the hydraulic jump.

Either of these techniques is effective. The method of depressing the apron is probably to be preferred since there is less scouring action at the

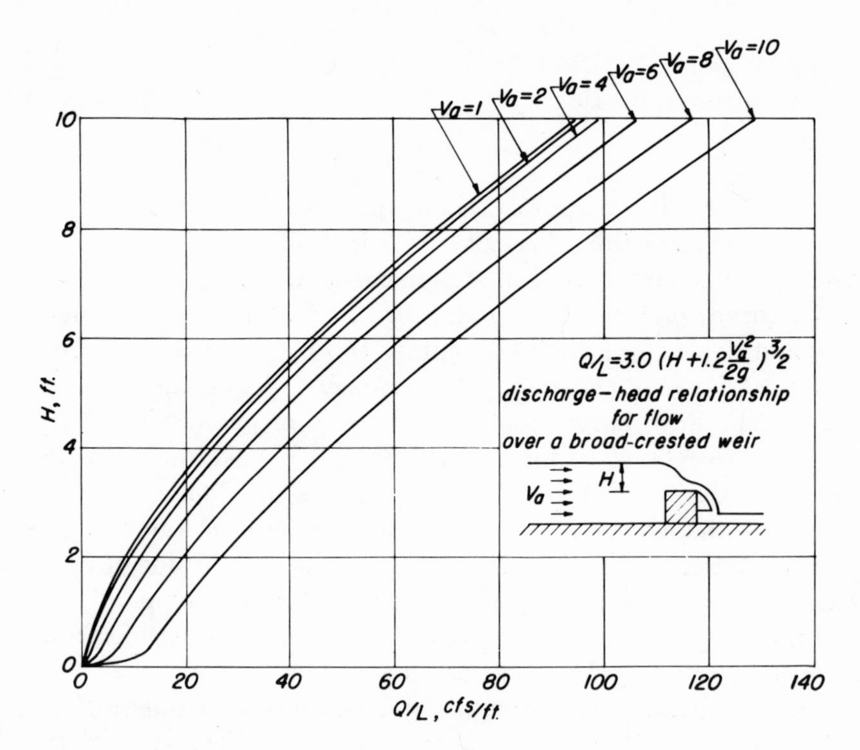

Fig. 63. Discharge-head relationship for flow over a broad crested weir, with $\alpha = 1.2$.

end of the apron. The amount of depression is determined as the difference between the natural tailwater depth and the depth required to form a jump. Tests have shown that a sill with a vertical face should be provided at the end of the apron. Sills with a sloping face have a tendency to throw the discharge up without creating the desired pool. In this case the flow remains concentrated and will cause excessive scour in the stream channel.

The broad-crested weir is probably the simplest method of producing the necessary pool since no extra excavation is required. However, the flow over the weir can be expected to plunge and possibly cause scour on the downstream side. This can be overcome by extending the apron downstream of the weir or by providing riprap in the channel below the weir.

The height of weir required to form the necessary pool is best established by model tests. Where this is impracticable, satisfactory performance can be provided by estimating the weir height required when a diverging type of apron is used. The hydraulic jump will then adjust its position to meet the end conditions. The weir height can be estimated from the relationships for broad-crested weirs. A common formula is

$$Q = CL\left(H + \alpha\frac{V_a^2}{2g}\right)^{3/2}$$

where Q = total discharge
L = length of weir
H = head on the weir
V_a = average velocity of the flow approaching the weir
α = velocity distribution correction factor
g = acceleration of gravity, 32.2 ft./sec.^{2}

It will be necessary to adjust the term $V_a^2/2g$ for nonuniform velocity distribution by means of the correction factor α. As an approximation, $\alpha = 1.2$ may be used for conservative results. The coefficient C may also be approximated as 3.00 for conservative results, resulting in the formula

$$\frac{Q}{L} = 3.00\left(H + 1.2\frac{V_a^2}{2g}\right)^{3/2}$$

which is shown graphically in Fig. 63. The value of V_a is computed from

$$V_a = \frac{Q}{d_2L}$$

The required weir height is then determined from

$$h = d_2 - H$$

where h = weir height
d_2 = tailwater depth required by the hydraulic jump
H = head on the weir

The head on the weir may be determined from Fig. 63. The discharge factor $Q/D^{5/2}$ should be converted to discharge per linear foot of weir, Q/L. The head, H, corresponding to the approach velocity may then be read directly. This relationship holds for broad-crested weirs with a vertical face for crest widths 2.5 to 3.0 times the head on the weir as shown in Fig. 64.

The apron stilling basin should be designed so that minor departures from the assumed tailwater depth will not cause the jump either to submerge the flow from the culvert or to be driven off the apron. Submergence is caused by the tailwater being too high, while downstream movement of the jump is caused by the tailwater being too low. It has been found

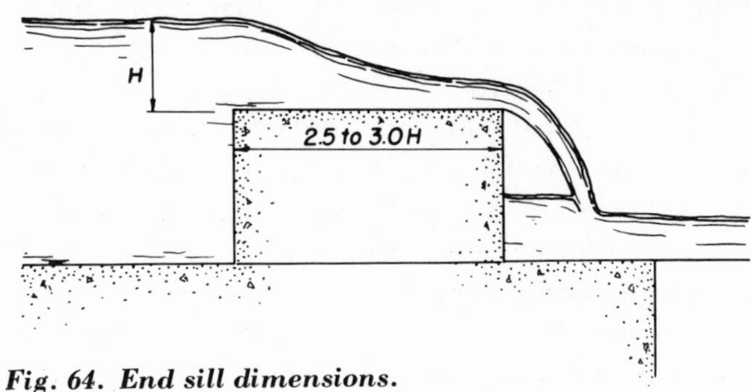

Fig. 64. End sill dimensions.

that the use of baffle blocks such as shown in Fig. 65 is advantageous in assuring the formation of the hydraulic jump on the apron. A diverging approach section may also be used to vary the approach conditions of flow in accordance with the pool depth established on the apron. It is advisable to design the apron so that at maximum discharge the hydraulic jump will originate within the diverging section. Any variation in pool

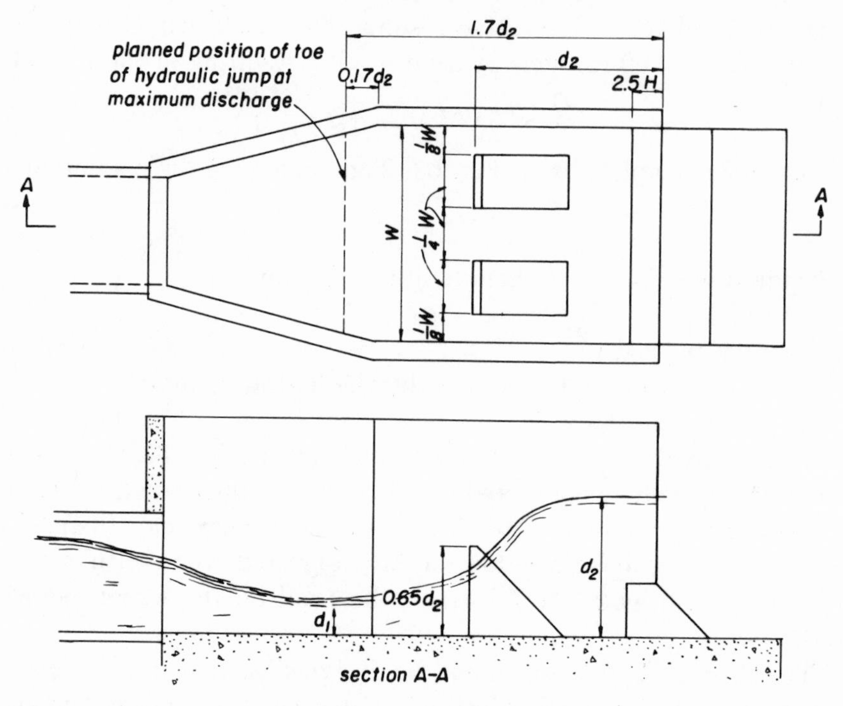

Fig. 65. A hydraulic jump outlet structure with baffle blocks and end weir.

depth on the apron will then have a self-correcting tendency since a change in position will cause a corrective change in the initial conditions. This effect may also be provided with an apron placed on a reasonably flat slope. The proportions for the hydraulic jump stilling basin shown in Fig. 65 were based in part on model tests made by the California Division of Highways at the City of Los Angeles Hydraulic Laboratory. The proportions shown are intended to serve only as a guide in establishing minimum dimensions. Departures may be made without seriously affecting the performance of the apron.

The apron should be of sufficient length to contain approximately 30 per cent of the hydraulic jump. For the values of q_c and d/D used in the curves of Fig. 62, the maximum length of the hydraulic jump is determined by

$$\frac{L_j}{D} = 5.6\,\frac{d_2}{D}$$

where L_j = length of hydraulic jump
D = pipe diameter
d_2 = tailwater depth

Wingwall Angle

No optimum wingwall angle has been determined for culvert outlets. The purpose of the wingwall other than to serve as a retaining wall is to guide the outlet flow in an efficient transition from a circular culvert to the flow channel.

For free-springing jets, wingwalls serve the purpose of protecting the embankment from bank-washing currents or eddies induced by the jet. Hence, the best angle must be determined by site conditions.

For the supported jet without tailwater effect, wingwalls are used to prevent the jet splash and high apron velocities from washing the embankment. The diffusion of the apron flow will be difficult and it will probably be impractical to attempt to control jet diffusion. Therefore, site conditions and apron length will govern the placement of the wingwalls.

Supported Jet with Tailwater Effect

The presence of tailwater at the culvert outlet will assist in the distribution of the outlet flow. The U.S. Bureau of Reclamation has devised an empirical formula for determining the maximum angle that diffusing flow can be expected to follow in rectangular channels. While not strictly applicable, this formula can be used to estimate the angle of wingwall that will be followed by flow from circular culvert outlets. This is

$$\tan\alpha = \frac{\sqrt{gd}}{3V}$$

where α = wingwall angle with respect to direction of flow
d = average depth on the apron
V = average velocity on the apron

From the considerations of the foregoing sections, it can be seen that the wingwall angle will be affected by the discharge constant q_c, pipe depth ratio d/D, width ratio at the end of the transition ϕ, and the tailwater depth ratio d_t/D. In any case, it is not considered desirable for wingwalls controlling hydraulic operation to diverge at a total included angle greater than 45 deg.

Apron Length

An apron extending between wingwalls for the complete length of the wingwalls should be provided where erosion protection is required. With the present data, the required length of apron from the culvert outlet to the end of the transition can only be approximated.

The length of apron for supported jets with no tailwater effect was given in the section "Supported Jets" as

$$L_a = 0.37 V_o \sqrt{D}.$$

The USBR gives the length of transition from a circular section to a rectangular section as

$$L = \frac{1}{5} V D$$

where L = length of transition
V = pipe discharge velocity
D = pipe diameter

This applies to outlets with an apron width ratio of $\phi = 1$ at the end of the transition. For diverging wingwalls, the apron length should be greater.

Where the flow follows the wingwalls, the apron length is given by

$$L_a = \frac{D(\phi - 1)}{2} \tan \alpha.$$

The apron for an outlet operating with a hydraulic jump should be long enough to contain 30 per cent of the length of the jump and provide a short distance downstream from the pipe outlet to permit formation of the jump. Until more experience and data are accumulated, it is advisable to provide a minimum overall apron length (culvert outlet to back of weir) equal to the length of the hydraulic jump. For the range of data given in Fig. 62, this will be given by

$$\frac{L_a}{D} = 5.6 \frac{d_t}{D}.$$

Hydraulic Jump Contained in the Culvert Pipe

The characteristics of flow in circular conduits will permit the establishment of a hydraulic jump in a pipe under certain circumstances. Fig. 61 shows the relationship between pressure-momentum and the relative depth in a pipe. Where the flow in the pipe is less than critical, a hydraulic jump is possible provided there is sufficient tailwater depth to cause its formation.

It will be noted that the steep slope of the curves for values of d/D greater than 0.5 limits the opportunity of jump formation in the pipe with a free surface. However, a hydraulic jump may form in a pipe without a free surface. It is also possible to enlarge the pipe and thus change the characteristics of the resulting jump. Fig. 61 may be used by entering the curves with values of $(P + M)/wD^3$ and q_c for the new pipe size in which the value of $P + M$ is maintained constant.

The formation of a hydraulic jump in a pipe may choke the pipe and cause it to fill, particularly if the inlet is submerged. To prevent this from happening, it is advisable to provide a vent pipe well upstream of the outlet to admit air.

It is sometimes possible to increase the efficiency of a culvert by causing the pipe to flow full, particularly on steep slopes. This can increase the discharge without raising the headwater depth. Due to entrance constriction, full flow may not occur until the open channel capacity of the pipe is exceeded. The characteristics of the hydraulic jump can be used to cause the pipe to fill prematurely and operate more efficiently. In this case, a vent pipe is undesirable. Designs employing this refinement should be studied carefully to be sure that the culvert will perform in the desired manner.

Cantilevered Outlets

The cantilevered type of culvert outlet is often used to avoid steep culvert slopes and to reduce the length of culvert. The free-springing jet issuing from this type of outlet is highly erosive. The best means of dissipating the energy from the free fall is by means of the plunge pool; i.e., the jet falls into a water-filled pool of sufficient depth to dissipate the energy. The pool may be excavated or formed naturally. In the latter case, material will be transported downstream and often large basins are eroded. If normal stream velocity is low, the material may be deposited a short distance downstream and cause shoaling. It is recommended that the basin be preshaped with protection for the banks to prevent erosion.

The necessary depth of the pool is often considered to be independent of the material and is determined by the stable depth, the depth of eventual erosion if left to natural processes. The stable depth is given by the empirical expression

$$d_s = 1.32 H_T^{0.225} q^{0.54}$$

Scour is controlled at the cantilevered outlet of this 42-in. culvert by means of a plunge pool.

where d_s = depth of scour below tailwater level
H_T = total head from the headwater elevation to pool elevation
q = discharge per unit width Q/D

However, recent research[5] indicates that type of material and time are involved in determining the scour that will result from this type of outlet.

The location of the pool center with respect to the pipe outlet is given by

$$L_p = V_o\sqrt{\frac{2H}{g}}$$

where L_p = horizontal distance from the pipe outlet to the pool
H = vertical distance of the pipe above the pool
V_o = outlet velocity
g = acceleration of gravity, 32.2 ft./sec.^{2}

Submerged Outlets

Culverts may be required to operate with the outlet submerged. This may be a permanent condition or may be due to depth-flow characteristics of the flow channel for the particular discharge. Unless the outlet is located well above the stream bed in a very wide channel, an erosion problem will exist. Outlets located near the stream bed should be provided with an apron and those in narrow channels should have wingwalls to prevent bank erosion from eddies set up by the submerged jet.

Submerged jets tend to remain concentrated and do not readily dissipate their energy. Velocities of 60 per cent of the culvert outlet velocity will persist to a distance downstream of the outlet equal to 6.2 pipe diameters for jets not confined by an apron or stream bed. For jets supported by a bottom plane, the velocities will be almost 100 per cent for distances up to $6.2D$. Apron velocities at $L > 6.2D$ for outlets located at apron level may be determined from the relationship

$$v = 6.2 \frac{V_o}{L/D}$$

where v = maximum apron velocity at distance L
L = distance from the outlet
D = pipe diameter
V_o = outlet velocity

Wingwall and Apron Length—Submerged Outlet

The total diffusion angle of submerged jets has been established by experiment to be approximately 22 deg. The length of apron is established by consideration of the relationship between apron and outlet velocities and distance from the outlet. Wingwalls may be built at any angle as long as the total angle of flare is greater than 22 deg., with the apron covering the enclosed area.

Impact Stilling Basin

The impact-type stilling basin developed by the USBR[2] provides one of the best and most efficient means of controlling the erosive potential of high-energy culvert discharge. The basin is effective over the complete discharge range. The design proportions shown in Fig. 66 have been developed for a minimum-size, yet adequate, outlet device. The operation of the basin has been found to be more efficient than a comparable hydraulic jump.

The principle of operation is to produce energy dissipation by causing the flow to strike the vertical hanging baffle. The flow is turned upstream by the horizontal portion of the baffle and the floor, generating vertical eddies. No tailwater is necessary for good operation; but with tailwater, performance is improved since it reduces outlet velocities. Fig. 67 shows a typical basin in operation at 80 per cent of maximum discharge.

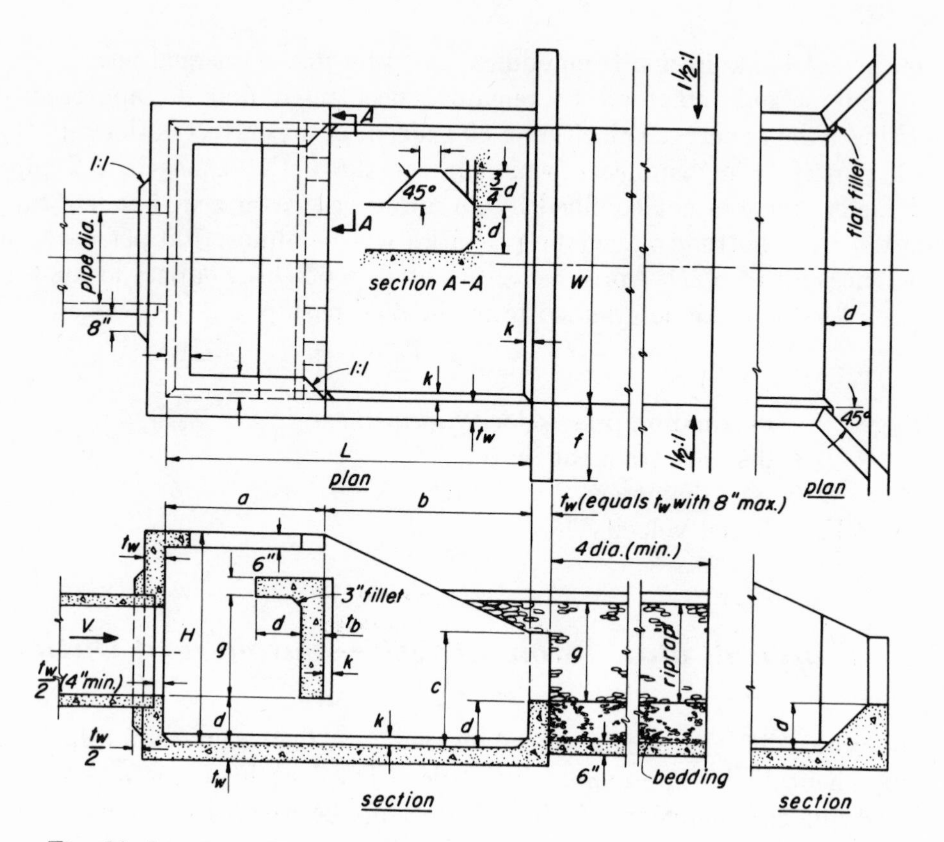

Fig. 66. Impact stilling basin design.

The design of the impact stilling basin depends only on the discharge and is independent of outlet velocity and pipe size as long as outlet velocities do not greatly exceed 30 fps.

The detailed dimensions of the basin are related to the width, which is determined by the discharge. Fig. 68 shows basin width for discharges up to 339 cfs, the upper limit recommended by the USBR. Instead of a single curve, an upper limit curve and a lower limit curve are given. Variation of basin width between these limits is not critical to the operation of the basin and permits the selection of convenient dimensions.

Table 13 lists dimensions for various discharges, together with suggested pipe sizes. The pipe size is unimportant to the operation of the basin and may be changed without changing the basin dimensions as long as the discharge is the same. If a basin width other than that given in Table 13 is required, the proportional dimension may be used. The riprap dimensions suggested in the table were determined from the empirical formula

$$V_b = 2.6\sqrt{d}$$

Fig. 67. An impact basin. *Courtesy of U.S. Bureau of Reclamation.*

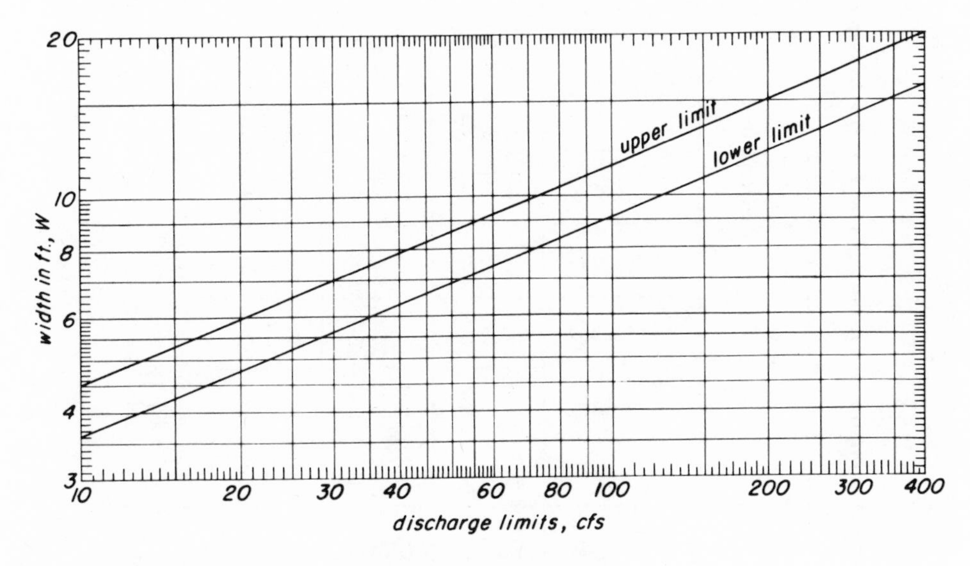

Fig. 68. Impact-type energy dissipator basin VI.

where V_b = bottom velocity, fps

d = diameter of rock in inches

This formula assumes the use of ordinary rock with a specific gravity of about 2.65.

TABLE 13. Stilling Basin Dimensions—Impact-Type Energy Dissipator (Basin VI)

Suggested pipe size*		Maximum discharge, cfs	Feet and inches										Inches					
Diam., in. (1)	Area, sq.ft. (2)	Q (3)	W (4)	H (5)	L (6)	a (7)	b (8)	c (9)	d (10)	e (11)	f (12)	g (13)	t_w (14)	t_f (15)	t_b (16)	t_p (17)	k (18)	Suggested riprap sizes (19)
18	1.77	21**	5-6	4-3	7-4	3-3	4-1	2-4	0-11	0-6	1-6	2-1	6	6½	6	6	3	4.0
24	3.14	38	6-9	5-3	9-0	3-11	5-1	2-10	1-2	0-6	2-0	2-6	6	6½	6	6	3	7.0
30	4.91	59	8-0	6-3	10-8	4-7	6-1	3-4	1-4	0-8	2-6	3-0	6	6½	7	7	3	8.5
36	7.07	85	9-3	7-3	12-4	5-3	7-1	3-10	1-7	0-8	3-0	3-6	7	7½	8	8	3	9.0
42	9.62	115	10-6	8-0	14-0	6-0	8-0	4-5	1-9	0-10	3-0	3-11	8	8½	9	8	4	9.5
48	12.57	151	11-9	9-0	15-8	6-9	8-11	4-11	2-0	0-10	3-0	4-5	9	9½	10	8	4	10.5
54	15.90	191	13-0	9-9	17-4	7-4	10-0	5-5	2-2	1-0	3-0	4-11	10	10½	10	8	4	12.0
60	19.63	236	14-3	10-9	19-0	8-0	11-0	5-11	2-5	1-0	3-0	5-4	11	11½	11	8	6	13.0
72	28.27	339	16-6	12-3	22-0	9-3	12-9	6-11	2-9	1-3	3-0	6-2	12	12½	12	8	6	14.0

*Suggested pipe will run full when velocity is 12 fps or half full when velocity is 24 fps. Size may be modified for other velocities by $Q = AV$, but relation between Q and basin dimensions shown must be maintained.

**For discharges less than 21 cfs, obtain basin width from curve of Fig. 42. Other dimensions proportional to W: $H = 3W/4$, $L = 4W/3$, $d = W/6$, etc.

Tailwater is not needed for the successful operation of the basin; however, performance will be improved with tailwater not exceeding

$$d + \frac{g}{2}$$

where d and g are defined as in the dimension sketch of Fig. 66. Excessive tailwater will cause flow to pass through the top of the baffle and should be avoided if possible. Should the apron become clogged with silt, the entire flow can pass over the baffle with reduced but acceptable performance. Notches in the lower edge of the baffle are for producing a scouring flow concentration to remove deposited silt.

The basin may be operated with pipes on slopes as large as 15 to 20 deg. without adversely affecting performance. For greater slopes a horizontal or sloping pipe approximately 2 diameters long should be placed just upstream of the stilling basin. For improved performance, the alternate end sill and 45-deg. wingwall plan should be used. The extra sill length distributes the flow over a wider area. This reduces the tendency to scour and also reduces the height of waves in the downstream channel.

The baffle action can cause a hydraulic jump to form in the pipe, and the pipe may fill or operate erratically, depending on a number of factors. For this reason it is recommended that the culvert pipe be vented a convenient distance upstream of the basin with a pipe one-sixth of the culvert diameter.

References

1. Albertson, M. L.; Dai, Y. B.; Jensen, R. A.; and Rouse, Hunter, "Diffusion of Submerged Jets," ASCE *Transactions*, 1950.
2. Bradley, J. N., and Peterka, A. L., "The Hydraulic Design of Stilling Basins," ASCE *Proceedings*, Vol. 83, October 1957, and *Journal of the Hydraulics Division*, No. Hy5, Papers No. 1401 to 1406, inclusive.
3. Chow, V. T., *Open-Channel Hydraulics*, New York, McGraw-Hill Book Co., 1959.
4. *Design of Small Dams*, Washington, D.C., U.S. Bureau of Reclamation, 1960.
5. *Drainage Structures, Design and Performance*, Highway Research Board Bulletin 286, Washington, D.C., 1960.
6. Forster, J. W., and Skrinde, R. A., "The Control of the Hydraulic Jump by Sills," ASCE *Transactions*, 1950.
7. Lane, E. W., and Kindsvater, C. E., "Hydraulic Jump in Enclosed Conduits," *Engineering News-Record*, December 29, 1938.
8. Rouse, Hunter, *Engineering Hydraulics*, New York, John Wiley & Sons, 1949.
9. Woodward, S. M., and Posey, C. J., *Hydraulics of Steady Flow in Open Channels*, New York, John Wiley & Sons, 1948.

7

Drop Inlets and Sag Culverts

DEPARTURES FROM THE USUAL TYPE OF CULVERT CONSTRUCTION are sometimes required when it is necessary to place the culvert invert below the natural grade of the drainage channel. These usually take the form of a drop inlet or a sag culvert, sometimes known as an inverted siphon.

Use of Drop Inlets

Drop inlets are useful where the headroom at the entrance is limited or where it is desirable to reduce velocity by inducing high energy losses at the entrance. A drop inlet type of culvert is placed below the natural drainage grade at the entrance and discharges directly into the natural drainage channel at the outlet. A typical drop inlet is illustrated in Fig. 69a.

Use of Sag Culverts

High drainage flow and limited headroom space produce difficult situations. In cases where the required culvert size is larger than can be accommodated in a normal culvert installation, it may be necessary to use a sag culvert. In this design, the invert of the culvert barrel is placed below the inlet and the outlet as shown in Fig. 69b.

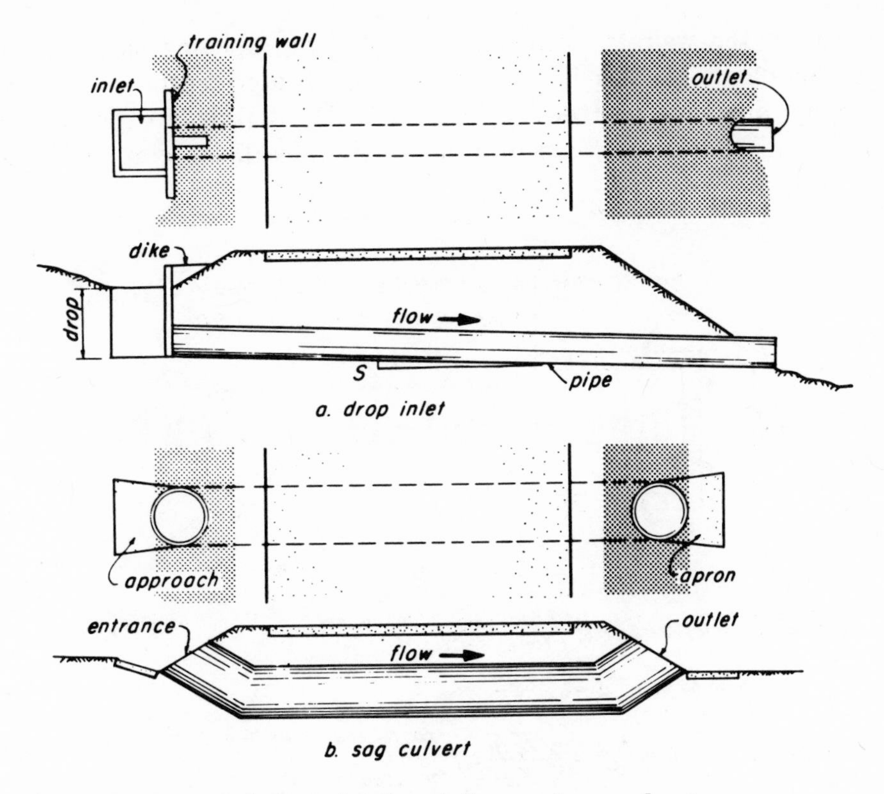

Fig. 69. Typical designs for drop inlets and sag culverts.

The hydraulic operation of a sag culvert is not necessarily objectionable. Hydraulic energy losses are potentially greater because of the vertical bends at either end and the greater length of pipe used in construction. Due to its configuration, a sag culvert will flow full, thus producing an outlet control situation.

The chief objections to the operation of a sag culvert are silting at low flows and stagnation during periods of no flow. Silting can be minimized by designing the culvert to produce self-cleansing velocities. Stagnation can be overcome in some cases by providing subsurface drains at the low point which are capable of draining the culvert in a reasonable period of time.

Drop Inlet Design

The flow in a drop inlet culvert is controlled (except at the highest flows) by the weir effect of the horizontal drop opening (Fig. 70). Balanced design will strive to provide a pipe of sufficient capacity to prevent submergence of the weir at normal flows. The drop opening should carry design flows without exceeding the limiting headwater depth.

Many different weir designs are possible. Blaisdell[1] experimented with several different types of drop inlet spillways that are applicable to

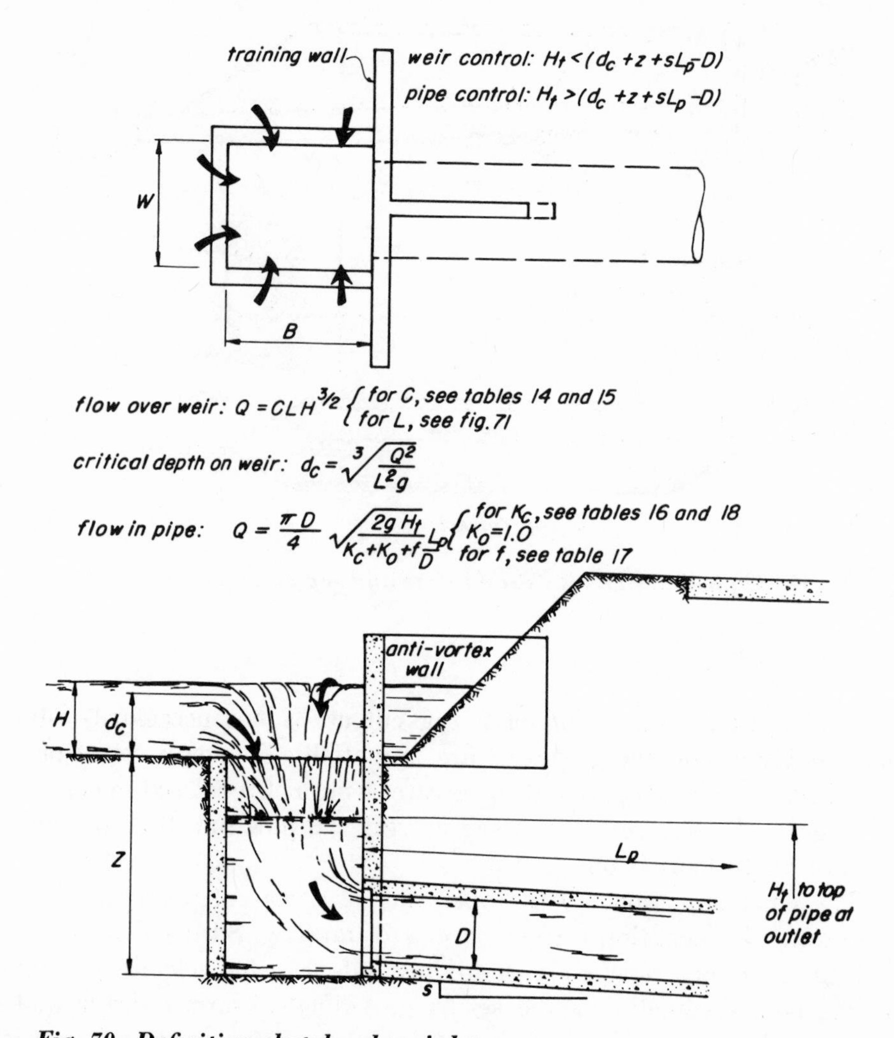

Fig. 70. Definition sketch—drop inlets.

culvert design. Those most applicable to drop inlet culverts are shown in Fig. 71.

The flow into the horizontal drop opening is given by

$$Q = CLH^{3/2}$$

which, expressed in the dimensionless terms of culvert hydraulics, becomes

$$\left(\frac{Q}{D}\right)^{5/2} = C\frac{L}{D}\left(\frac{H}{D}\right)^{3/2}$$

where Q = discharge, cfs
D = culvert pipe diameter, ft.
L = weir length, ft.
H = headwater depth measure with respect to the weir, ft.
C = discharge coefficient

The weir length is determined by the geometry of the drop opening (Fig. 70) and the approach flow to the inlet. The discharge coefficient is deter-

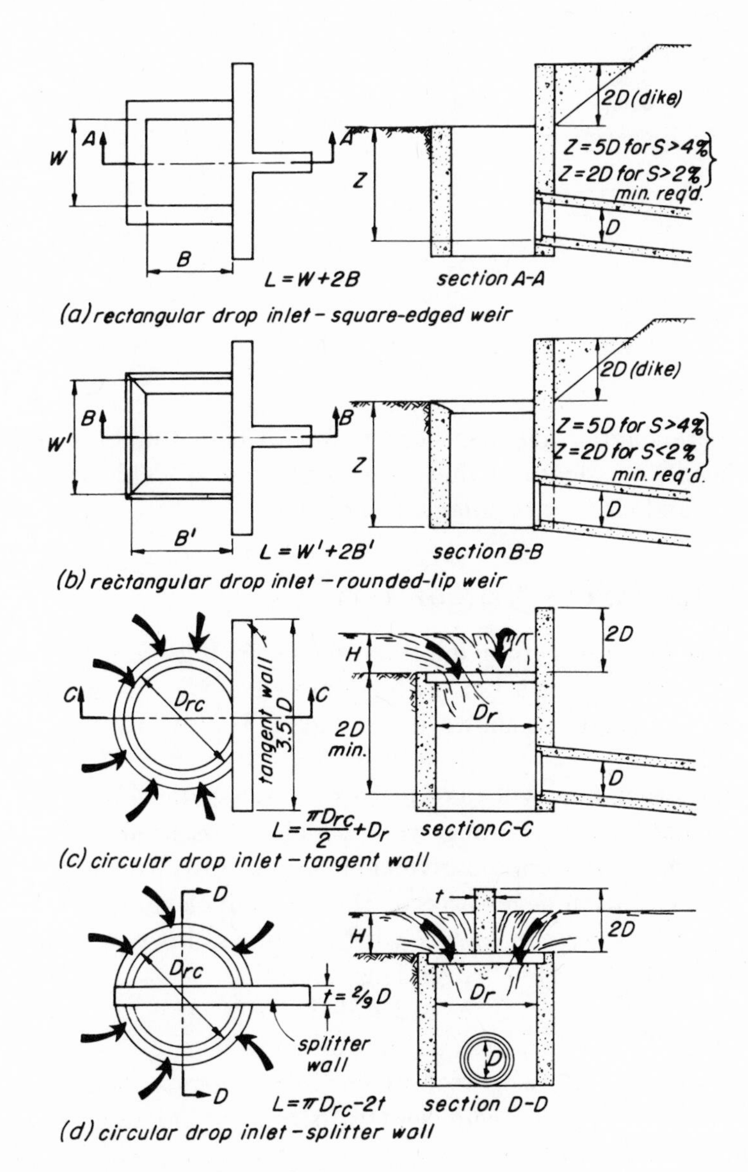

(a) rectangular drop inlet - square-edged weir
(b) rectangular drop inlet - rounded-lip weir
(c) circular drop inlet - tangent wall
(d) circular drop inlet - splitter wall

Fig. 71. Drop inlet design.

TABLE 14. Weir Coefficients for Rectangular Drop Inlets

H/D	Values of C	
	$Q/D^{5/2}<4$	$Q/D^{5/2}>4$
.05	0.966	—
.10	3.18	1.05
.20	3.28	2.40
.30	3.32	2.94
.40	3.33	3.22
.50	3.34	3.38
.60	3.35	3.50
.80	3.36	3.64
1.00	3.36	3.74

TABLE 15. Weir Coefficients for Circular Drop Inlets

H/D_{rc}	C for max. error of ± 5%
0.06–0.08	2.60
0.08–0.10	2.82
0.10–0.20	3.10
0.20–0.50	3.41
0.50	3.46
H/D_{rc}	Avg. C
.07	2.60
.10	2.92
.15	3.13
.20	3.25
.25	3.32
.30	3.37
.35	3.40
.40	3.42
.45	3.44
.50	3.46

mined experimentally and has been found to be a function of geometry and the headwater depth. Values of C are given in Tables 14 and 15 for rectangular and circular openings, respectively.

RECTANGULAR DROP INLET

Examples of the rectangular inlet are shown in Figs. 71a and 71b. Weir length is determined for a box with square edges by the inside perimeter of the box. The length as shown in the figures is given by

$$L = W + 2B.$$

This assumes that flow will take place over three edges only. The fourth edge is replaced by a training wall, which is essential for satisfactory operation. The design formulas given here apply only if this wall is provided and the pool elevation never exceeds the top wall elevation.

The length of weir for a box with a rounded lip is measured at the high point on the lip. Thus length is given by

$$L = 2B' + W'$$

where B' and W' are measured as shown in Fig. 71.

Drop inlet culverts with rectangular inlets operate most satisfactorily when the height of drop is sufficient to permit considerable submergence of the pipe entrance without submerging the weir. For culvert pipes on a slope greater than 4 per cent, the depth of drop should be at least 5 pipe diameters. For slopes less than 2 per cent, the depth of drop need not be more than 2 pipe diameters.

Submergence of Rectangular Drop Inlet

A rectangular drop inlet will be submerged when the water level in the vertical riser is higher than the critical depth over the weir. The depth of water in the riser is controlled by the flow characteristics of the culvert pipe operating with either inlet or outlet control. Critical depth for weir flow (Fig. 70) is given by

$$d_c = \sqrt[3]{\frac{Q^2}{L^2 g}}$$

where d_c = critical depth, ft.
Q = discharge, cfs
L = weir length, ft.
g = acceleration of gravity, 32.2 ft./sec.^{2}

Rectangular Drop Inlet Discharge Coefficient

The weir discharge coefficients for rectangular drop inlets given in Table 14 are determined by

$$C = 3.38\left(1 - \frac{1}{250H/D}\right)^{3/2} \text{ for } \frac{Q}{D^{5/2}} < 4$$

and by

$$C = 4.10\left(L - \frac{1}{16.7H/D}\right)^{3/2} \text{ for } \frac{Q}{D^{5/2}} > 4$$

Values of C interpolated from Table 14 are of sufficient accuracy for most purposes.

Flow in Submerged Rectangular Drop Inlets

If the depth of water in the vertical riser is above the critical depth for weir flow, the drop inlet will be submerged. Fow is then determined by the relationship

$$Q = \frac{\pi D^2}{4}\sqrt{\frac{2gH_t}{K_c + K_o + fL/D}}$$

where H_t = total head, ft., measured from the headwater surface in the riser to the crown of the culvert outlet
K_c = entrance loss coefficient
K_o = outlet loss coefficient, usually taken as 1.0
f = Darcy-Weisbach friction factor in which

$$f = 185\,\frac{n^2}{D^{1/3}}$$

L = length of pipe

This form of the formula ignores the effect of friction in the riser which, for short risers, is insignificant. Weir submergence (Fig. 70) will exist when

$$H_t > (d_c + Z + SL_p - D)$$

where d_c = critical depth of flow on weir
Z = height of riser
S = slope of pipe
L_p = length of pipe
D = pipe diameter

TABLE 16. Entrance Loss Coefficients for Rectangular Drop Inlets

Socket end of pipe projecting slightly into riser		Square-edge pipe opening into riser	
Slope, per cent	K_e	Slope, per cent	K_e
0	.12	0	1.2
5	.12	5	.95
10	.13	10	.87
20	.13	20	.82
30	.17	30	.81

***TABLE 17. Darcy-Weisbach Friction Factor* f *for Various Pipe Sizes and Manning's* n**

	Values of f				
D \ n	.010	.012	.013	.024	.025
6	.0233	.0336	.0394	.1342	.1456
12	.0185	.0266	.0313	.1066	.1156
18	.0162	.0233	.0273	.0931	.1010
24	.0147	.0211	.0248	.0846	.0918
30	.0136	.0196	.0230	.0785	.0852
36	.0128	.0185	.0217	.0739	.0802
42	.0122	.0175	.0206	.0702	.0762
48	.0117	.0168	.0197	.0671	.0729
54	.0112	.0161	.0189	.0645	.0700
60	.0108	.0156	.0183	.0623	.0676
66	.0105	.0151	.0177	.0604	.0655
72	.0102	.0147	.0172	.0586	.0636
84	.0097	.0139	.0163	.0557	.0604

Entrance loss coefficients, K_c, to be used for submerged rectangular drop inlets for both square-edge and round-lip weir are given in Table 16. They have been experimentally determined and are influenced by the slope of the culvert pipe.

Friction Factors

Table 17 is a tabulation of equivalent Darcy-Weisbach friction factors for various n values and various pipe sizes. This table is based on the formula:

$$f = 185\frac{n^2}{D^{1/3}}.$$

Anti-Vortex Wall

Blaisdell's work has shown that an anti-vortex wall is essential for satisfactory operation of a drop inlet. In the case of a rectangular drop inlet, a back training wall and dike will provide satisfactory operation. The dike extending from the training wall to the embankment (Fig. 71a) prevents circulation around the wall. The presence of circulation impairs the operation of the drop inlet and requires a larger inlet for the same flows. The design procedure herein presented is based upon the presence of a training wall and dike.

The height of the training wall and dike should be as high as the expected headwater or 2 diameters, whichever is less. This is shown in Fig. 71.

Culvert Pipe

The culvert pipe is designed in the same manner as the conventional culvert. However, the turbulent nature of the water at the entrance will cause the pipe to flow full sooner after submergence of the entrance than in the normal culvert installation. The curves of Fig. 41 in Chapter 4 can be used to determine the operational characteristics of the pipe. If it is at all possible for the pipe to flow full, it will do so. If the flow is not great enough to fill the pipe, it will operate with inlet control, even though the entrance is submerged. Inlet control in this case is in reference to the pipe entrance in the riser and not to the weir at the entrance to the drop inlet. Entrance loss coefficients for conventional culvert installations may be used as estimates of entrance losses as long as the weir is not submerged by the water in the riser.

Circular Drop Inlets

The construction of drop inlets can be simplified by building circular drop inlets of precast concrete pipe. The same principles of design apply to the circular inlet as to the rectangular. The most satisfactory designs are shown in Figs. 71c and 71d. The rectangular weir discharge formula

$$Q = CLH^{3/2}$$

applies equally well to the circular rim. Values of the discharge coefficient for the circular opening are determined from

$$C = 3.60\left(1 - \frac{0.013}{H/D_{rc}}\right)^{3/2}$$

and are given in Table 15. The weir length shown in Fig. 71 takes into account the effect of the anti-vortex devices on the approach flow.

The riser height required to prevent drowning out of the inlet weir before the culvert pipe flows full need not be more than 2 diameters, as shown in Fig. 71. The diameter D_r of the riser should not be less than $1.25D$.

Submergence—With a full-flowing pipe, the inlet weir will become submerged in the same manner for a circular inlet as for a rectangular inlet. The same design formulas may be used, including the formula for determining critical depth on the weir. However, the orifice loss coefficients for submerged weir flow will be different and are given in Table 18.

Anti-Vortex Devices—The anti-vortex devices that are satisfactory for circular drop inlets are shown in Figs. 71c and 71d. They are the tangent wall and the splitter wall. Experiment has shown that operation is essentially the same for either device. The height of the wall should be equal to either the maximum expected headwater H or 2 pipe diameters, whichever is less. In either case, no circulation should be permitted around the wall, as this will impair the efficiency of the operation. The splitter wall should be extended into the embankment and the tangent wall should be provided with a dike extending into the embankment. Other anti-vortex devices have been developed that will also ensure satisfactory operation.

TABLE 18. Entrance Loss Coefficients for Circular Drop Inlets, 20 Per Cent Slope

Inlet crest	Anti-vortex wall	Conduit entrance	$\frac{D_r}{D}$	K_e*
Square edge	Splitter	Groove	1.78	.66
.25D radius	Splitter	Groove	1.78	.42
.25D radius	Splitter	Groove	1.25	.61
.25D radius	Tangent	Groove	1.78	.50

*These values should be increased for slopes less than 20 per cent and may be decreased for greater slopes.

Those shown here are most satisfactory for culvert applications. In no case should a circular drop inlet be constructed without an anti-vortex device.

Drop Inlet—Example Problem

Design a rectangular and a circular drop inlet to carry a flow of 50 cfs at a head on the weir of 1.0 ft. The total available drop (ground level at upstream to ground level at downstream) is 9 ft. The length of culvert pipe is 200 ft. The socket end of a concrete pipe will be placed flush with the riser wall. The outlet will remain unsubmerged for the highest expected flow.

Solution Using Rectangular Riser

Step 1. Determine pipe slope and riser height. As a first approximation, select

$$\text{slope of pipe} = 1 \text{ per cent}$$
$$\text{depth of riser} = 9 - 0.01 \times 200 = 7 \text{ ft.}$$

Remarks: A riser 7 ft. deep may be undesirable for practical reasons, while one 5 ft. deep may be more acceptable; therefore, select

$$\text{depth of riser} = 5 \text{ ft.}$$
$$\text{slope of pipe} = \frac{9 - 5}{200} = 2 \text{ per cent.}$$

Step 2. Determine pipe size. Proceed by selecting and evaluating performance of several different pipe sizes:

(*a*) *Try 24-in. pipe.*

$$\frac{Q}{D^{5/2}} = \frac{50}{5.65} = 8.85 \text{ and } \frac{L}{D} = \frac{200}{2} = 100.$$

Optimum critical slope (from Fig. 38, Chapter 3) = 1.45 per cent. Type of control (from Fig. 45, Chapter 4):

$$(S_c)_{op}\frac{L}{D} = 0.0145 \times 100 = 1.45 \text{ and}$$

$$s_o = \frac{2.0}{1.45} = 1.38.$$

Pipe can be expected to flow full (outlet control) since control length curves show that pipe will fill for values of $Q/D^{5/2} > 6.4$. Required depth of water in riser from nomograph (Appendix C):

For $L = 200$ ft.

$D = 24$ in.

$Q = 50$ cfs

find $H = 18$ ft.

Remarks: The head required to produce the required flow in a 24-in. pipe exceeds that which is permissible.

(b) *Try 30-in. pipe.*

$$\frac{Q}{D^{5/2}} = \frac{50}{9.9} = 5.05 \text{ and } \frac{L}{D} = \frac{200}{2.5} = 80.$$

Optimum critical slope (from Fig. 38, Chapter 3) = 1.3 per cent. Type of control (from Fig. 45, Chapter 4):

$$(S_c)_{op}\frac{L}{D} = 0.013 \times 80 = 1.04 \text{ and}$$

$$s_o = \frac{2.0}{1.3} = 1.54.$$

Pipe can be expected to flow part full (inlet control) since control length curves show that pipe will flow part full for values of $Q/D^{5/2} < 7.2$. Required depth of water in riser from nomograph for inlet control (Appendix B, Fig. B-3):

$$\frac{H}{D} = 1.95 \text{ for } Q = 50 \text{ and } D = 30 \text{ in.}$$

$$H = 1.95 \times 2.5 = 4.87 \text{ ft.}$$

Since $H <$ riser depth, 30-in. pipe will be satisfactory.

Step 3. Determine outlet velocity. From Manning's equation,

$$V = \frac{1.486}{n}R^{2/3}S^{1/2}$$

where $n = 0.012$

$S = 0.02$

Determine R from curve of hydraulic elements (Fig. 36, Chapter 3) for d/D determined from culvert operation diagram (Fig. 41, Chapter 4). For $s_o = 1.54$,

$$\frac{Q}{D^{5/2}} = 5.05$$

$$\frac{d}{D} = 0.71$$

Then $R = 1.19 \times \frac{D}{4} = 1.19 \times \frac{2.5}{4}$

$R = 0.744$

Then $V = \frac{1.486}{0.012}(0.744)^{2/3}(0.02)^{1/2}$

$V = 14.4$ fps.

Step 4. Determine weir length.

$$Q = CLH^{3/2}$$

$$\text{or } L = \frac{Q}{CH^{3/2}}$$

Select C from Table 14 for $Q/D^{5/2} = 5.05$ and $HW/D = 1/2.5 = 0.40$. Select $C = 3.22$, since $Q/D^{5/2} > 4.0$. Then $L = \dfrac{50}{3.22 \times 1^{3/2}} = 15.5$ ft. required. Use a box inlet 5.5 ft. with a training wall $= 1.0$ ft. high.

(*a*) *Check for weir control.*

$$d_c = \sqrt[3]{\frac{1}{g}\left(\frac{Q}{L}\right)^2}$$

$$d_c = \sqrt[3]{\frac{1}{32.2}\left(\frac{50}{15.5}\right)^2}$$

$$d_c = 0.658 \text{ ft.}$$

Then $(d_c + Z + SL - D) = (0.685 + 5.0 + 0.02 \times 200 - 2.5)$

$(d_c + Z + SL - D) = 7.185.$

Also $H_t = (H + SL - D) = (4.87 + 0.02 \times 200 - 2.5)$

$H_t = 6.37$ ft.

Since $6.37 < 7.185$

$$H_t < (d_c + Z + SL - D).$$

Weir controls flow into the culvert.

Design Summary of Box Drop Inlet Culvert

Design conditions:

$Q = 50$ cfs
$HW = 1.0$
$L = 200$ ft.

Design selections:

Riser 5.0 ft. deep
Pipe slope 2 per cent
Concrete pipe 30-in. diameter
Square-edge box inlet 5.5x5 ft.
Training wall 1.0 ft. high

Solution Using Circular Riser

From the design of a box-shaped drop inlet, it was found that a weir length of approximately 15 ft. was required. A precast pipe with a 60-in. diameter will provide this length and may be used on the first trial. Therefore, using a 60-in. circular concrete pipe with the socket end forming the weir,

$$D_r = 60 \text{ in. and } D_{rc} = 65 \text{ in.} = 5.41 \text{ ft.}$$

To determine the weir coefficient, use Table 15. Estimate H. Then

$$\frac{H}{D_{rc}} = \frac{1}{5.41} = 0.185.$$

Select $C = 3.10$. Determine length of weir (from Fig. 71) using splitter wall:

$$L = \pi D_{rc} - 2t, \text{ where } t = \frac{2}{9}D$$

$$L = 3.14 \times 5.41 - 2 \times \frac{2}{9} \times 5.41$$

$$L = 14.78 \text{ ft.}$$

Determine operating head from $Q = CLH^{3/2}$. Then

$$HW = \left(\frac{Q}{CL}\right)^{2/3}$$

$$HW = \left(\frac{50}{3.10 \times 14.78}\right)^{2/3}$$

$$HW = 1.059 \text{ ft.}$$

Recheck the discharge coefficient:

$$\frac{H}{D_{rc}} = \frac{1.059}{5.41} = 0.196$$

From Table 15, $C = 3.25$ (average value). Then $HW = 1.03$ ft., which checks the computations with reasonable accuracy.

Check for location of control:

$$d_c = \sqrt[3]{\frac{1}{g}\left(\frac{50}{14.78}\right)^2} = 0.709$$

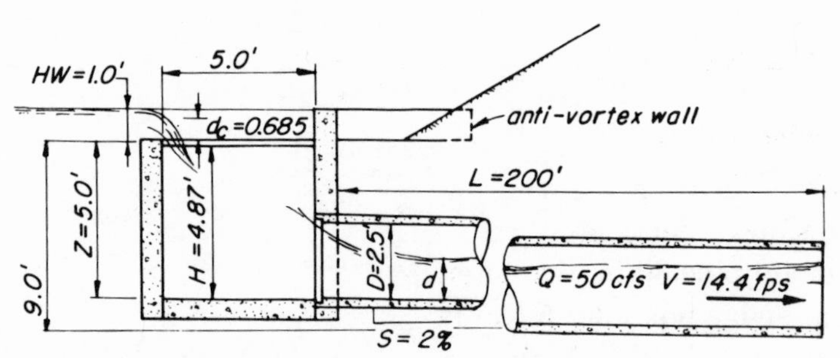

a. rectangular drop inlet design and operation example

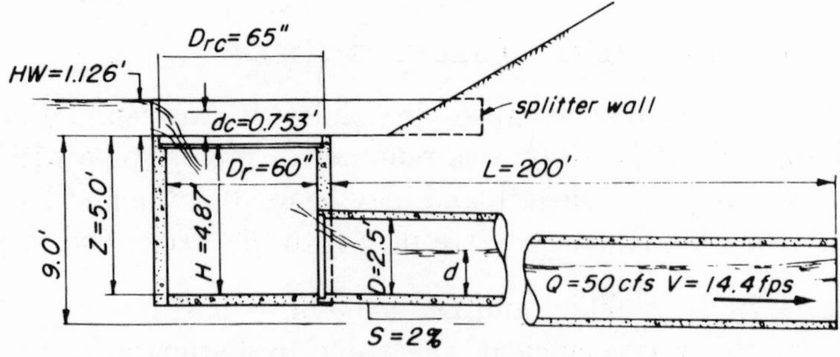

b. circular drop inlet design and operation example

Fig. 72. Drop inlet design examples.

Then $(d_c + Z + SL - D) = (0.709 + 5.0 + 4.0 - 2.5) = 7.209$ and $H_t = 6.37$ (previously determined).

Since $6.37 < 7.253$, or $H_t < (d_c + Z + SL - D)$, the control will be located at the weir.

Design Summary

A 60-in. riser pipe will be satisfactory if the criteria governing headwater depth can be raised slightly. If headwater criteria cannot be adjusted, it will be necessary to use a 66-in. riser pipe.

Entrance Comparison (See Fig. 72)

1. Square box inlet 5.5x5 ft. with 1.0-ft.-high training wall will operate at a head of 1.0 ft.
2. Circular 60-in. concrete riser pipe inlet with socket end forming the weir will operate at a head of 1.13 ft. with a 1.03-ft.-high splitter.

Sag Culverts

The design of a sag culvert is for the most part similar to the design of a conventional culvert flowing full. This assumes that the invert of the

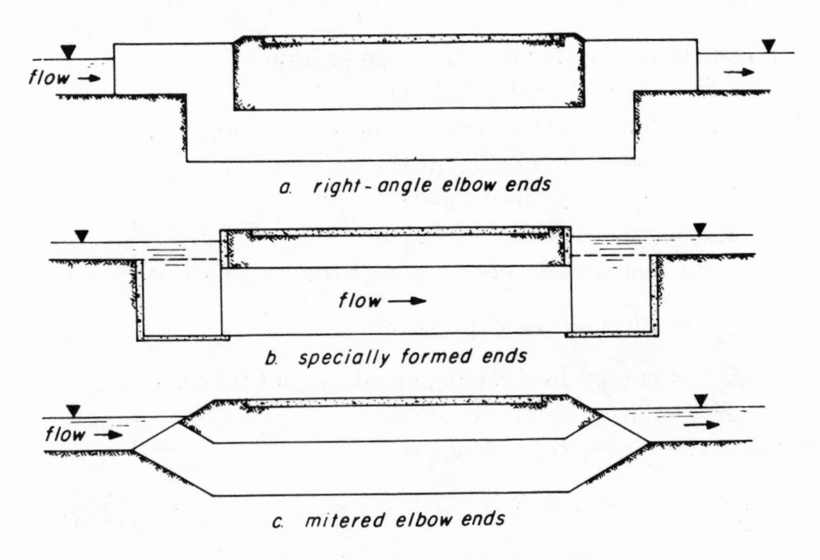

Fig. 73. Examples of sag culvert configurations.

culvert entrance is below the outlet invert and forces the culvert to flow full at all times. In this case open channel flow is not a consideration. However, where it is only necessary to drop the entrance invert a small amount so that the crown of the culvert is above the outlet invert, it is definitely possible to have open channel flow. The analysis of the flow in these cases will require considerable experience in the application of hydraulic fundamentals.

In those cases where it is only necessary to drop the culvert invert a small amount, it will probably be more satisfactory to use a multiple-barrel installation. Since a division of flow will permit the use of smaller pipe, it is possible to design an adequate culvert with the allowable headroom and without the objectionable characteristics of the sag culvert.

Several applications of the sag culvert design are shown in Fig. 73. It will be noted that they differ from conventional culvert design in:

1. Entrance and outlet configuration
2. The presence of vertical bends
3. The depressed elevation of the culvert invert with respect to the inlet and the outlet

This section will deal only with those installations in which the crown of the culvert pipe is below the headwater and tailwater elevations.

SAG CULVERT DESIGN RELATIONSHIPS

Flow in a sag culvert, as illustrated in Fig. 74, is expressed by Bernoulli's theorem. Neglecting the velocity of approach and downstream velocity, this is

$$HW + SL' = \left(K_e + K_b + f\frac{L}{D} + K_b' + K_o\right)\frac{V^2}{2g} + H_T$$

in which HW = headwater depth at the entrance
S = normal channel slope
L' = horizontal distance from the entrance to the outlet
V = average velocity in the culvert
H_T = tailwater depth at the outlet
K_e = entrance loss coefficient
K_b = energy loss coefficient at the first vertical bend
$f\frac{L}{D}$ = friction loss expression
K_b' = energy loss coefficient at second vertical bend
K_o = outlet loss coefficient

By grouping the terms, this becomes

$$HW - H_T + SL' = \left(K_e + K_b + K_b' + K_o + f\frac{L}{D}\right)\frac{V^2}{2g}.$$

Unless the outlet is designed to recover the kinetic energy of flow in the pipe, the factor K_o will be unity. The difference in headwater depth and tailwater depth $(HW - H_T)$ and the fall due to slope is more simply expressed as head H. The friction effect can be expressed in terms of the Manning roughness factor through the expression

$$f = 185 \frac{n^2}{D^{1/3}}.$$

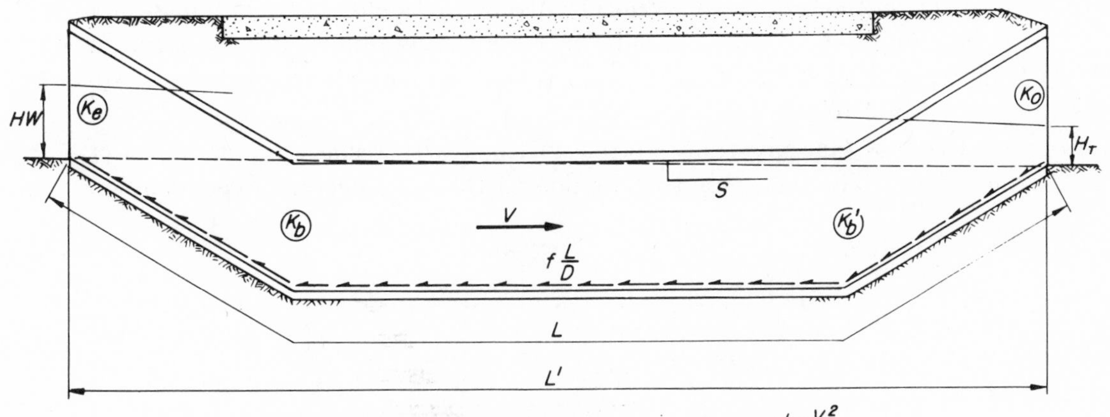

Fig. 74. Definition sketch for flow relationship in a sag culvert.

By making these substitutions and introducing discharge Q in place of velocity V, the above expression becomes

$$H = 0.0252 \left[(K_e + K_b + K_b') + 1 + 185 \frac{n^2 L}{D^{4/3}}\right] \frac{Q^2}{D^4}$$

If this is made dimensionless by dividing by the pipe diameter, an equation similar to the full-flowing straight culvert results:

$$\frac{H}{D} = 0.0252 \left[1 + (K_e + K_b + K_b') + 185 \frac{n^2}{D^{1/3}} \frac{L}{D}\right] \left(\frac{Q}{D^{5/2}}\right)^2$$

Nomographs for Analysis of Sag Culvert

The analysis of the hydraulic operation of a sag culvert can be made by means of the nomographs for full-flowing culverts presented in Appendix C. To use these nomographs for this purpose, the entrance coefficient scale must be entered with the combined effect of the entrance and the two bends. Hence, the factor K_e in the nomograph becomes $K_e + K_b + K_b'$.

Solution of the nomograph gives the difference in elevation of the headwater and tailwater surfaces, H. The headwater depth HW is determined from consideration of the tailwater depth H_T and the natural channel slope SL, so that

$$HW = H_T - SL + H.$$

ENTRANCE LOSS COEFFICIENTS FOR SAG CULVERT

There are very little data on entrance loss coefficients for sag culverts. However, a good approximation of entrance loss effects can be made by application of the entrance coefficients for conventional culverts given in Chapter 4 when the entrance geometry is similar. These coefficients are repeated in Table 9, Chapter 5.

Inlets of sag culverts are often enlarged with respect to the barrel of the culvert. The losses that occur due to the entrance are dependent on

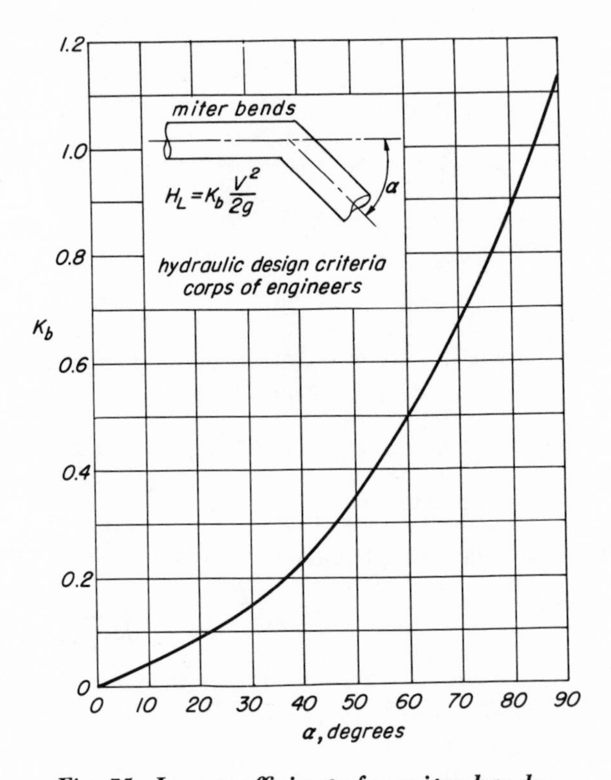

Fig. 75. Loss coefficients for miter bends.

the velocity of flow through the inlet and, because of the enlargement, will be less than for a conventional inlet. It will be necessary to adjust the entrance loss coefficient to account for any enlargement. Since the average velocity in the pipe barrel is used to calculate all losses,

$$K_e = \left(\frac{A_p}{A_e}\right)^2 K_e \text{ standard}$$

where K_e = entrance loss coefficient to be used in calculating entrance losses

K_e standard = entrance loss coefficient for the conventional type culvert without an enlargement, values in Table 9, Chapter 5

A_e = area of enlarged entrance

A_p = area of pipe

Bend Losses

The bends in a sag culvert are usually constructed as an abrupt change in direction. Losses from bends of this type are higher than from those built as gradual curves. Loss coefficients are consequently higher than might normally be expected. However, the losses in a sag culvert due to bends can be minimized by minimizing the number of bends and the angular change in direction.

Fig. 75 has been prepared from data presented in the U.S. Army Corps of Engineers' publication *Hydraulic Design Criteria.*[3] The losses experienced at bends are related to the total change in direction.

Design Features of Sag Culverts

As previously pointed out, the sag culvert is a special application of the straight barrel culvert. As such, the use of headwalls and endwalls is similarly dictated by special conditions in some installations. Outlet energy dissipators will probably never be required in view of the special application of the sag culvert.

Anti-vortex devices are not required for satisfactory operation of a sag culvert. This is due to the elevation of the outlet, which forces the barrel to flow full.

Sag Culvert—Example Problem

A 300-ft. culvert is to be placed under a 4-ft.-high roadway with an embankment slope of 2½ to 1. It is to carry 75 cfs at a maximum headwater depth of 3 ft. The slope of the flow channel at the location of the embankment is 0.2 per cent. The normal stream depth at this discharge is 1 ft. The top of the pipe is to have a minimum cover of 2 ft. and is to be placed on undisturbed ground for its entire length.

Determine the type of culvert to be used, its size, and its installation.

Solution:

The design for a straight projecting concrete pipe is determined from the design nomographs discussed in Chapter 5.

It is found that to carry 75 cfs, a culvert

42 in. in diameter will operate at headwater depth of 4.9 ft. (flowing-full nomograph)

48 in. in diameter will operate at a headwater depth of 4.6 ft. (culvert capacity chart)

54 in. in diameter will operate at a headwater depth of 3.8 ft. (culvert capacity chart)

Obviously, a pipe large enough to carry the flow without exceeding the headwater depth limitation will be too large for the available headroom. Therefore, it will be necessary to use a sag culvert.

Construct the culvert entrance with an enlarged opening equal to twice the area of the barrel. Place the entrance and outlet at the toe of the embankment slope. Set the culvert barrel on a 0.2 per cent slope. The size of the concrete pipe is determined by finding the diameter and the headwater depth for the following design data:

Q = 75 cfs

Slope = 0.2 per cent

Friction factor = 0.012

Angle change = 22 deg.

Entrance loss coefficient $= 0.50 \times \dfrac{A_p{}^2}{A_e{}^2} = 0.5 \times \dfrac{1}{4}$

$$K_e = 0.125$$

Computations:

Assume 42-in.-diameter pipe.

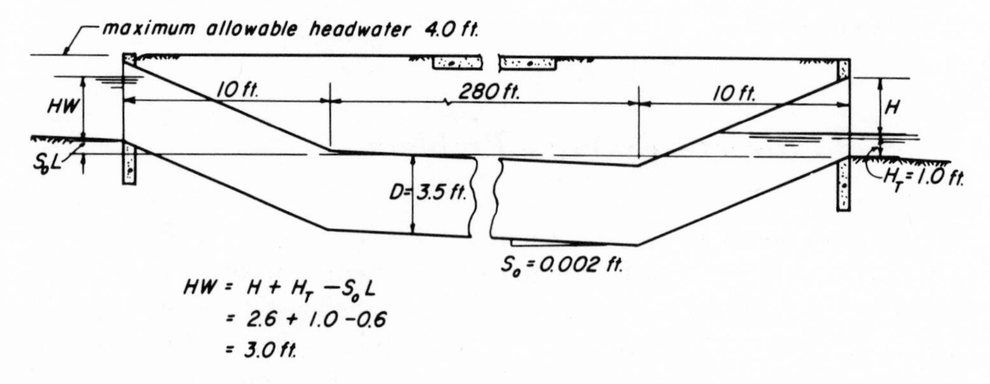

Fig. 76. Sag culvert—example problem.

Then $K_b = 0.1 = K_b'$ (Figs. 74 and 75)

$$(K_e + K_b + K_b') = 0.125 + 0.1 + 0.1 = 0.325$$

$H = 2.6$ ft., from Fig. C-2, Appendix C.

The headwater depth is determined by

$$HW = H_T + H - SL$$

$$HW = 1.0 + 2.6 - 0.002 \times 300$$

$$HW = 3.0 \text{ ft.}$$

A 42-in.-diameter culvert installed as in Fig. 76 will operate satisfactorily.

This example is a typical case in which a sag culvert may be required. Normal culvert installations cannot be used since the dimensions of the required pipe exceed the headroom available for the culvert. By depressing the pipe, the required headroom is obtained. Improved hydraulic operation is achieved by submerging the outlet to lower the hydraulic grade line, permitting the use of a smaller pipe than would otherwise be possible.

References

1. Blaisdell, F. W., *Hydraulics of Closed Conduit Spillways*, Technical Paper Nos. 12 and 18, Series B, University of Minnesota, Hydraulic Laboratory, St. Anthony Falls, 1958, Parts I through VII.
2. *Design of Small Dams*, Washington, D.C., U.S. Bureau of Reclamation, first edition, 1960, Chapter VII, Spillways.
3. *Hydraulic Design Criteria*, tenth issue of *Charts*, U.S. Army Corps of Engineers, Vicksburg, Miss.

8

Advantages of Concrete Pipe Culverts

THE PRESENT PRACTICE OF HIGHWAY ENGINEERING IS BASED on the highest standards ever used in highway construction. These improved standards require the construction of high fill embankments, deep cuts, and structures which are justified by the expected length of useful life of new roadways. These new roadways may be regarded as permanent installations capable of serving indefinitely. The culverts used in modern highway construction are an integral part of the embankment and should be built as permanent as the embankment.

Culvert structures are an increasingly important part of the total cost of highway construction. Attention to this detail is of major importance, since a well-functioning culvert can avert major damage or traffic interruption. The added cost of careful design and construction to prevent flooding is well justified in the light of cost of repair to the roadway, possible lawsuits for damage to adjacent property, or the possibility of traffic accidents. In addition, suitable culvert design can effect significant economies in both installation and future maintenance.

Highway engineers thoroughly familiar with all types of culvert design and construction are aware of the ideal suitability of concrete pipe for culvert construction. Concrete has been used extensively for lining all types of water channels. It is recognized as the construction material best suited for hydraulic applications. Concrete pipe combines the hydraulic advantages of smoothness and circular shape in a prefabricated product that is easily installed.

Concrete and reinforcing steel are used to produce pipe of various strengths to meet varying load-carrying requirements. Economy is effected without sacrificing performance by a supply of pipe that is built to meet the hydraulic and structural requirements of the job. The versatility of reinforced concrete design enables the fabrication of pipe of special designs to meet unique conditions. Specially fitted sections or designs for special construction procedures attest to the versatility of concrete pipe.

Concrete pipe plants are well distributed around the country. A concrete pipe plant is probably less than 100 miles from most construction sites. This means that the pipe is readily available when and where it is needed. These plants produce pipe that is a closely controlled quality product using local materials and manufactured by skilled local workers. Concrete pipe has a proven experience record, assuring performance without change as long as needed—and longer.

Additional cost savings for concrete pipe culverts may be obtained by designs that make full use of the superior hydraulic properties of concrete pipe. These hydraulic characteristics permit the smallest possible size pipe to be used for the job. They also assure low first cost and, due to the inherent quality of concrete, low annual cost.

Concrete pipe culverts are simple to build and are not easily damaged in placement of the embankment.

The outstanding advantages of concrete pipe culverts may be tabulated as follows:

Maximum hydraulic efficiency
Pretested strength
Demonstrated durability
Local availability
Construction adaptability
Low maintenance
High salvage value
Engineered economy

Concrete pipe is the superior pipe for culverts. It meets all culvert requirements including economy. Savings through performance are first

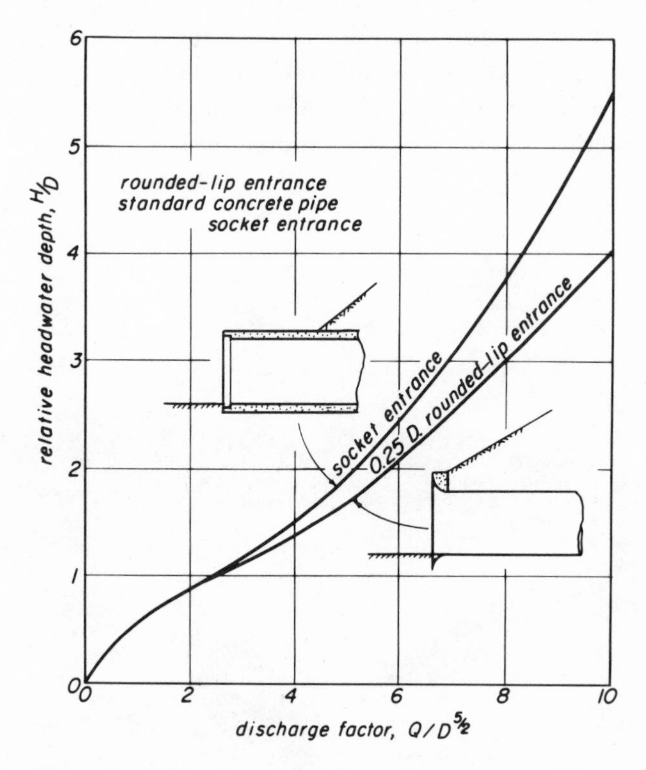

Fig. 77. Inlet control comparison curves for rounded entrances and grooved-edge entrances in headwalls.

realized in the hydraulic design. The design principles that have been discussed in detail in the preceding chapters are emphasized here in specific application to concrete pipe for culverts.

Efficient Entrances

The flow characteristics of natural watercourses are altered and disturbed by the installation of a culvert, regardless of the efficiency of the structure. The major effect of a culvert is a drastic change in the "flow-area-depth" relationships of the natural watercourse. This is, in effect, a restriction in the stream. The operation of culvert entrances produces further restriction by constricting the flow in the culvert barrel. In Chapter 4 it was pointed out that all culverts must necessarily operate with some amount of ponding at the entrance. Due to the detrimental effect of excessive ponding, it is highly desirable to minimize the restricting effect of culverts by making use of the most efficient entrance shapes.

The rounded-lip entrance has been found to be the shape allowing least ponding for standard highway culverts. Experiment has shown that the performance of the groove end of tongue-and-groove concrete pipe closely approximates the performance of a small-radius rounded-lip entrance. The excellent performance characteristics of concrete pipe entrances are demonstrated by a comparison of the dimensionless inlet control performance curves for an entrance with a rounding of $0.25D$ and the groove entrance of a concrete pipe as shown in Fig. 77. A specific example of the

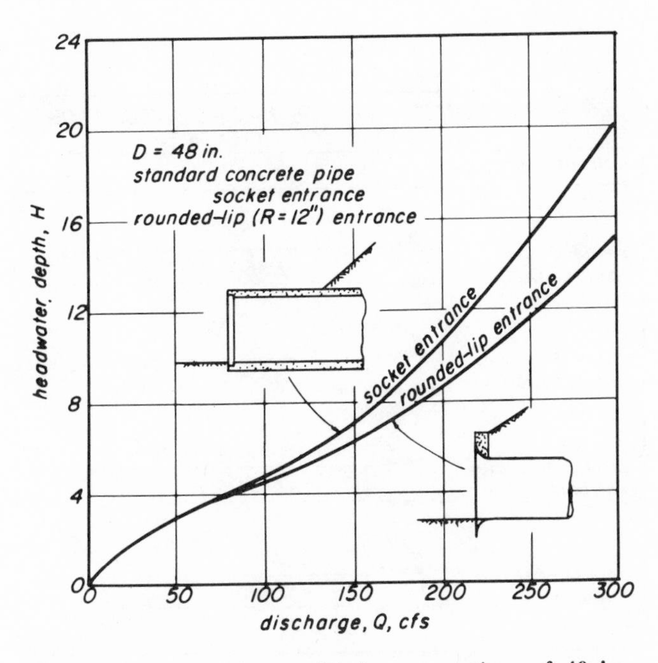

Fig. 78. Comparison of inlet operation of 48-in.-diameter pipe with rounded entrances and grooved-edge entrances in headwalls.

same effect for a 48-in. pipe is shown in Fig. 78. Further improvement in the performance of the groove entrance is obtained by providing a headwall. For standard culvert inlets, there is little to be gained by further improvements of the natural groove provided with tongue-and-groove or bell-and-spigot concrete pipe.

Concrete pipe entrances have a structural use as well as a decidedly beneficial effect on the discharge-headwater relationship in inlet control. For culverts that operate with inlet control and with the entrance submerged, it is important to minimize potential flotation of the partly filled pipe. Efficiently operating grooved entrances of concrete pipe reduce flotation forces, due to deeper depths of flow at the entrance. The weight of concrete pipe is of further benefit in this respect.

The discharge advantage of concrete pipe entrances operating with inlet control is retained when the pipe flows full with outlet control. Comparative discharge characteristics are indicated by the discharge coefficients illustrated in Fig. 79. The higher coefficients indicate higher discharges at equal headwater depths in the classical discharge relationship given by

$$Q = C_D A \sqrt{2gH}$$

where the discharge coefficient is expressed as C_D. The discharge coefficient is related to entrance geometry, and large C_D values result from efficient flow patterns.

It will be noted that entrances formed with the groove end of con-

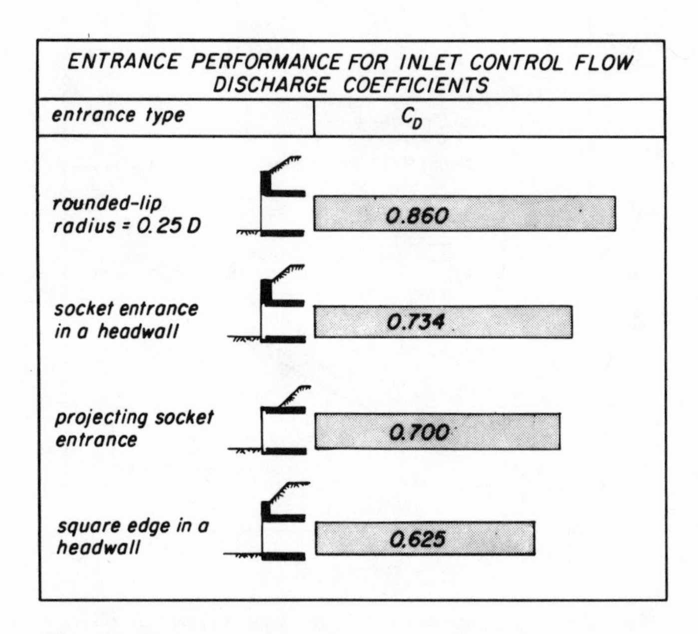

Fig. 79. Entrance capacity comparison for concrete pipe in inlet control.

crete pipe provide nearly ideal performance as compared to entrances with a rounded lip.

Efficient Barrel Characteristics

The discharge capacity of pipe culverts is governed to a large extent by the performance of the culvert barrel. A culvert operating with inlet control is in reality a two-part hydraulic system in which each part operates more or less independently of the other. With inlet control, the potential capacity of the part-full barrel exceeds that of the entrance. The upper discharge limit for which this holds true is determined by the performance of the barrel in accepting and transporting the flow as delivered by the inlet. The upper discharge limit at which a culvert will function with inlet control for a particular entrance is determined by the relative roughness of the barrel.

Adaptability of pipe for culverts is illustrated in this 12-barrel installation. The high flows and minimum allowable headwater depths in this application require the superior hydraulic performance provided by concrete pipe.

In practical application, the greatest discharge capacity will generally be realized with inlet control operation. The roughness of the culvert wall controls the flow depth in the barrel and is a determining factor in the transition from inlet control to outlet control. Depth of flow in smooth-wall pipe is less than in rough-wall pipe, other conditions being the same. This increases the range of inlet control operation for smooth-wall pipe.

Pipe wall roughness is an important factor in outlet control operation since additional headwater depth is required to overcome the effect of friction due to roughness. It follows that culvert performance is decidedly enhanced for both inlet control and outlet control operation by use of pipe with low roughness characteristics.

It has been established that concrete pipe produces minimum frictional resistance as compared with the friction characteristics of ideally smooth pipe. In Fig. 80 the friction relationships for several sizes of concrete pipe are compared with the ideally smooth pipe curve. The friction factors, f, shown are used in the friction formula

$$h_f = f \frac{L}{D} \frac{V^2}{2g}$$

Values of f may be converted to n for use in the Manning's equation for open channel flow. This relationship is shown in Fig. 81 for concrete pipe and rough-wall pipe. It will be noted that the concrete pipe closely approximates the most desirable characteristics. In practice, a constant value of n is used for all sizes of pipe. Although laboratory tests have determined n for concrete pipe in some cases to be as low as 0.010, it is common to use a value of 0.012 for design purposes. This value is shown

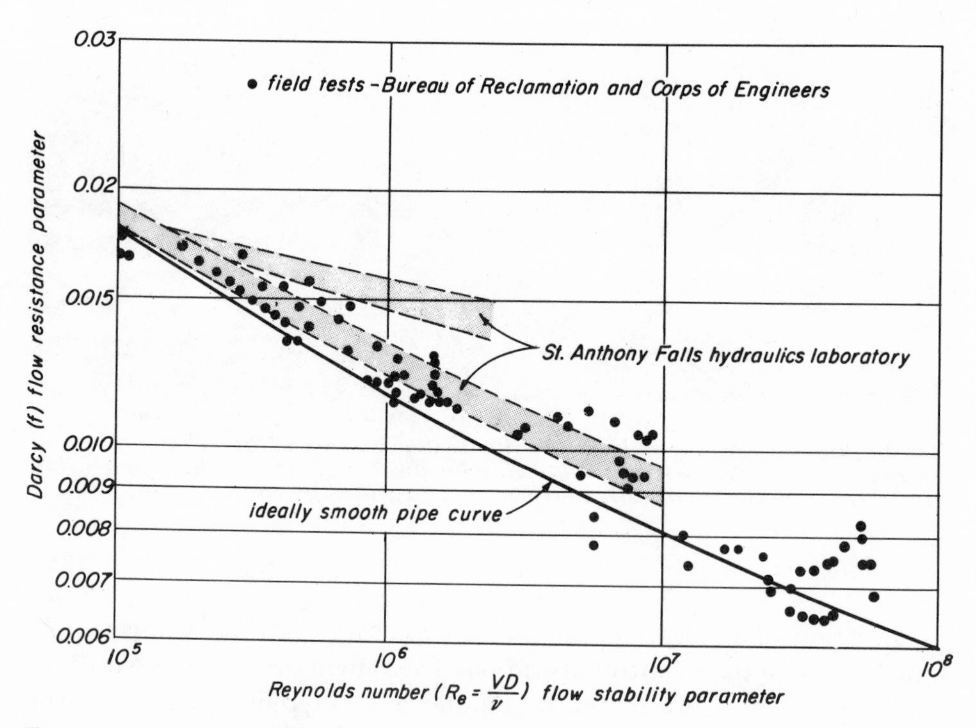

Fig. 80. Friction coefficients for concrete pipe.

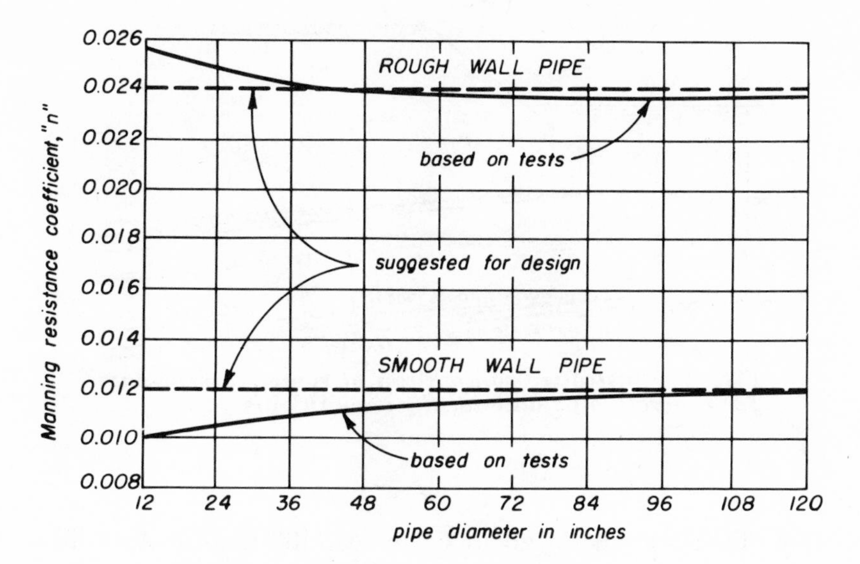

Fig. 81. Manning's n *values for concrete pipe.*

for comparison in Fig. 81 and indicates the factor of safety that exists in hydraulic design for concrete pipe culverts.

Efficient Operation at Minimum Slopes

Barrel slope may be considered as an energy-supplying factor in culvert performance. In inlet control, the effect of barrel friction is overcome by energy added to the flow system by means of the slope. If the barrel slope is sufficiently steep, inlet control will be assured through the entire operating discharge range. If the slope is exactly equal to the rate of friction loss, the depth of flow in the culvert barrel will remain essentially unchanged. It is desirable to provide a slope that will maintain inlet control operation over a predetermined discharge range. Smooth barrel walls require only minimum slopes, while rough barrel walls require a substantial increase in the slope to produce the same flow depth.

Generalized slope relationships have been established for comparable barrel performance for various degrees of wall roughness. A means of comparing the open channel properties of pipe barrels is provided by the concept of optimum critical slope discussed in Chapter 4. This comparison applied to ideally smooth pipe and concrete pipe is shown schematically in Fig. 82. This figure shows that the ideal slope for pipe of wall materials such as glass, drawn brass, or acrylic plastic is one that will produce a fall

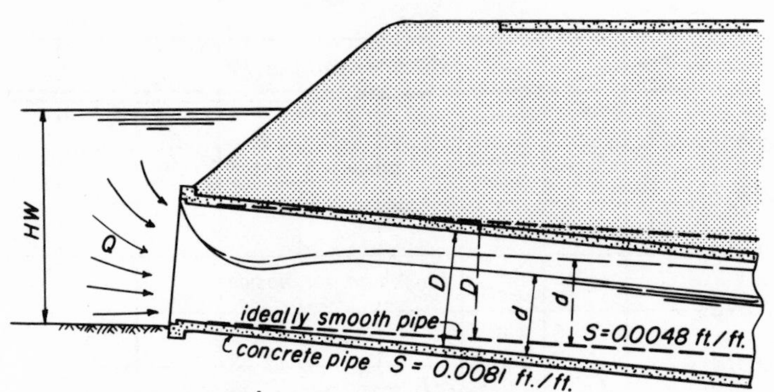

Fig. 82. Illustrative comparison of slope requirements for concrete pipe and ideally smooth pipe.

in a 30-in.-diameter pipe of about $5\frac{3}{4}$ in. per 100 ft. of length. The slope of a concrete pipe of the same size to produce the same hydraulic effect is only $9\frac{3}{4}$ in. per 100 ft. of length. Comparable slopes for pipe of other materials can be determined. The slope for a 30-in. corrugated pipe would be four times greater than for the concrete pipe, or 39 in. per 100 ft. of length. Inasmuch as the available slope is often limited, it is desirable to use materials requiring the least slope.

Culvert slope is of outstanding importance in both inlet and outlet control culvert operations. The discharge range for which inlet control operation will exist is controlled by slope. In outlet control operation, slope directly influences the headwater depth.

Minimum Friction Losses

Friction is always present to some varying degree in water flowing in pipe culverts. The frictional resistance to flow of water along wall surfaces is proportionate to the rate of flow and the roughness of the surface. Friction is present with ideally smooth surfaces as well as extremely rough surfaces, but to a far lesser degree.

The force to overcome the effect of friction in a full pipe is provided by the energy level of the headwater pool. The major part of the total energy head is used to overcome barrel friction losses. Losses of any kind require additional headwater energy to produce flow. Due to the low roughness properties of concrete pipe, discharge capacities for the same energy in the headwater pool are substantially higher than for pipe of most other materials. The low-friction characteristics of concrete pipe compare favorably with ideally smooth pipe, often permitting the use of

TABLE 19. Friction-Head Comparison for Ideally Smooth Pipe and Concrete Pipe 100 Ft. Long, Flowing Full

Velocity	5 fps					10 fps				
Pipe size, in.	12	24	36	48	60	12	24	36	48	60
Discharge, cfs	3.9	15.6	35.1	62.4	97.5	7.8	31.2	70.2	125	195
Ideally smooth pipe, ft.	.54	.23	.14	.102	.078	1.86	.82	.52	.37	.28
Concrete pipe, ft.	.62	.29	.16	.107	.081	2.17	1.01	.57	.39	.29

smaller size pipe to carry the same discharges as larger pipes of rougher material.

Friction head, the portion of the headwater depth that must be used to overcome friction forces developed by the flow, is given by the standard formula for friction flow

$$h_f = f \frac{L}{D} \frac{V^2}{2g}$$

The friction head h_f is the depth of water required to overcome friction produced by flow with a velocity of V. The friction factors, f, previously discussed, are experimentally determined and are given in the curves of Fig. 80. The length L and the diameter D are geometric properties of the particular pipe. The importance of the smoothness of concrete pipe is illustrated in the comparison of friction-head forces for concrete pipe and ideally smooth pipe in Table 19. For this comparison, pipes 100 ft. long and with diameters ranging from 12 to 60 in. are used for velocities of 5 and 10 fps.

From this comparison it is evident that the performance of concrete pipe closely corresponds to the performance of ideally smooth pipe. Interpreted in another way, the design discharge will be transported through the culvert at the lowest headwater depth by the use of concrete pipe.

Efficient Culvert Operation

The naturally smooth walls and good entrance shape of concrete pipe result in efficient culvert operation. These characteristics should be optimized at every opportunity to transport the design discharge within

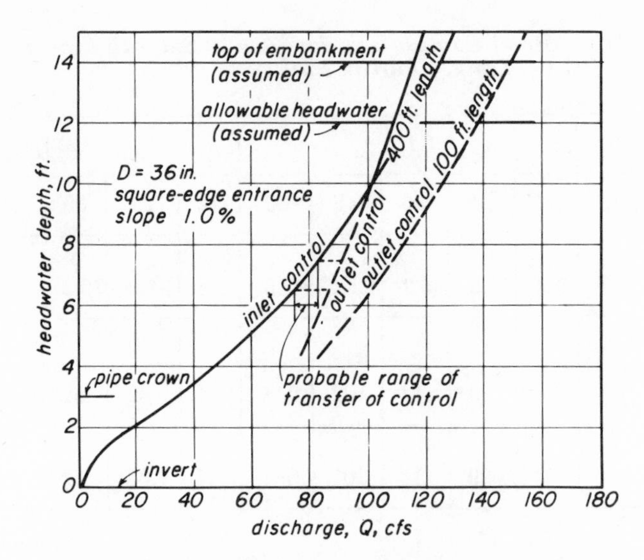

Fig. 83. Effect of length on operation of a 36-in.-diameter concrete culvert pipe.

the headwater limitations, using the smallest possible pipe. It has been established that comparable performance can be provided for various types of pipe by controlling the factors that influence the flow. In this way comparable culvert designs of equal flow capacity can be developed

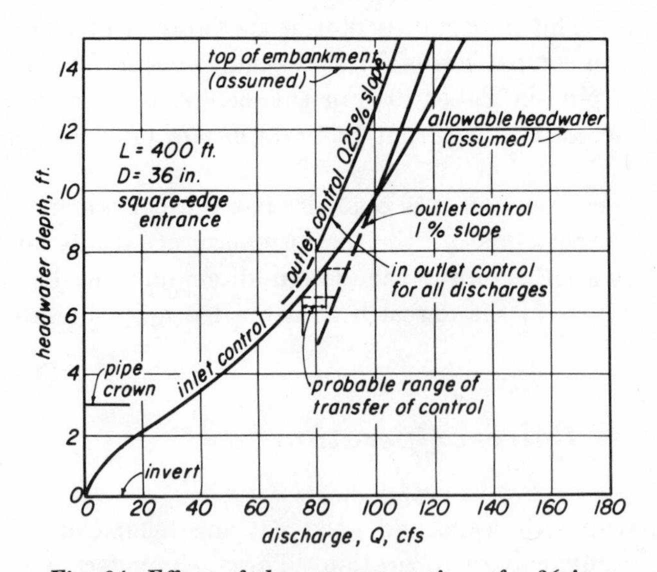

Fig. 84. Effect of slope on operation of a 36-in.-diameter concrete culvert pipe.

for various sizes of pipe, entrance shapes, slopes, or roughness qualities. Once designs providing satisfactory hydraulic performance are established, a selection can be made that best meets the requirements of economy, durability, etc. It will usually be found from all considerations that concrete pipe is the best choice.

An indication of the wide selection of potential designs may be demonstrated by considering various factors in culvert operation. Fig. 83 illustrates the effect of length in the operation of a 36-in. concrete pipe culvert with a square-edge headwall entrance and a pipe slope of 1 per cent. The curve for inlet control operation is shown in comparison with the outlet control operation curves for pipes 100 ft. long and 400 ft. long. The outlet control curve for a pipe 100 ft. long indicates the desirability of outlet control performance, in this case, for the assumed conditions of installation. However, further investigation will show that outlet control for this case is unattainable since the open channel capacity of the concrete pipe exceeds the capacity of the entrance with inlet control over the illustrated discharge range. If the length is increased to 400 ft., as shown in the comparative curve, the open channel capacity of the culvert is reduced and the culvert will begin to operate with outlet control when a discharge of approximately 80 cfs is reached. Initially, this will cause an advantageous increase in discharge capacity over that with inlet control operation. This advantage is lost by the time the allowable headwater (assumed for this case) is reached. Further investigation will show that similar performance results with a corrugated pipe 100 ft. long placed at a slope of 4 per cent.

The effect of slope on culvert operation is illustrated in Fig. 84 for the 400-ft.-long culvert of Fig. 83. Culvert operations for the 1 per cent slope are discussed above. A reduction in the slope from 1 per cent to 0.25 per cent causes the outlet control curve to rise above the inlet control curve. A culvert of this length and slope will operate with outlet control for all practical discharges. This is the same general effect as would be experienced for a 100-ft. culvert on a 1 per cent slope using corrugated pipe, as shown in Fig. 85. The outlet control curves shown in this figure are for the same length and slope of culvert but for material with different roughness properties. The rougher culvert will operate with outlet control for all discharges and is comparable to the 400-ft.-long concrete culvert at a 0.25 per cent slope shown in Fig. 84.

Figs. 83, 84 and 85 illustrate the principles involved in making comparable culvert designs. In each of these cases the importance of the smooth-wall properties of concrete pipe on culvert operation is evident since the entrance characteristics in all cases are the same. The superiority of concrete pipe culverts over those of corrugated pipe is even more outstanding when the more efficient concrete socket entrance is used. Fig. 86

Fig. 85. Effect of roughness on a 36-in.-diameter culvert pipe.

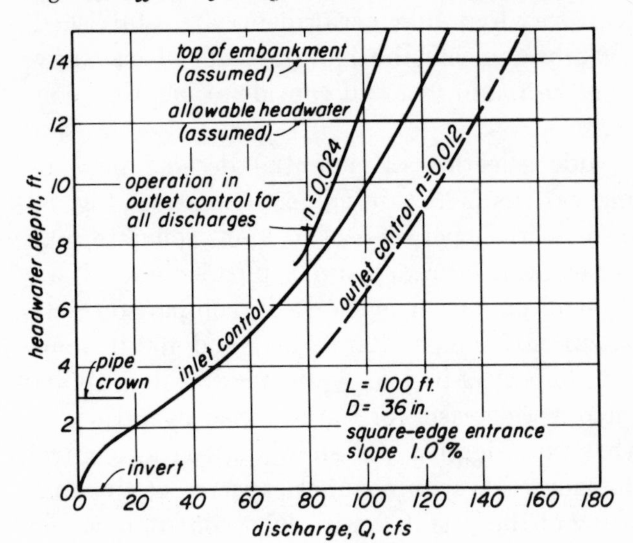

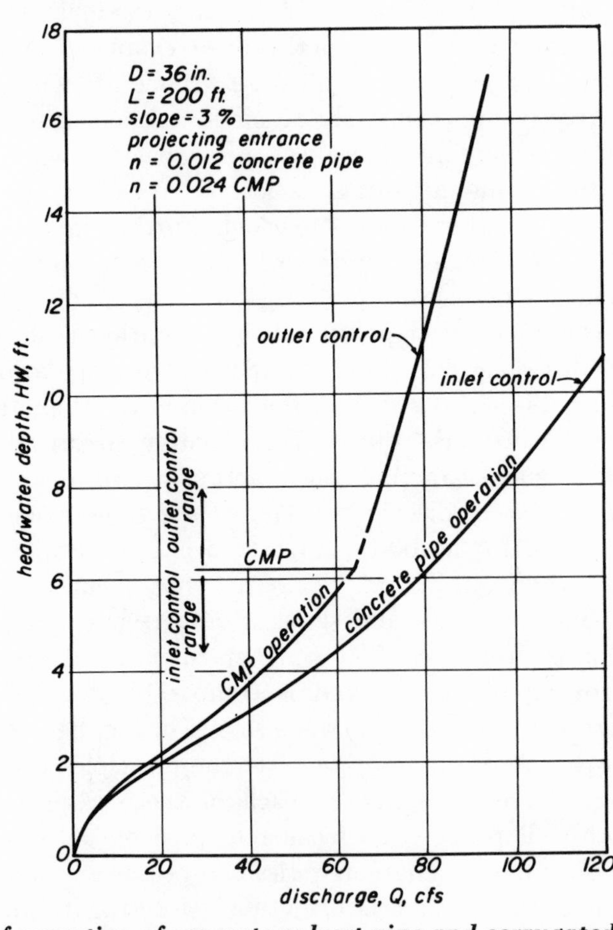

Fig. 86. Comparison of operation of concrete culvert pipe and corrugated culvert pipe.

compares the performance of two types of culverts selected and installed as counterparts. This illustration is for 200-ft.-long, 36-in. projecting culverts on a 3 per cent slope. The curve falling to the right is the performance of a concrete pipe and the curve to the left is the performance of a corrugated pipe. The superior entrance and low roughness characteristics of concrete pipe result in much higher discharge capacities at the same headwater depths.

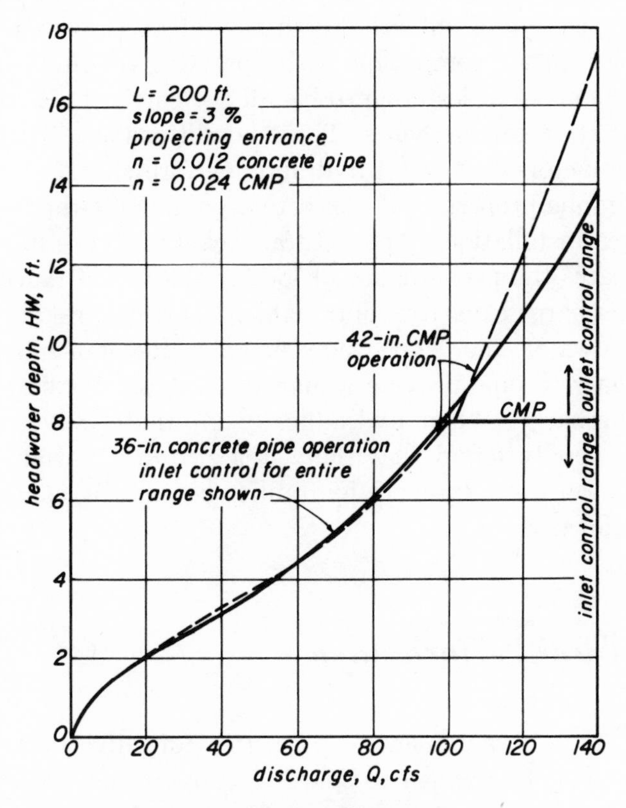

Fig. 87. Operation of comparable concrete and corrugated culvert pipe designs.

Designs for various types of pipe may be altered to obtain discharge characteristics that are approximately comparable. By making the rougher pipe one 6-in. size larger, its performance is improved and closely duplicates the smaller concrete pipe at all but the higher headwater depths, as shown in Fig. 87. In the upper discharge range, the rough-wall pipe operates with outlet control at rapidly increasing headwater depth while the concrete pipe continues to operate with inlet control. In this range the operating curves diverge, with the smaller concrete pipe carrying an increasingly greater discharge by comparison. The concrete pipe continues to operate with inlet control due to its greater open channel capacity.

Summary of Hydraulic Performance

Although simple in appearance, pipe culverts pose a complex problem in design. The objective of culvert design should be to construct the most economical installation compatible with operating requirements. Material and labor costs make it desirable to install the smallest size pipe that will meet the operating requirements. These conditions are satisfied by optimizing all the factors that affect hydraulic performance.

The hydraulic properties of concrete pipe make it the best choice for all pipe culvert installations. The natural socket entrance of concrete pipe closely duplicates the performance of ideally shaped entrances to provide the highest discharge capacities obtainable. Near-ideal roughness qualities minimize headwater and slope requirements. Recommended roughness factors for concrete pipe provide a margin of safety for flow in excess of the design discharge. When hydraulically alternate culvert designs are made, it is generally found that there is a size differential and that the smaller pipe is concrete. In every hydraulic comparison, concrete pipe will provide superior performance.

Structural Performance

Strength is a basic requirement of pipe used for culverts. Concrete pipe can be supplied with strength to spare to support the weight of the embankment above it. But strength must be paid for, and unused strength is a waste of money just as is unused flow capacity. For this reason, reinforced concrete pipe is manufactured in five different standard strength classifications so that the required size and strength can be selected for the most economical installation. Special strength designs are manufactured when required.

The loads that must be supported by the culvert are applied as a combination of dead-weight load and settlement loads. Dead-weight load is the weight of the fill material directly above the pipe. Settlement loads result from the consolidation of the fill material adjacent to the pipe. The loads are related to the size of the pipe and are similar for all types of pipe of the same size.*

*See Appendix E for references on pipe strengths, loads, and construction practices.

Meets Rigid Specifications

Engineering products and materials are commonly produced to meet specified standards of recognized engineering organizations. Concrete pipe is an engineering product that is produced to meet high engineering standards. Because of these standards, the user of concrete pipe is assured of known structural performance and quality in the final product.

Reinforced concrete culvert pipe is manufactured to meet the specifications of the American Society for Testing and Materials (ASTM). These specifications provide for five standard pipe strength classifications and define minimum strength requirements for each class. These specifications also set dimensioning standards, material standards, minimum steel requirements, and standards of workmanship. The specifications for concrete pipe are the most rigid standards established for any culvert material.

Specifications for reinforced concrete pipe are also issued by the American Association of State Highway Officials (AASHO), the federal government, and the American Railway Engineering Association (AREA). In general, reinforced concrete pipe meeting ASTM specifications will also meet the specifications of these other organizations. The applicable specifications for reinforced concrete culvert pipe are: ASTM C76, AASHO M170, Federal SS-P-00375a, and AREA Specification for Reinforced Concrete Culvert Pipe.

Load-Bearing Strength

The concrete pipe specifications state minimum performance standards. Verification of performance is provided before installation by the three-edge bearing test, which subjects the pipe to abnormally severe loading. Because of this test, the culvert designer may be confident of the supporting quality of concrete pipe.

Research has shown that the installed supporting strength of concrete pipe exceeds the strength of the pipe in the three-edge bearing test. It has been found that installing the pipe and constructing the embankment around the pipe increase the pipe's load-bearing capability. Simple design procedures have been developed to incorporate the important structural and load-bearing factors. The effect of bedding is important to design because it can increase the supporting strength of the pipe, in some cases by more than 300 per cent. The design formulas permit consideration and evaluation of the physical characteristics of the foundation material and embankment material.

Structural predictability is a significant advantage of culvert designs for concrete pipe. Fundamentally sound design procedures for rigid pipe applications enable engineers to design each structure for the specific conditions of the particular site. The designer has complete control over the design computations.

The rigid nature of concrete pipe means that it is self-supporting and that the pipe will be the same shape both in the ground and out. The structural strength of concrete pipe is attained through controlled manufacturing processes, not at the time of field installation. Although "kick-it-in-the-trench" construction techniques cannot be used with assurance of achieving a good job, reasonable attention to the good practices that should be used for all types of pipe will assure excellent results.

Concrete culvert pipe structures provide a sense of confidence-of-performance. Pipe strengths are known to be reliable. Loads on the pipe are determined accurately in accordance with the science of soil mechanics. The effect of construction method on loads and supporting strengths is evaluated. The end result is an installation that has been properly designed, not selected by guess.

Durability

Highway embankments are expected to serve for an indefinite time, although the highway itself may become obsolete or inadequate. Depending upon the rate of development of future requirements, highways may reach the stage of obsolescence at an early age or last well beyond the design period. The culverts emplaced in the embankments should be expected to have a life expectancy equal to and exceeding the useful design life of the highway. This assures satisfactory service during the initial design period and enhances the salvage value of the roadway when modifications and expansions are required.

The need for durability in culvert structures is self-evident. As part of the embankment, the culvert should be functional as long as the embankment is in existence. The severity of this requirement is, of course, unknown and will vary considerably. It can be concluded, however, that good culvert design requires the selection of a culvert material that will be structurally sound, with little or no decrease in flow capacity for a period greatly exceeding the design period.

Other requirements related to durability should be considered in the economic analysis for culvert selection. The most important in this respect is flow capacity after years of service. The flood-like flows that culverts are designed to carry may occur soon after the culvert is built or near the end of the designed service life of the highway. In either case, the culvert must be functional. Hydraulic design should actually be made for future flow capacity. Friction factors for concrete pipe are recommended in the light of this important provision. The concrete pipe sizes selected will continue to meet the design requirements after years of service.

Maintenance is an important item in determining the real cost of culverts. Concrete pipe, through years of service, has demonstrated outstanding superiority in this regard. Concrete pipe retains its hydraulic efficiency in entrance design and flow capacity after years of hard knocks from maintenance equipment and floating debris. The hard, dense surface of concrete pipe retains its smoothness; therefore it retains its original flow characteristics. As a result of its smoothness, there is little tendency for the accumulation of silt in culvert barrels, eliminating the need for frequent cleaning. When cleaning is required, mechanical equipment may be used without danger of damage to any part of the structure.

Because of its durability, concrete pipe is salvageable. On occasion, culverts are removed for various reasons, such as relocation, emplacement of larger structures, or making way for improvements. The rigid nature of concrete pipe and its short sectional lengths permit removal without damage. The pipe may be re-used in other locations, thus effecting substantial saving. This fact should always be considered at the time the design is made.

Durability has a direct influence on the annual cost of a culvert installation. Annual cost and not first cost establishes the true cost of a culvert installation. Although there are some uncertainties in predicting the annual cost, it can be evaluated as the sum of the following:

1. Prorated first cost over the expected use period
2. Yearly debt service based on first cost
3. Yearly maintenance

Experience has shown that the cost of these three items is less for a properly designed concrete pipe culvert than for a culvert of any other type of material. Including the salvage value, the annual cost of a concrete pipe culvert is most attractive to the user.

Concrete pipe has been used for culverts for over 100 years, and it was used in other installations long before its first use in culverts. In all this experience it has not been possible to establish a definite upper limit to the useful life of concrete pipe. For practical purposes the useful life is often taken to be 100 years. Yet experience records of early pipe installations indicate that concrete pipe is capable of serving much longer than 100 years. Today, concrete culvert pipe is a much improved product, using quality materials and manufactured with better methods than ever before. Thus, there is every reason to believe that the useful life of concrete culvert pipe is much in excess of 100 years.

Construction Adaptability

An important feature of any construction material is its adaptability to different applications and construction procedures. As it is rigid and self-supporting, concrete pipe may be handled with conventional construction equipment. Wherever mechanical equipment is involved, some abuse is inevitable, such as impact from machines and material, unusual loads in storage and construction, and environmental exposure due to extreme climatic variations. Concrete pipe can be readily adapted to the various construction procedures without costly damage.

The adaptability of concrete pipe is illustrated by this use of elliptical pipe.

Concrete pipe may be installed in many ways, provided the load and support conditions are considered. Due to the rigidity of the pipe walls, mitered cuts may be made at culvert ends without danger of collapse. Special foundation problems may be solved by use of concrete pipe, since its structural behavior is well known and reliable. Problems of flotation are largely overcome by the weight of concrete pipe and the independent action of each pipe section. The need for these special qualities of concrete pipe is often unforeseen and may arise at any time. However, these qualities are available when concrete pipe is used.

There are many outstanding features of concrete pipe that are taken for granted. One of these is the convenient length of concrete pipe sections—not too long and not too short. The length of section makes it easier to prepare the bedding for the pipe and permits the laying operation to closely follow preparation of the bedding. The short lengths permit easy adjustment to the bedding without developing significant undesirable beam action. The short lengths may be laid on long-radius curves without resort to special sections. The special tongue-and-groove ends of the pipe are manufactured with clearances that permit this flexibility in alignment, which is also useful for differential vertical adjustments under load. The combination of convenient length and interlocking pipe ends provides the advantages of flexibility while retaining the superior structural action of cross-section rigidity. This latter feature eliminates the danger of progressive failure by collapse, which may occur with purely flexible pipe.

Although sometimes considered troublesome, the weight of concrete pipe is extremely useful in construction of the embankment. Due to its weight, the alignment of the pipe is not readily disturbed during placement of the fill material. Material may be tamped under the haunches of the pipe with little danger of shifting its position. A moderate amount of piling of material on one side will not easily move the pipe, nor, with reasonable care, will the operation of mechanized equipment. Heavy equipment may also be moved over the pipe after a moderate amount of cover has been placed.

Adaptability to construction operations is an important feature in the installed cost of a culvert. Concrete pipe is built to take it both during and after construction.

Local Availability

Concrete pipe is available from local sources in most areas. Concrete pipe producers stockpile a large inventory of most sizes and classes of pipe and can make prompt delivery as pipe is needed. Since plants are nearby, transportation costs are small. This means more pipe for the money. It also eliminates the need for a large stockpile at the job site and often means that the pipe can be delivered to the point of use. Eliminating the need for double handling is a big factor in cutting costs on jobs.

Close cooperation is assured when it is possible to work with a local producer. Special orders are rapidly processed and emergency deliveries are quickly arranged. Close control is assured since lines of communication are short and direct. The local pipe producer values local patronage and is interested in providing service as well as a quality product.

Concrete culvert pipe stockpiled at the producer's yard, ready for use.

Concrete pipe is a local product manufactured by local labor from local materials. Local business is good business because it supports local economy while providing the best service available. Money spent on concrete pipe stays within the community.

Guide Lines for Pipe Culvert Design

The design of a pipe culvert is not an easy job. Regardless of the type of material used or the computations involved, considerable time and effort are expended on each culvert installation. The purpose of this effort is, as in the case of any other structure, to establish the culvert that will perform a specific function in an economical way that is compatible with all aspects of the project.

Culvert installations for modern highways represent a considerable expenditure which is wasted if the culverts do not perform in accordance with the need. On the other hand, culvert structures with greater than needed capabilities are unnecessarily expensive. It is the engineer's duty to determine what is needed and what will meet the need at the least cost.

The complexities of culvert design require a functional understanding of culvert hydraulics and structural behavior. It is possible that the problem of economics will require more than one solution involving the consideration of more than one type of material. The only reasonable basis for evaluation in these cases is comparable hydraulic designs that will carry the same discharges at comparable headwater depths. The flow characteristics of each design should be clearly understood. Then, before the final decision is reached, other factors such as durability and cost may be considered.

When comparable designs are made for different materials, the advantages of concrete pipe culverts cited in this chapter will become outstandingly clear. An examination of the physical properties of the two major materials used for pipe culverts provides a basis for some general observations that may be used as a guide in pipe culvert design:

1. The most desirable hydraulic operation is always achieved with the smoothest pipe wall. The walls of concrete pipe are twice as smooth as its unlined flexible counterpart.
2. Culvert entrance shape is important to culvert operation. Entrance efficiency is built into every section of concrete pipe in the groove edge used for joining pipe sections.
3. The required pipe size may be reduced if it is feasible to increase the allowable headwater depth. This is true for all types of pipe.
4. The slope required for comparable hydraulic operation of equal size pipe is always much less for the smooth-wall pipe. To achieve comparable pipe barrel operation, concrete pipe requires only one-fourth as much slope as unlined standard flexible pipe of the same size.
5. Improved hydraulic pipe characteristics permit use of smaller size pipe without sacrificing performance. It will generally be found in comparable hydraulic designs that the flexible pipe must be larger than the concrete pipe.
6. The earth load to be supported and, therefore, the required pipe strength will be the least with the smallest pipe that will satisfy the hydraulic requirements. The hydraulic characteristics of concrete pipe will assure minimum support requirements.
7. Concrete pipe culverts may be installed quickly with a small working force. Labor costs are held to a minimum.
8. Concrete pipe is not easily damaged in storage, handling, or installation. Contractors know that such damage losses are minimal with concrete pipe; therefore, contingency provisions in their bids may be reduced.
9. The extremely durable quality of concrete pipe reduces the annual cost. Long life, no replacement cost, reduced maintenance, and high salvage value are factors that cannot be ignored.
10. Concrete pipe is available from local sources to assure ready delivery from a large inventory. In addition, the purchase of local materials boosts local economy.

Concrete pipe is a basic construction material engineered for its intended use. Quality is assured by adherence to recognized engineering standards. Its consistently high quality and excellent hydraulic and structural performance have inspired the confidence of engineers in all areas. The choice of concrete pipe for a culvert is never wrong. An investment in concrete pipe for culverts is good business and sound engineering.

Appendices

Appendix A

Culvert Capacity Charts

EACH CULVERT CAPACITY CHART APPLIES TO A SERIES OF SIZES of a given type of barrel and entrance for a range of discharge rates. For each size of culvert shown, there are one or more curves; one is solid, which denotes inlet control of the headwater-discharge relationship, and the other curves shown by short or long dashes refer to outlet control of the headwater-discharge relationship. All these curves are further identified by an index number, $L/100S_o$, which is length in feet divided by slope of barrel in per cent.

The solid line for each size culvert gives the maximum discharge obtainable with a given headwater depth. For any value of $L/100S_o$ less than that indicated on the solid curve, no decrease in headwater can be obtained for a given discharge. (Comparison of curves for different types of entrance, however, will show differences in headwater at a given discharge, depending on the type of entrance.) At any point on the solid line, the culvert can be assumed to be operating with inlet control; i.e., the headwater depth will depend solely on the entrance and the barrel will not flow full.

The short and long dashed curves indicate the headwater-discharge relationship for culvert operation with outlet control. In this case the headwater depth is dependent on length, slope, and resistance losses. The culvert barrel will be flowing partly full until the headwater is substantially above the crown elevation at the entrance; it will flow full for increasing proportions of the barrel length as the discharge increases. On the charts where there is no dashed line for a given size, the operating headwater for outlet control is so nearly identical with that for inlet control that the solid curve can be used without significant error.

Curve Arrangement

The curves are arranged so that linear interpolation for the headwater may be made between the inlet control (solid) and outlet control (dashed) curves according to the value of $L/100S_o$ for a given culvert size. Thus, if the numerical value of $L/100S_o$ (based on site conditions) is halfway between that for the solid curve and the dashed curve for a given size culvert, HW for a given Q can be interpolated as the midpoint between the two curves. Interpolation can also be made for the capacity, Q, of a given culvert for a given HW in the same manner.

Linear interpolation for any intermediate size that is commercially available may also be made between curves for two culvert sizes. In this case, if $L/100S_o$ for site conditions is equal to or less than that on the solid curve for either adjacent culvert size, interpolate directly between the solid curves according to height of barrel. When $L/100S_o$ for the site is greater than that shown on adjacent solid curves, interpolate first for $L/100S_o$ at each adjacent size and then interpolate between these points to locate a headwater point for the intermediate size. Precision is not necessary since the size selected for the design Q seldom requires the full depth of the headwater allowable at the site.

The charts may also be applied to the selection of culvert size where the barrel slope S_o is zero. In such a case the value of $L/100S_o$ cannot be computed. This difficulty may easily be surmounted by assuming a small slope for the barrel for the purpose of computing a value of $L/100S_o$. In general, use $S_o = 0.002$ for concrete barrels and $S_o = 0.004$ for corrugated metal barrels. First read an actual HW from the charts using this hypothetical $L/100S_o$; then increase the chart value of actual HW by the assumed amount of fall in the barrel flow line, LS_o, introduced in this procedure. A slope of 0.2 per cent or 0.002 for concrete and paved corrugated metal culverts is sufficient to obtain a value of $L/100S_o$ to use in the charts. For unpaved corrugated metal culverts, the use of a hypothetical slope of 0.4 per cent is advisable.

The dotted horizontal lines on the charts are constructed at HW depths that are twice the individual barrel diameter. In selecting the actual operating HW that is less than twice the barrel diameter, a high degree of accuracy can be obtained by use of these charts. On the other hand, for actual operating HW above this dotted line, the accuracy in determining HW for outlet control flow decreases with certain combinations of lengths, slopes, and roughness of barrel section. For cases where accuracy is necessary for outlet control, HW above twice the barrel rise can be computed with confidence by using flowing-full nomographs; enter the appropriate nomograph with the size of culvert determined by use of these charts.

In the range of low headwater design, these culvert capacity charts are extremely good. They have a range of headwater design from less than submergence of the inlet to about 1.5 times the barrel diameter. It is in this range of flow that the flowing-full culvert nomographs have least application.

An inspection of the culvert capacity charts will reveal that not all commercial sizes of pipe are included. On the other hand, several sizes of pipe which may not be readily available from all manufacturers *are* included. Therefore, the designer should check sizes that have been listed as commercially available against what is actually available in his design locality. In the circular sections, the 3-in. sizes have been left out of the culvert capacity charts for clarity.

Data Necessary to Use Capacity Charts

The design problem is to select a culvert that will convey the estimated flood discharge without exceeding the allowable (permissible) headwater depth. In certain localities it has been found through experience that particular types of culvert barrels and entrances are favored in lieu of other types. The designer should be aware of this in determining the final culvert installation.

To select a culvert size from the capacity charts, certain data concerning the site must be established:

1. Flood discharge Q in cubic feet per second.
2. Outlet channel depth in relation to critical depth in the barrel.
3. Allowable headwater AHW in feet.
4. Length L of the culvert in feet.
5. Slope S_o of the culvert barrel in feet per foot.
6. Index number $L/100S_o$.

Procedure for Using Charts

With the information in the preceding section, the culvert capacity charts can be used to select culvert size for most design problems. The following is a step-by-step procedure for using the charts:

1. From the estimate of length and slope of culvert barrel, compute $L/100S_o$.
2. Select the appropriate chart, depending on type of barrel and

entrance. In many cases the required sizes for different types of barrel and entrance may be desired for economic comparison.

3. Enter the chart with the discharge Q and move up to the allowable headwater AHW. Such a point is shown on the chart example by the symbol ⓧ.
   a. The first solid line below this point ⓧ gives size of culvert and actual headwater if $L/100S_o$ for the site is not greater than the value shown on the curve. The solid line will apply for any length culvert provided $L/100S_o$ is equal to or less than the value stated on the curve.
   b. For any larger $L/100S_o$ there is a possibility that actual HW for this size culvert may exceed AHW. If $L/100S_o$ for the site is greater than the value on the solid curve of step 3a, the actual headwater is read by interpolating along the ordinate for the given Q (see previous discussion on curve arrangement). Refer to symbol ⓧ on any chart for the example. If this point is appreciably above the AHW, the trial size of culvert is too small and the next larger size must be investigated.

Example

From site location, the following data for chart use were determined:

1. Estimate of discharge is $Q = 400$ cfs.
2. AHW, considering freeboard, is 9.0 ft.
3. Length of culvert barrel is about 320 ft.; headwalls are used because of high fill.
4. Slope of barrel placed on natural stream grade is approximately 0.008 ft. per foot.

Step procedure in using charts:

1. Compute $L/100S_o = 320/100 \times 0.008 = 320/0.8 = 400$.
2. Select appropriate chart (refer to section on data necessary to use capacity charts). Compare circular concrete and circular corrugated metal barrels, both with square edge in headwall entrance, for this site. Therefore, charts are selected that meet requirements of discharge, entrance condition, and type of barrel.
3. Enter the chart for the metal barrel first and with the discharge $Q = 400$ cfs; move up to the intercept of $AHW = 9.0$ ft. Compare $L/100S_o = 400$ to values on chart, sections 3a and 3b of procedure, and select proper size culvert. For this case, barrel size

would be D = 96 in., operating at an actual HW = 8.3 ft. Repeat procedure with concrete barrel chart and select appropriate size. For this case, the barrel size would be D = 84 in., operating at an actual HW = 9.0 ft.

Procedure for Cases Outside Chart Limits

If the downstream tailwater will submerge the crown of the culvert outlet, the charts do not apply. This condition must be established with reasonable certainty to justify a design procedure other than use of the charts. If established, the appropriate capacity chart may be selected by inspection to approximate the culvert size. Then use the nomograph for a culvert of this type flowing full.

Where the outlet is not submerged but the culvert $L/100S_o$ value is greater than any shown on the chart for the culvert barrel and entrance type, the nomograph for a culvert of this type flowing full may be used. Again, a trial size culvert for use of the nomograph may be obtained by inspection of the appropriate design chart. Then follow instructions for use of full-flow nomographs. *Caution:* For small rates of flow in relation to the barrel size and the culvert outlet not submerged by tailwater, a free water surface will exist inside the culvert, decreasing in depth downstream and approaching critical depth near the outlet. Since full flow is not occurring in these cases, the nomograph solution will give a headwater depth greater than required. In general, such cases may be recognized by the small head loss obtained in the nomograph solution and the resulting calculated headwater depth of less than about $1.2D$. In these cases a better estimate of the actual headwater depth may be made on the design chart by extrapolating a position for a site value $L/100S_o$ curve above the chart curve.

Where the allowable headwater depth is greater than can be read from the curves of the appropriate chart, one of the nomographs must be used.

1. Use the appropriate nomograph for inlet control operation when $L/100S_o$ is equal to or less than that of the inlet control curve (solid line) of the design chart.
2. Use the appropriate nomograph for a culvert flowing full when $L/100S_o$ is greater than that of the inlet control curve.

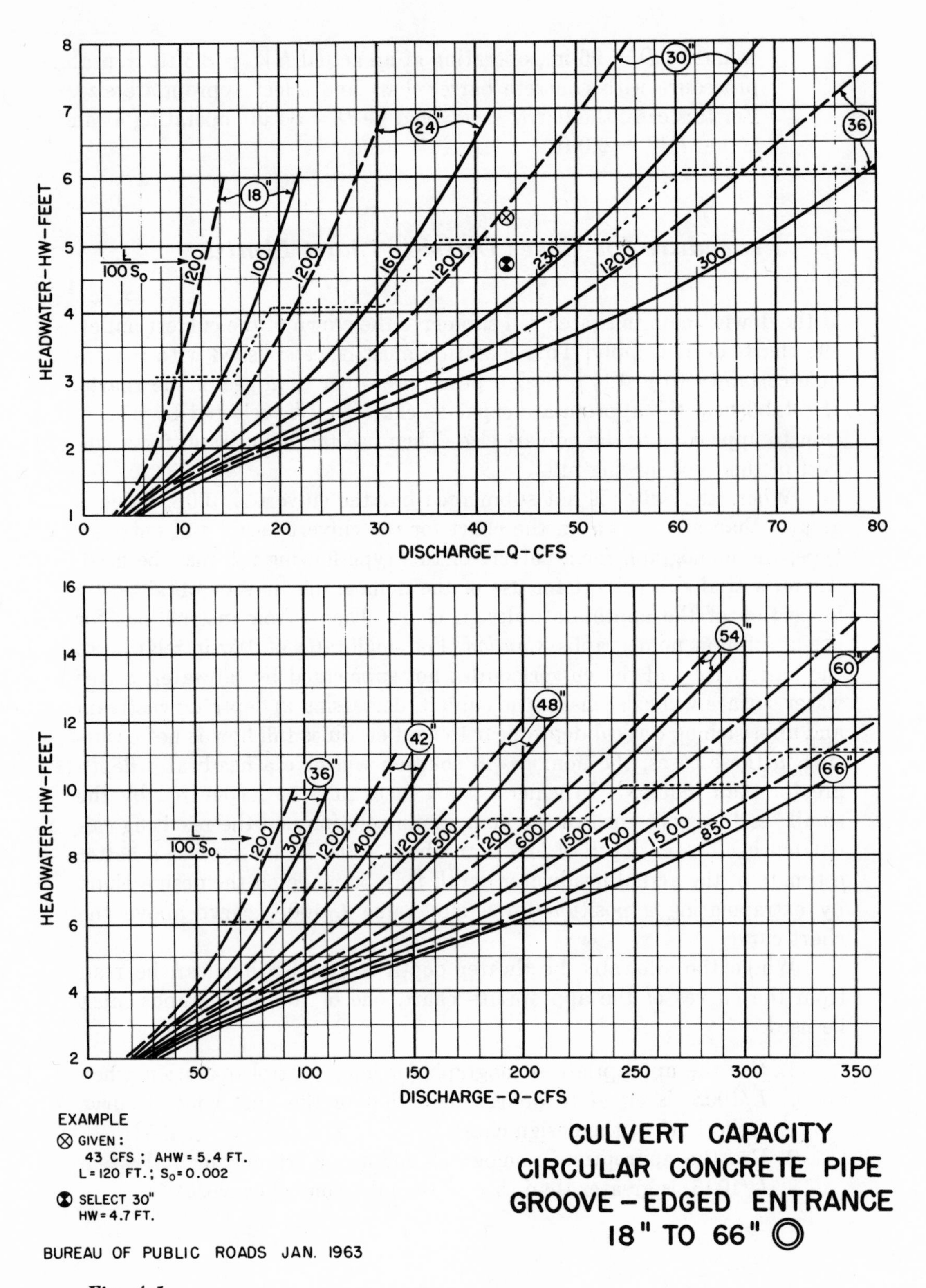
HEADWATER-HW-FEET
DISCHARGE-Q-CFS
18"
24"
30"
36"
L / 100 S₀
1200
100
160
230
300
42"
48"
54"
60"
66"
400
500
600
700
850
1500
EXAMPLE
⊗ GIVEN :
43 CFS ; AHW = 5.4 FT.
L = 120 FT. ; S₀ = 0.002
SELECT 30"
HW = 4.7 FT.
BUREAU OF PUBLIC ROADS JAN. 1963
CULVERT CAPACITY
CIRCULAR CONCRETE PIPE
GROOVE - EDGED ENTRANCE
18" TO 66"

Fig. A-1

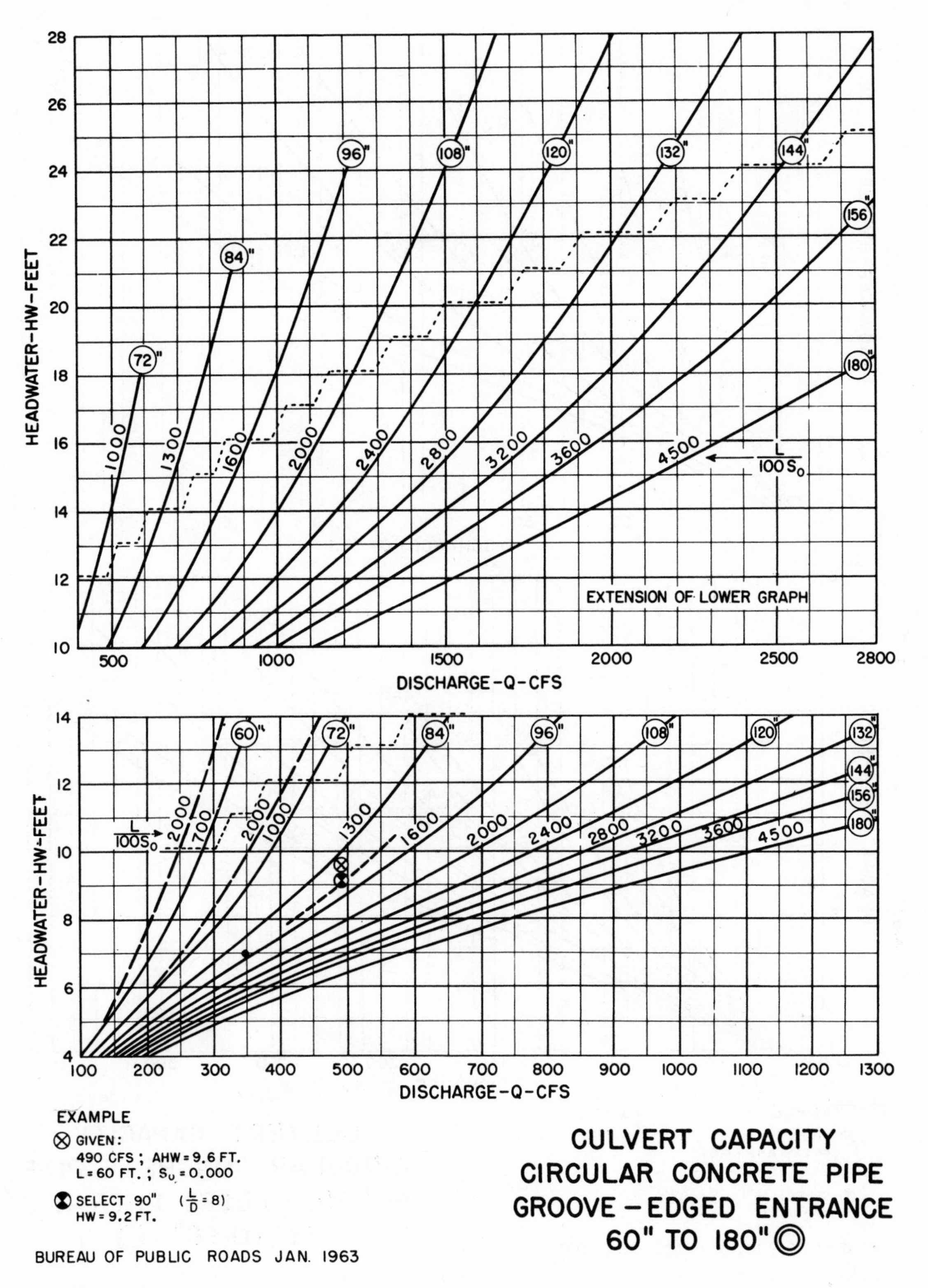
HEADWATER-HW-FEET
DISCHARGE-Q-CFS
EXTENSION OF LOWER GRAPH
72"
84"
96"
108"
120"
132"
144"
156"
180"
60"
1000
1300
1600
2000
2400
2800
3200
3600
4500
700
$\frac{L}{100 S_0}$
EXAMPLE
GIVEN:
490 CFS ; AHW = 9.6 FT.
L = 60 FT. ; S_0 = 0.000
SELECT 90" ($\frac{L}{D}$ = 8)
HW = 9.2 FT.
CULVERT CAPACITY
CIRCULAR CONCRETE PIPE
GROOVE-EDGED ENTRANCE
60" TO 180"
BUREAU OF PUBLIC ROADS JAN. 1963

Fig. A-2

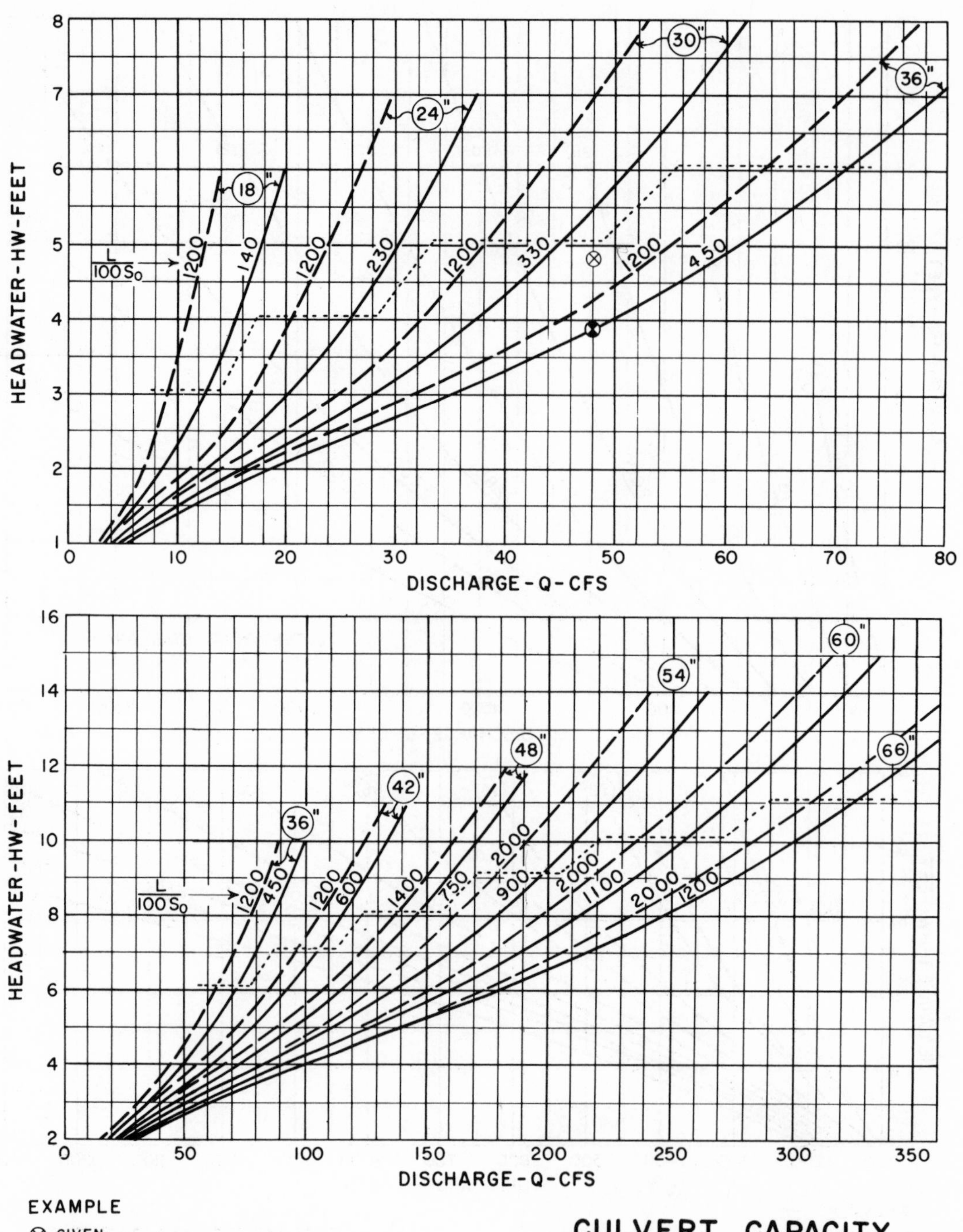

EXAMPLE

⊗ GIVEN:
48 CFS; AHW = 4.8 FT.
L = 60 FT.; S_0 = 0.003

SELECT 36"
HW = 3.9 FT.

BUREAU OF PUBLIC ROADS JAN. 1963

CULVERT CAPACITY
CIRCULAR CONCRETE PIPE
SQUARE-EDGED ENTRANCE
18" TO 66" ◎

Fig. A-3

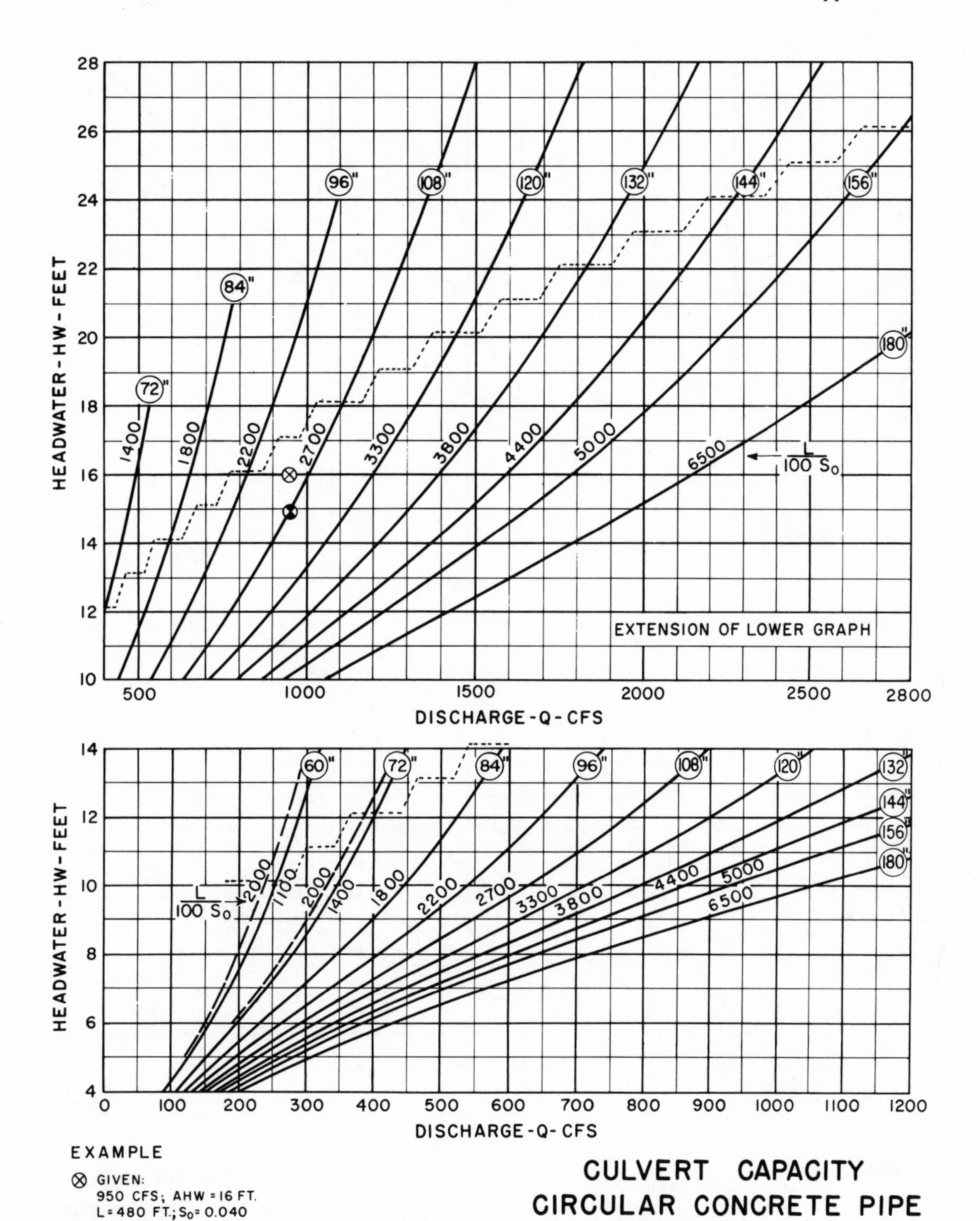

BUREAU OF PUBLIC ROADS JAN. 1963

Fig. A-4

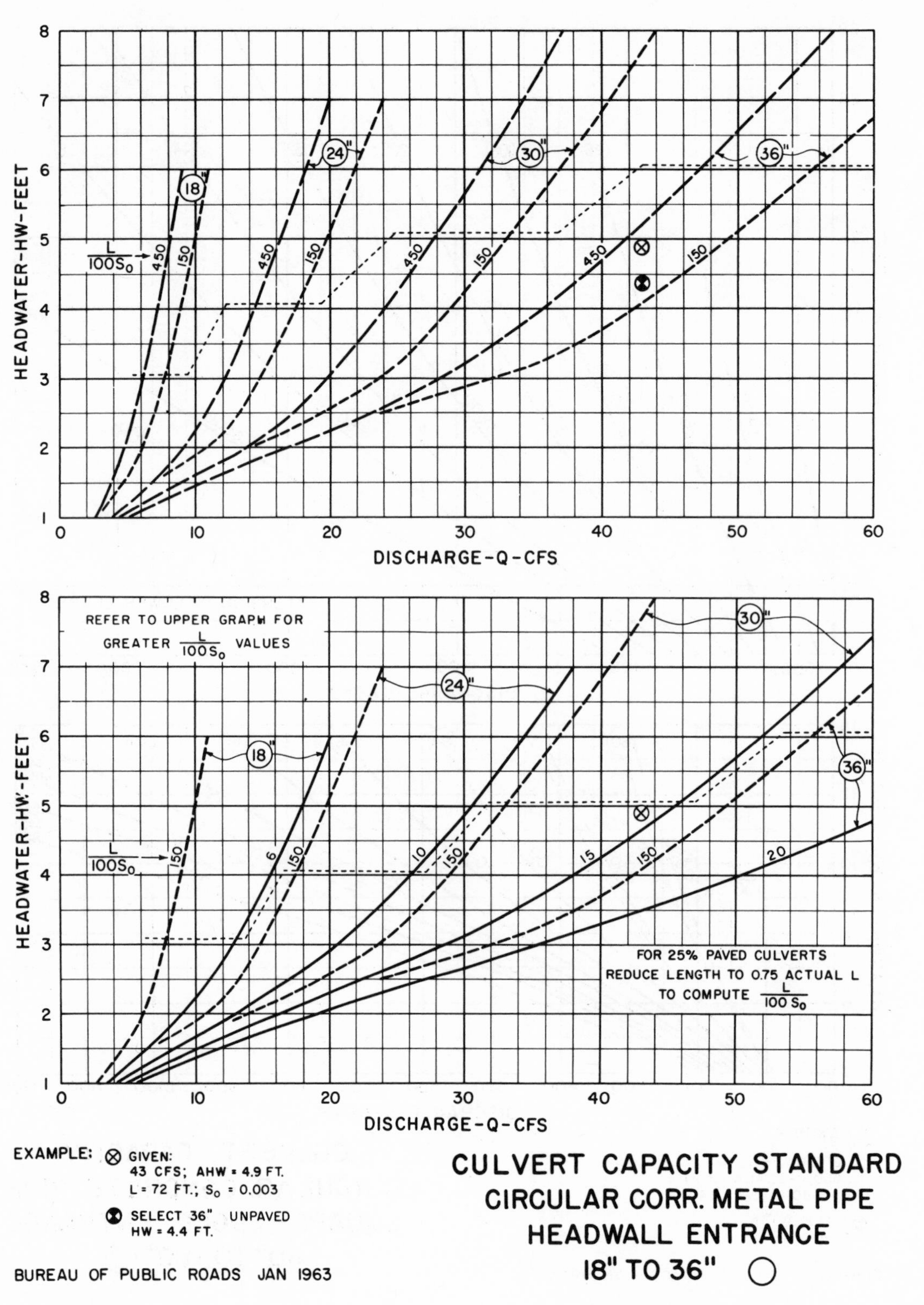
HEADWATER-HW-FEET
DISCHARGE-Q-CFS
L/100S₀
18"
24"
30"
36"
450
150
REFER TO UPPER GRAPH FOR GREATER L/100S₀ VALUES
6
10
15
20
FOR 25% PAVED CULVERTS REDUCE LENGTH TO 0.75 ACTUAL L TO COMPUTE L/100 S₀
EXAMPLE: GIVEN: 43 CFS; AHW = 4.9 FT. L = 72 FT.; S₀ = 0.003
SELECT 36" UNPAVED HW = 4.4 FT.
BUREAU OF PUBLIC ROADS JAN 1963
CULVERT CAPACITY STANDARD
CIRCULAR CORR. METAL PIPE
HEADWALL ENTRANCE
18" TO 36"

Fig. A-5

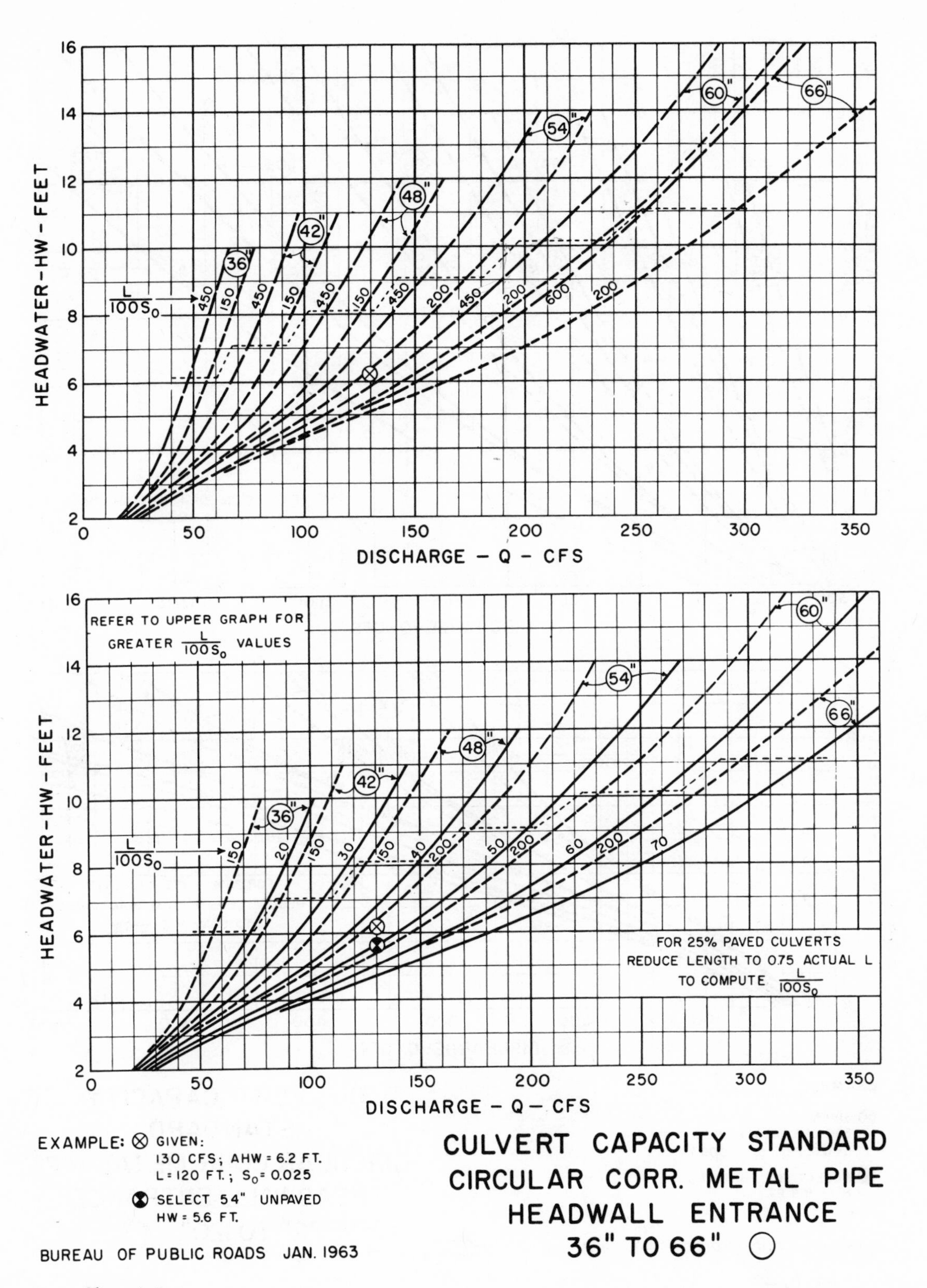
HEADWATER - HW - FEET
DISCHARGE - Q - CFS
L / 100 S_0
36"
42"
48"
54"
60"
66"
REFER TO UPPER GRAPH FOR GREATER L / 100 S_0 VALUES
FOR 25% PAVED CULVERTS REDUCE LENGTH TO 0.75 ACTUAL L TO COMPUTE L / 100 S_0
EXAMPLE: ⊗ GIVEN:
130 CFS; AHW = 6.2 FT.
L = 120 FT.; S_0 = 0.025
SELECT 54" UNPAVED
HW = 5.6 FT.
BUREAU OF PUBLIC ROADS JAN. 1963
CULVERT CAPACITY STANDARD
CIRCULAR CORR. METAL PIPE
HEADWALL ENTRANCE
36" TO 66" ○

Fig. A-6

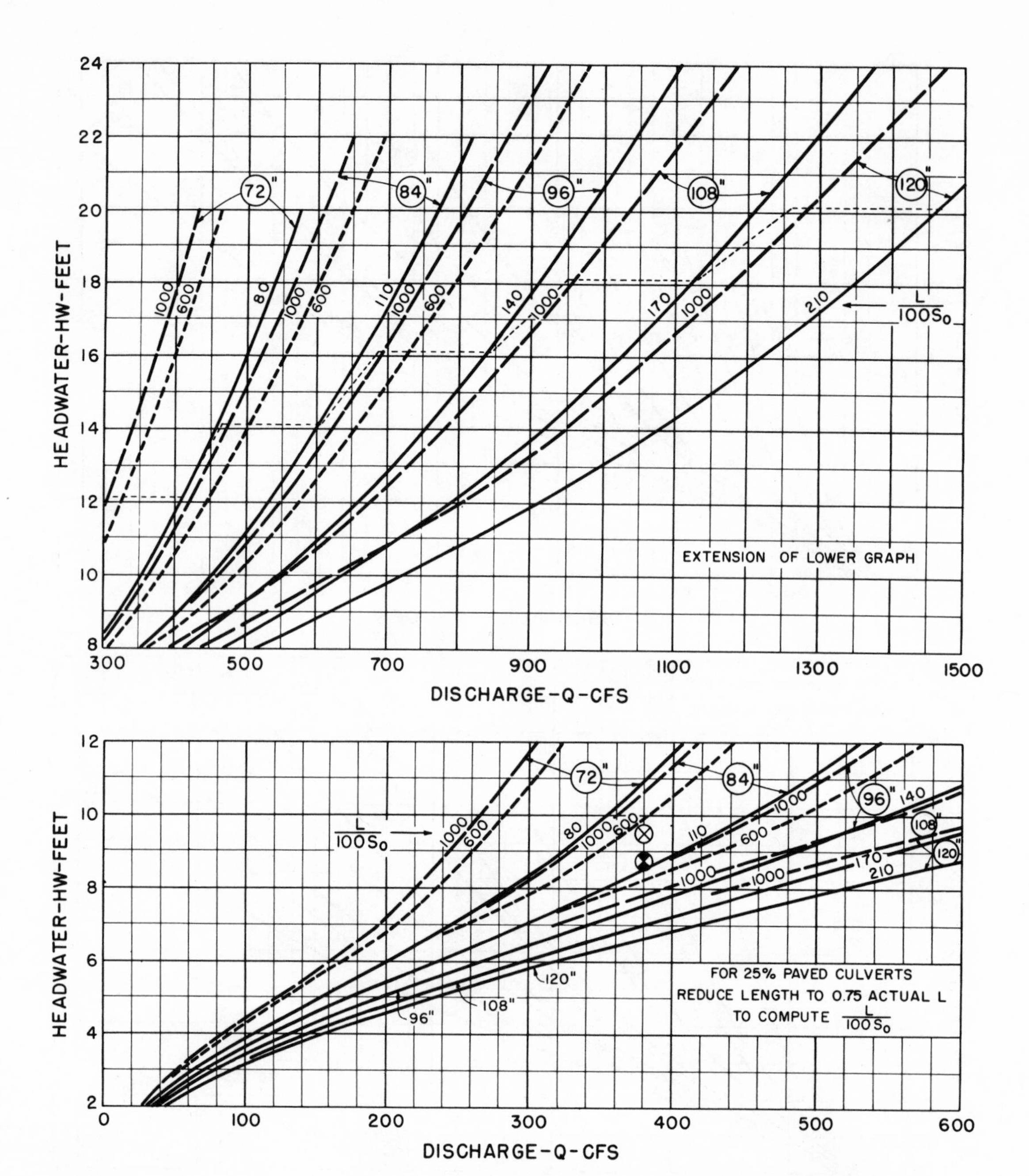

EXAMPLE

⊗ GIVEN:
380 CFS; AHW = 9.5 FT.
L = 120 FT.; S_0 = 0.0083

SELECT 84" UNPAVED
HW = 8.8 FT.

BUREAU OF PUBLIC ROADS JAN. 1963

CULVERT CAPACITY
STANDARD
CIRCULAR CORR. METAL PIPE
HEADWALL ENTRANCE
72" TO 120" ○

Fig. A-7

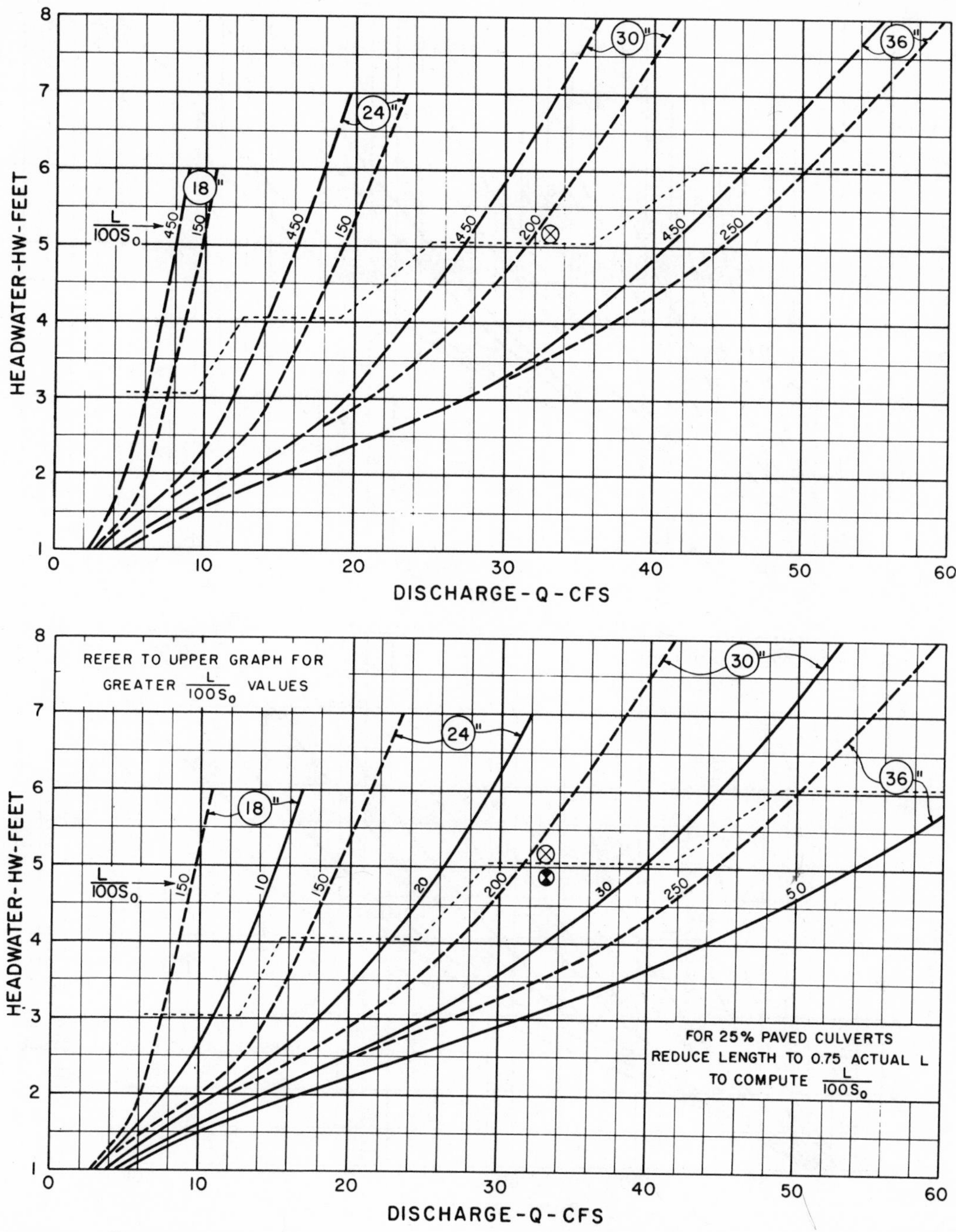

EXAMPLE: ⊗ GIVEN:
33 CFS; AHW = 5.2 FT.
L = 70 FT.; S_0 = 0.005

SELECT 30" UNPAVED
HW = 4.9 FT.

BUREAU OF PUBLIC ROADS JAN. 1963

CULVERT CAPACITY STANDARD
CIRCULAR CORR. METAL PIPE
PROJECTING ENTRANCE
18" TO 36" ◯

Fig. A-8

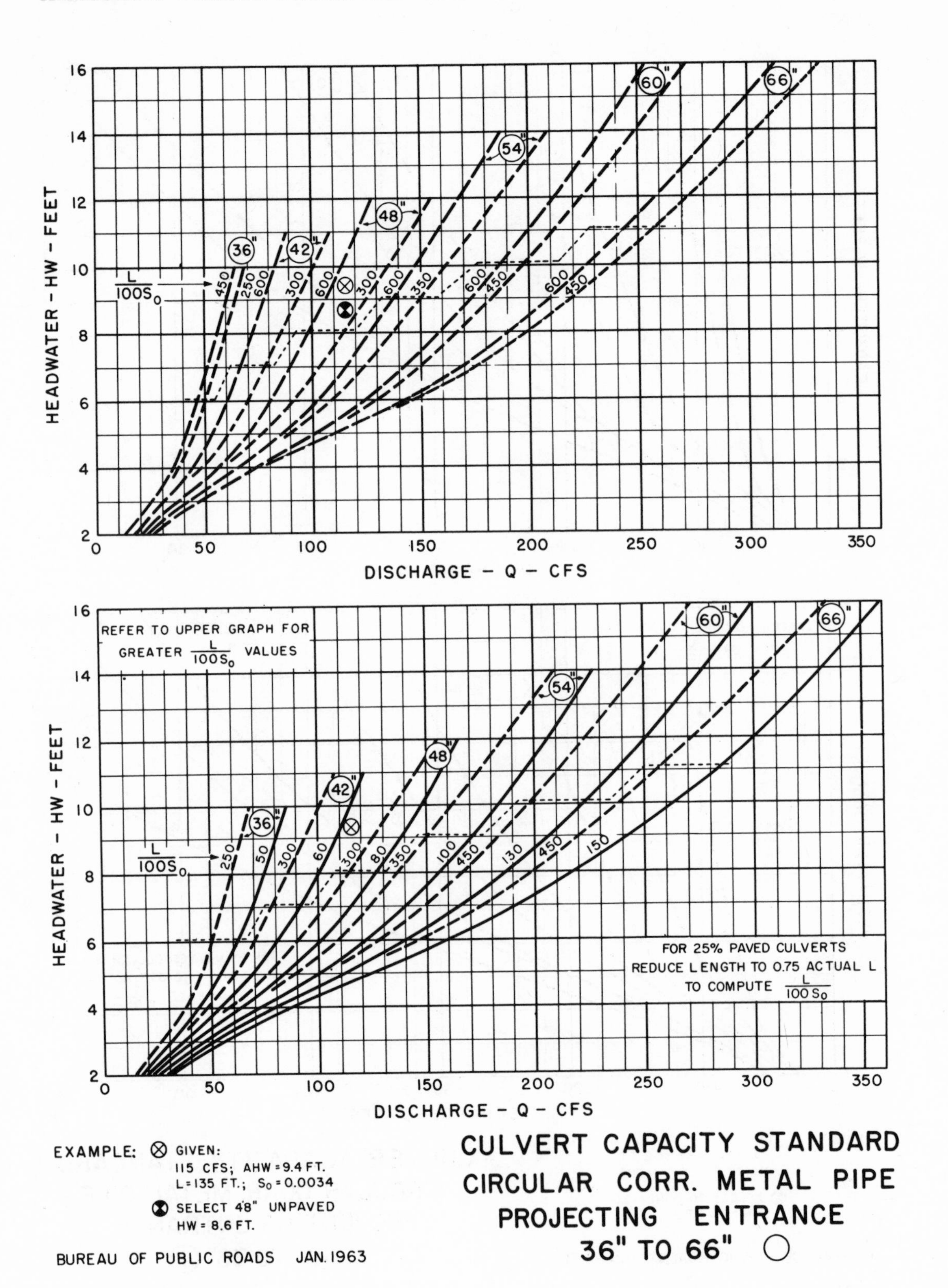

HEADWATER - HW - FEET
DISCHARGE - Q - CFS
36"
42"
48"
54"
60"
66"
L / 100S₀
REFER TO UPPER GRAPH FOR GREATER L/100S₀ VALUES
FOR 25% PAVED CULVERTS REDUCE LENGTH TO 0.75 ACTUAL L TO COMPUTE L/100S₀
EXAMPLE: GIVEN: 115 CFS; AHW = 9.4 FT. L = 135 FT.; S₀ = 0.0034
SELECT 48" UNPAVED HW = 8.6 FT.
BUREAU OF PUBLIC ROADS JAN. 1963
CULVERT CAPACITY STANDARD
CIRCULAR CORR. METAL PIPE
PROJECTING ENTRANCE
36" TO 66"

Fig. A-9

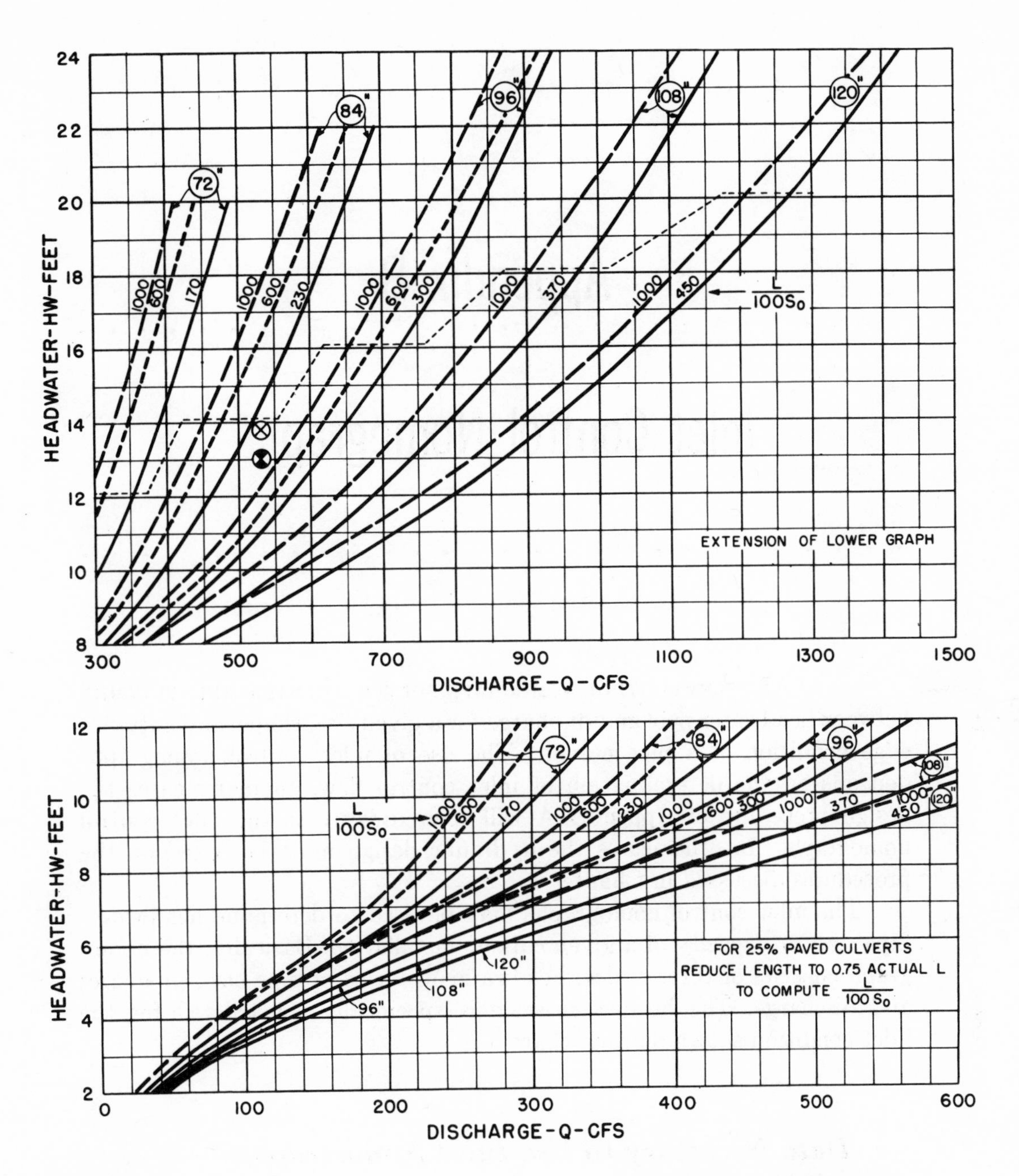

EXAMPLE

⊗ GIVEN:
530 CFS; AHW 13.8 FT.
L = 270 FT; S_0 = 0.0060

SELECT 90" UNPAVED
HW = 13.0 FT.

CULVERT CAPACITY
STANDARD
CIRCULAR CORR. METAL PIPE
PROJECTING ENTRANCE
72" TO 120" ○

BUREAU OF PUBLIC ROADS JAN. 1963

Fig. A-10

Appendix B

Inlet Control Nomographs

AN INLET CONTROL NOMOGRAPH SOLVES THE BASIC RELATIONSHIP between headwater pool and discharge for a given size, shape, and entrance edge condition of a pipe culvert. The use of inlet control nomographs depends on the determination of inlet control flow. In many cases the design procedure of Appendix A will refer directly to the inlet control nomographs. In other cases the hydraulic design must be based on the procedures discussed in Chapter 4.

The inlet control nomographs may be used to determine headwater, pipe size, or capacity of a given culvert installation. Basically, the nomograph consists of three scales: headwater in terms of pipe size; pipe size; and discharge. The headwater scale is specifically constructed for the inlet condition shown on each chart.

Data Necessary to Use Inlet Nomographs

To select a culvert size from these nomographs, certain basic data concerning the site must be established:

1. Flood discharge Q in cubic feet per second.
2. Outlet channel depth in relation to critical depth in the barrel.
3. Allowable headwater AHW in feet.
4. Length L of the culvert in feet.

5. Slope S_o of the culvert barrel in feet per foot.
6. Index number $L/100S_o$.

Procedure for Using Inlet Nomographs

These culvert nomographs can be used only for inlet control flow design. The following is a step-by-step procedure for their use:

1. Determine if these nomographs are applicable by:
   a. Following procedure outlined in Appendix A for culvert capacity charts, or
   b. Following procedure outlined in Chapter 4 to determine type of flow control.
2. Select the appropriate nomograph, depending on type of barrel and entrance.
3. Enter the nomograph with discharge and an assumed size pipe. In most cases approximate size can be determined from culvert capacity charts.
4. Using a straightedge, connect the discharge Q and pipe diameter D; extend the line to intersect the headwater scale HW/D to the right.
5. Read the headwater in terms of pipe diameter, HW/D, and convert this to headwater HW by multiplying by pipe diameter D in feet.
6. Compare the HW to the permissible headwater.
7. Repeat steps for other assumed pipe sizes if necessary.

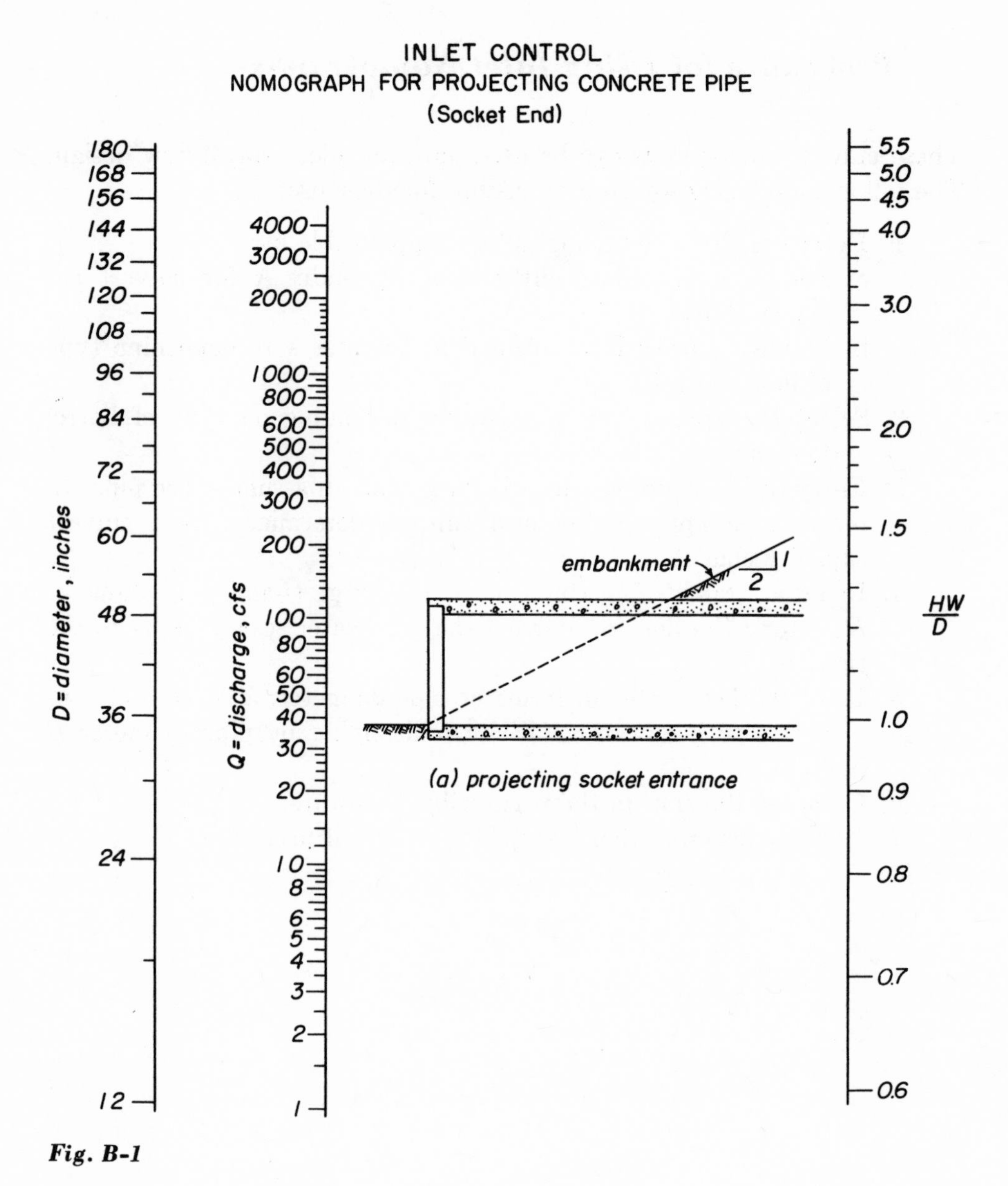
INLET CONTROL
NOMOGRAPH FOR PROJECTING CONCRETE PIPE
(Socket End)
D = diameter, inches
180
168
156
144
132
120
108
96
84
72
60
48
36
24
12
Q = discharge, cfs
4000
3000
2000
1000
800
600
500
400
300
200
100
80
60
50
40
30
20
10
8
6
5
4
3
2
1
HW/D
5.5
5.0
4.5
4.0
3.0
2.0
1.5
1.0
0.9
0.8
0.7
0.6
embankment
1
2
(a) projecting socket entrance

Fig. B-1

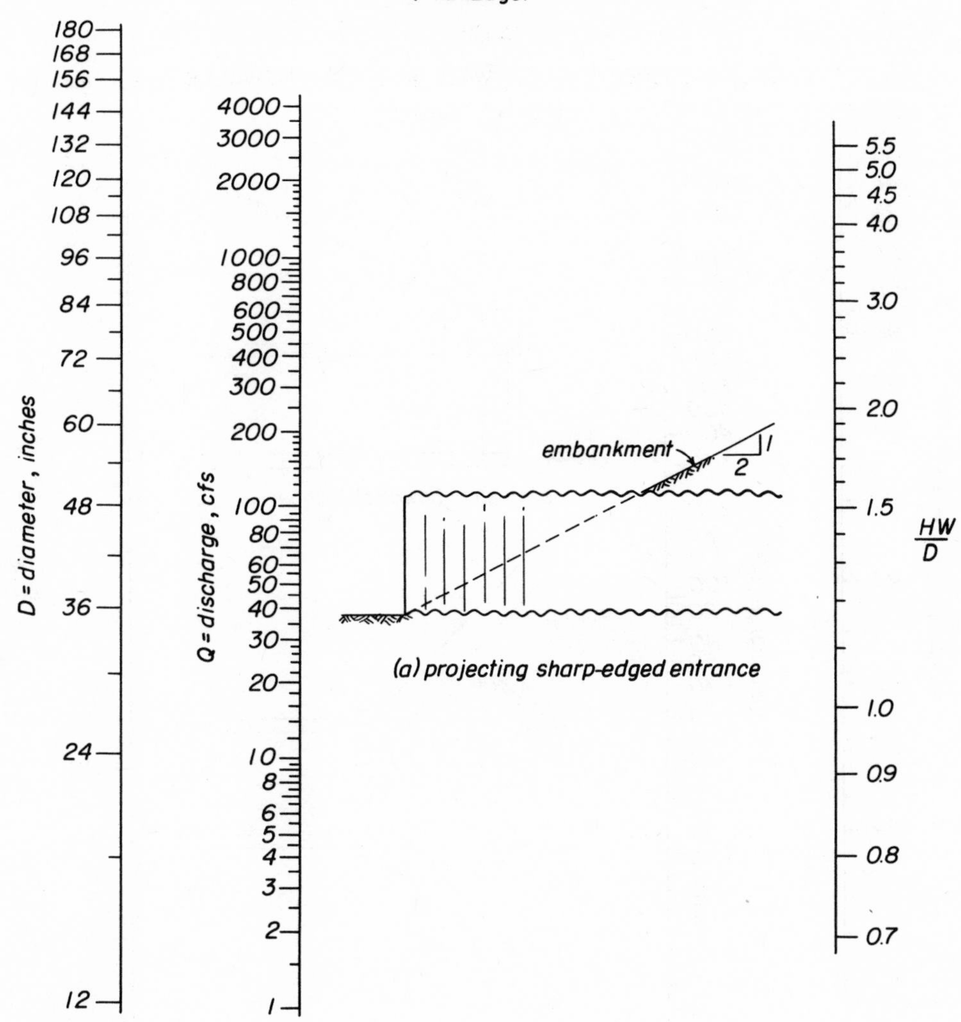
INLET CONTROL
NOMOGRAPH FOR PROJECTING CMP ENTRANCE
(Thin Edge)
D = diameter, inches
180
168
156
144
132
120
108
96
84
72
60
48
36
24
12
Q = discharge, cfs
4000
3000
2000
1000
800
600
500
400
300
200
100
80
60
50
40
30
20
10
8
6
5
4
3
2
1
embankment
1
2
(a) projecting sharp-edged entrance
5.5
5.0
4.5
4.0
3.0
2.0
1.5
1.0
0.9
0.8
0.7
HW/D

Fig. B-2

INLET CONTROL
NOMOGRAPH FOR CONCRETE PIPE WITH HEADWALL
(Socket Opening)
AND
CONCRETE PIPE WITH HEADWALL AND 45° WINGWALLS
(Socket Opening)

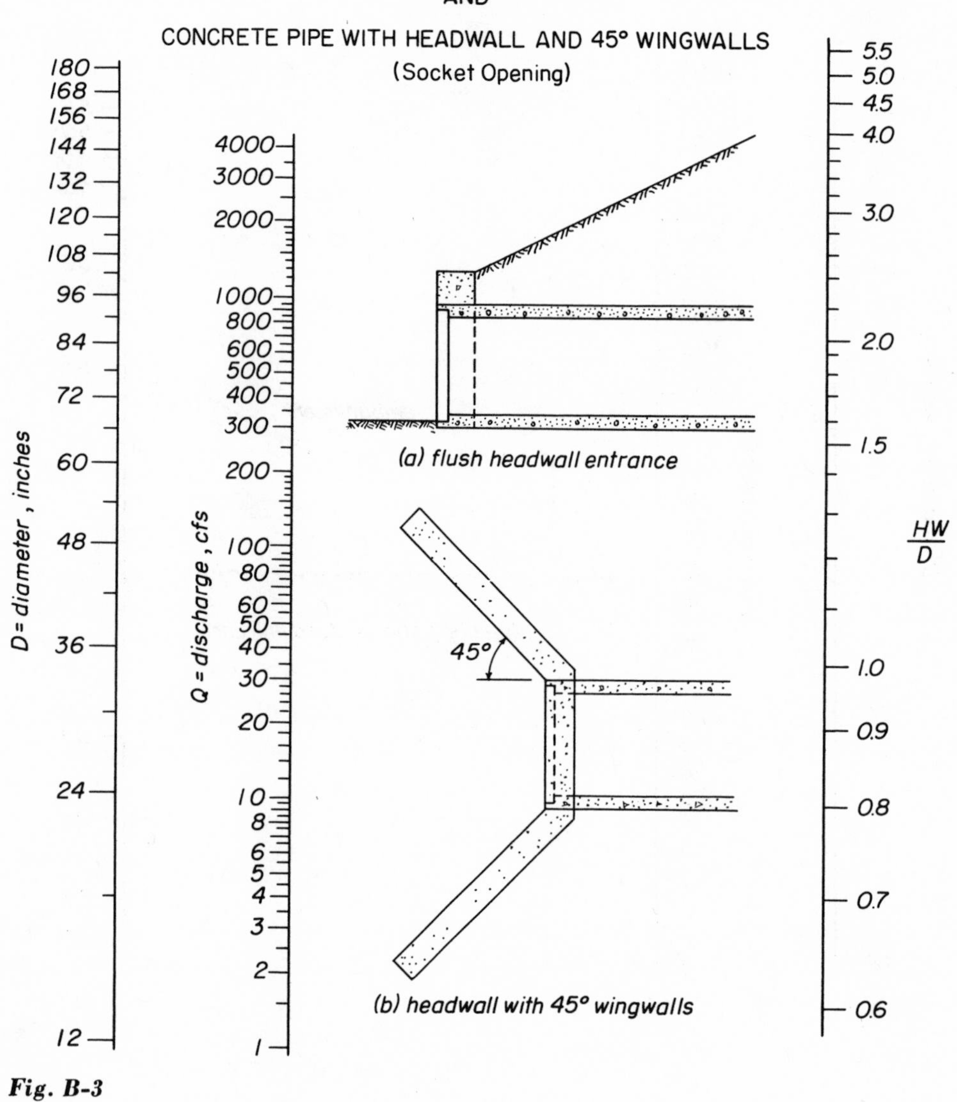

Fig. B-3

INLET CONTROL
NOMOGRAPH FOR SQUARE-EDGED ENTRANCE IN A HEADWALL

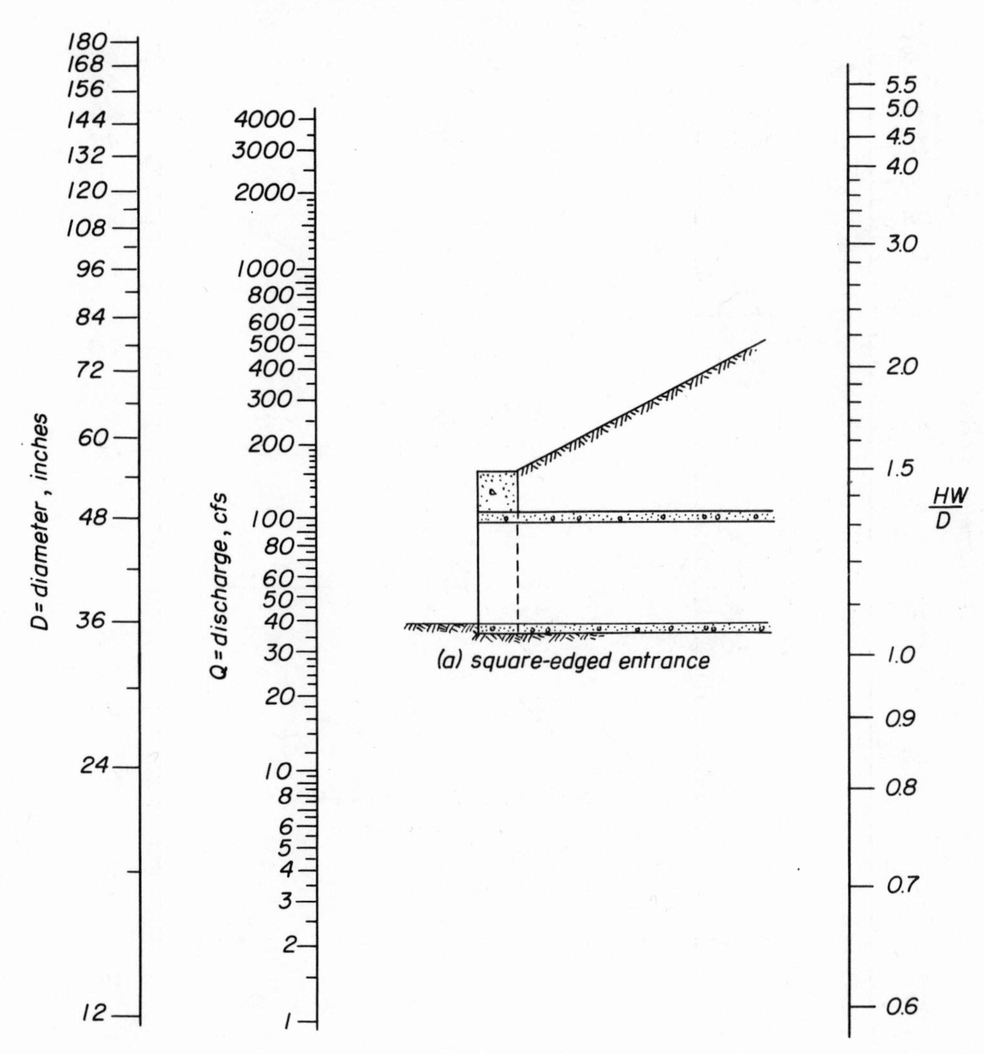

Fig. B-4

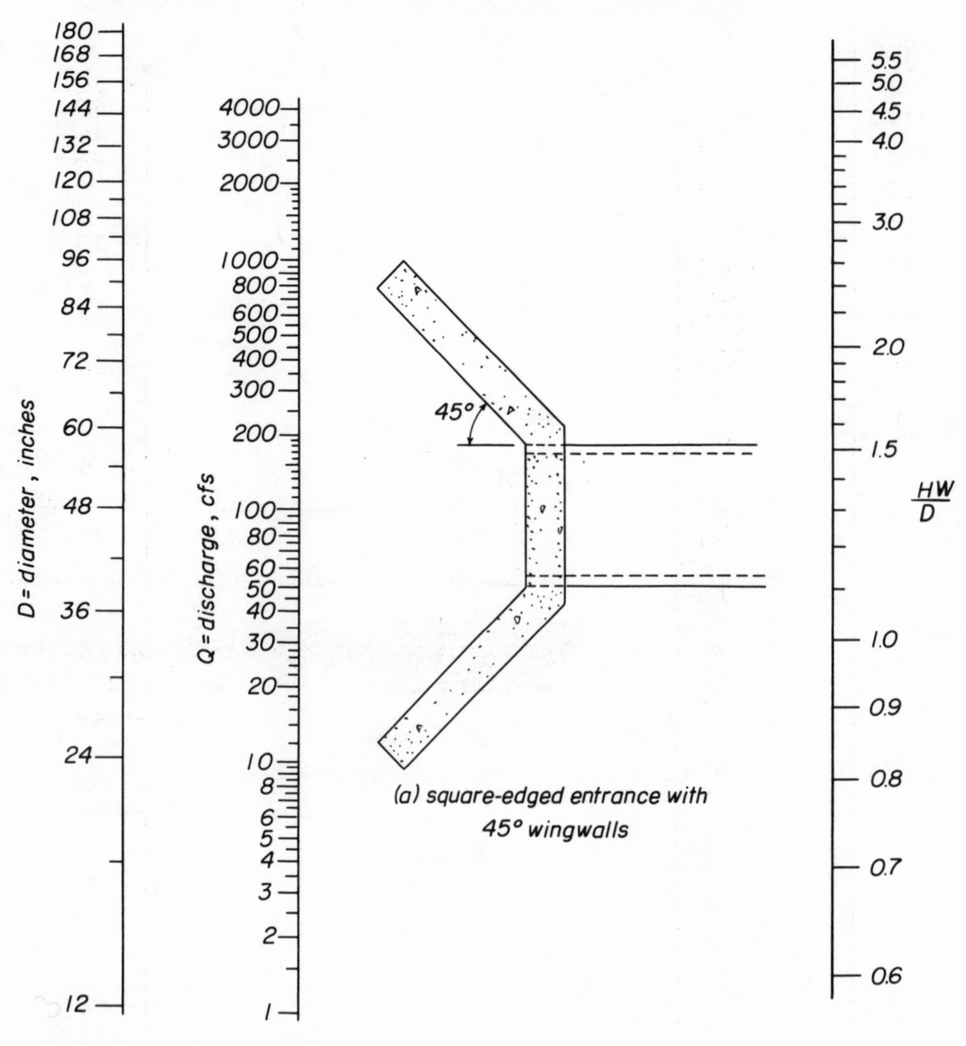
INLET CONTROL
NOMOGRAPH FOR SQUARE-EDGED ENTRANCE WITH 45° WINGWALLS
D = diameter, inches
180
168
156
144
132
120
108
96
84
72
60
48
36
24
12
Q = discharge, cfs
4000
3000
2000
1000
800
600
500
400
300
200
100
80
60
50
40
30
20
10
8
6
5
4
3
2
1
45°
(a) square-edged entrance with
45° wingwalls
5.5
5.0
4.5
4.0
3.0
2.0
1.5
1.0
0.9
0.8
0.7
0.6
HW/D

Fig. B-5

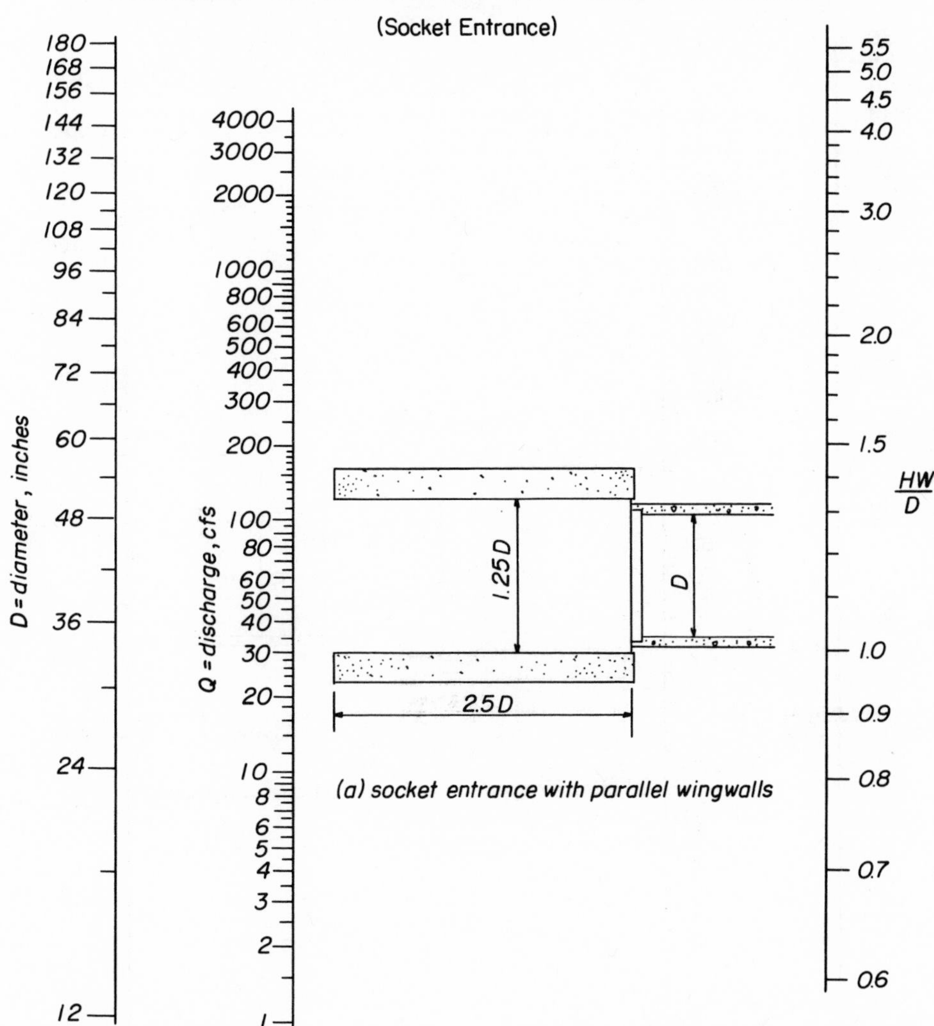
INLET CONTROL
NOMOGRAPH FOR CONCRETE PIPE WITH PARALLEL WINGWALLS
(Socket Entrance)
D = diameter, inches
180
168
156
144
132
120
108
96
84
72
60
48
36
24
12
Q = discharge, cfs
4000
3000
2000
1000
800
600
500
400
300
200
100
80
60
50
40
30
20
10
8
6
5
4
3
2
1
1.25 D
D
2.5 D
(a) socket entrance with parallel wingwalls
HW/D
5.5
5.0
4.5
4.0
3.0
2.0
1.5
1.0
0.9
0.8
0.7
0.6

Fig. B-6

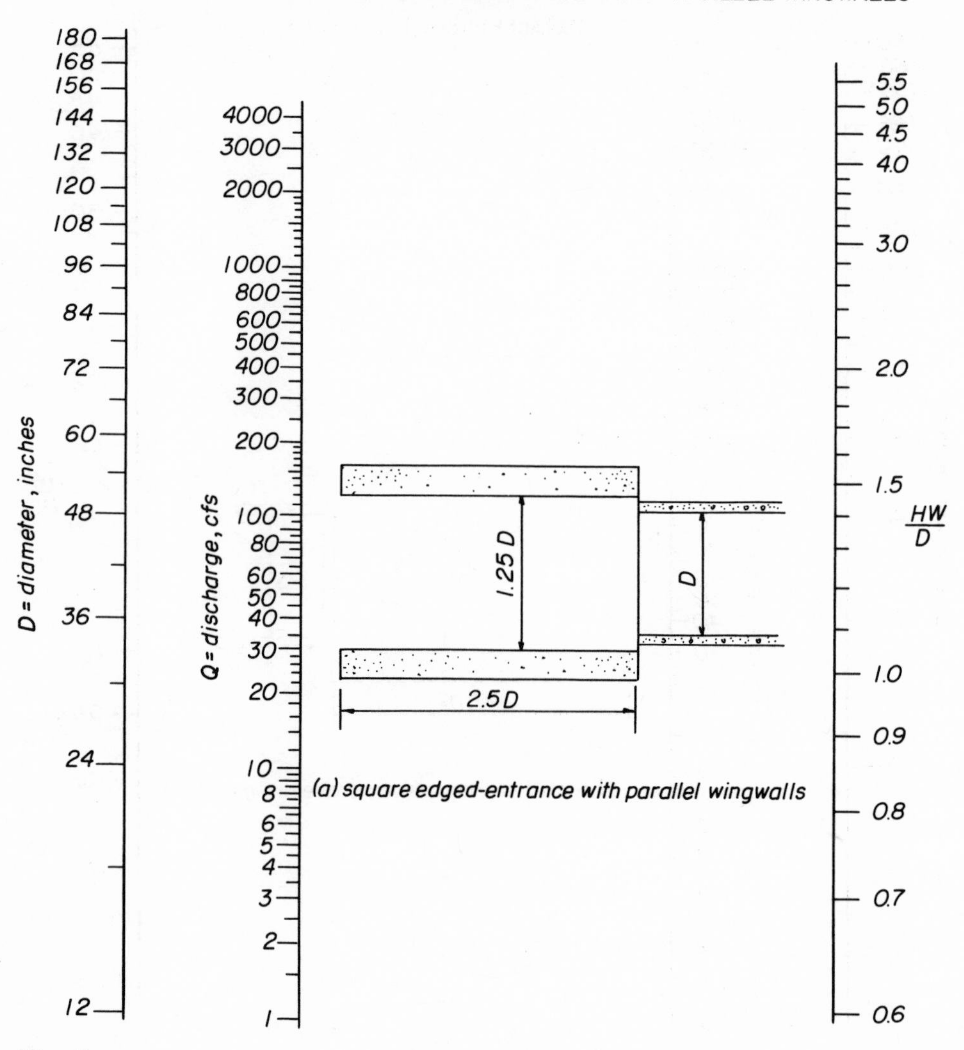
INLET CONTROL
NOMOGRAPH FOR SQUARE-EDGED ENTRANCE WITH PARALLEL WINGWALLS
D = diameter, inches
180
168
156
144
132
120
108
96
84
72
60
48
36
24
12
Q = discharge, cfs
4000
3000
2000
1000
800
600
500
400
300
200
100
80
60
50
40
30
20
10
8
6
5
4
3
2
1
HW/D
5.5
5.0
4.5
4.0
3.0
2.0
1.5
1.0
0.9
0.8
0.7
0.6
1.25 D
D
2.5 D
(a) square edged-entrance with parallel wingwalls

Fig. B-7

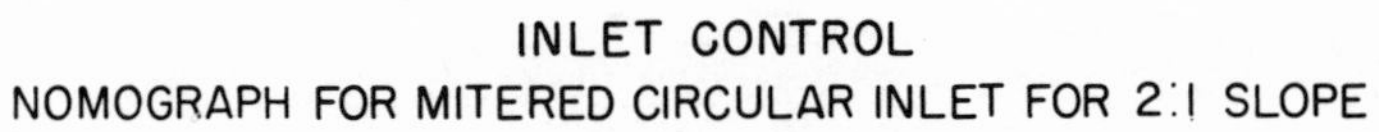
INLET CONTROL
NOMOGRAPH FOR MITERED CIRCULAR INLET FOR 2:1 SLOPE

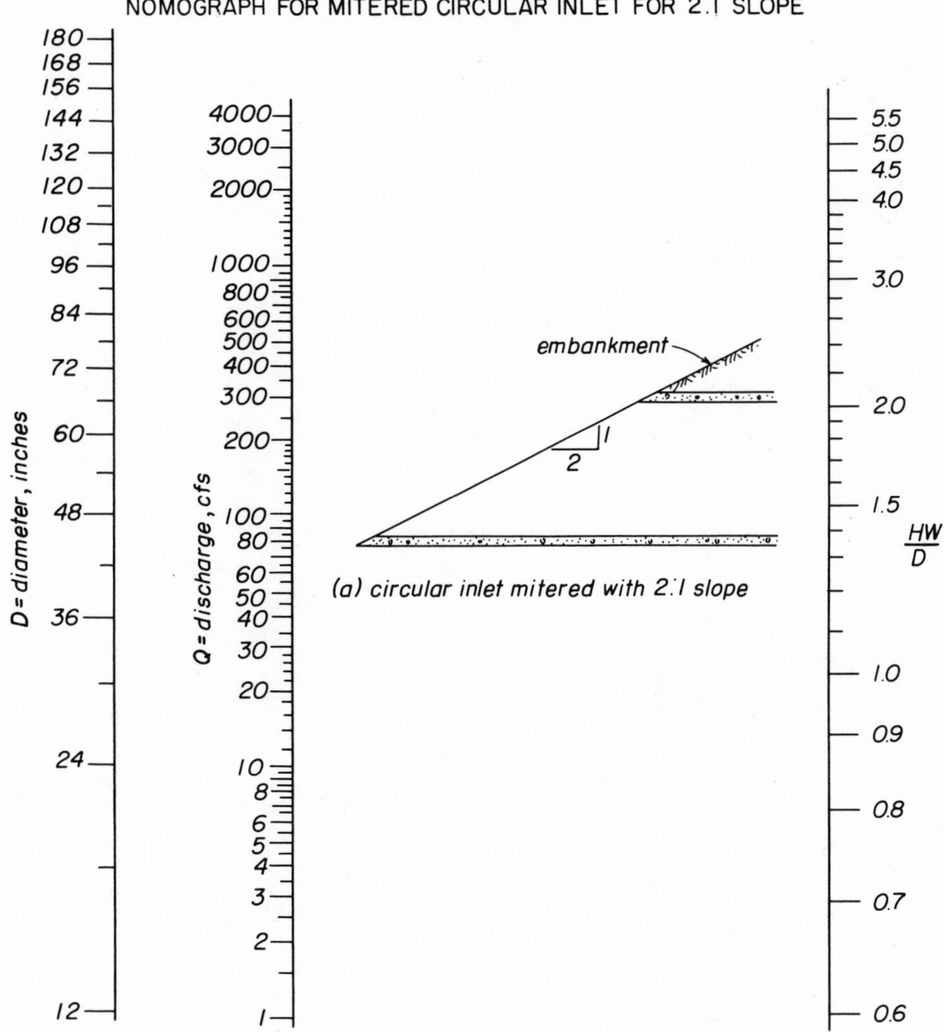
D = diameter, inches
180
168
156
144
132
120
108
96
84
72
60
48
36
24
12
Q = discharge, cfs
4000
3000
2000
1000
800
600
500
400
300
200
100
80
60
50
40
30
20
10
8
6
5
4
3
2
1
embankment
1
2
(a) circular inlet mitered with 2:1 slope
HW/D
5.5
5.0
4.5
4.0
3.0
2.0
1.5
1.0
0.9
0.8
0.7
0.6

Fig. B-8

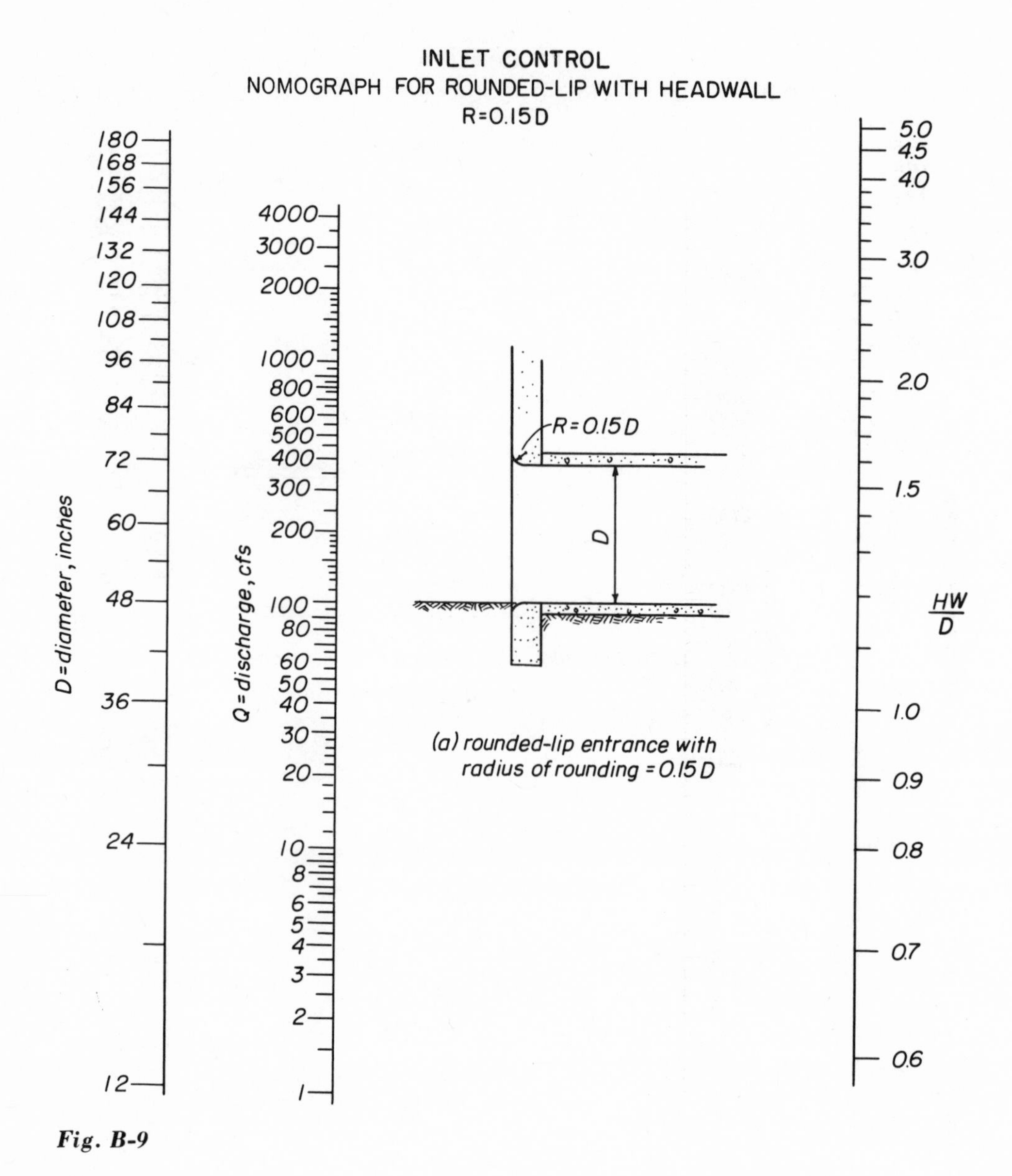
INLET CONTROL
NOMOGRAPH FOR ROUNDED-LIP WITH HEADWALL
R=0.15D
180
168
156
144
132
120
108
96
84
72
60
48
36
24
12
D=diameter, inches
4000
3000
2000
1000
800
600
500
400
300
200
100
80
60
50
40
30
20
10
8
6
5
4
3
2
1
Q=discharge, cfs
R=0.15D
D
(a) rounded-lip entrance with
radius of rounding = 0.15D
5.0
4.5
4.0
3.0
2.0
1.5
HW/D
1.0
0.9
0.8
0.7
0.6

Fig. B-9

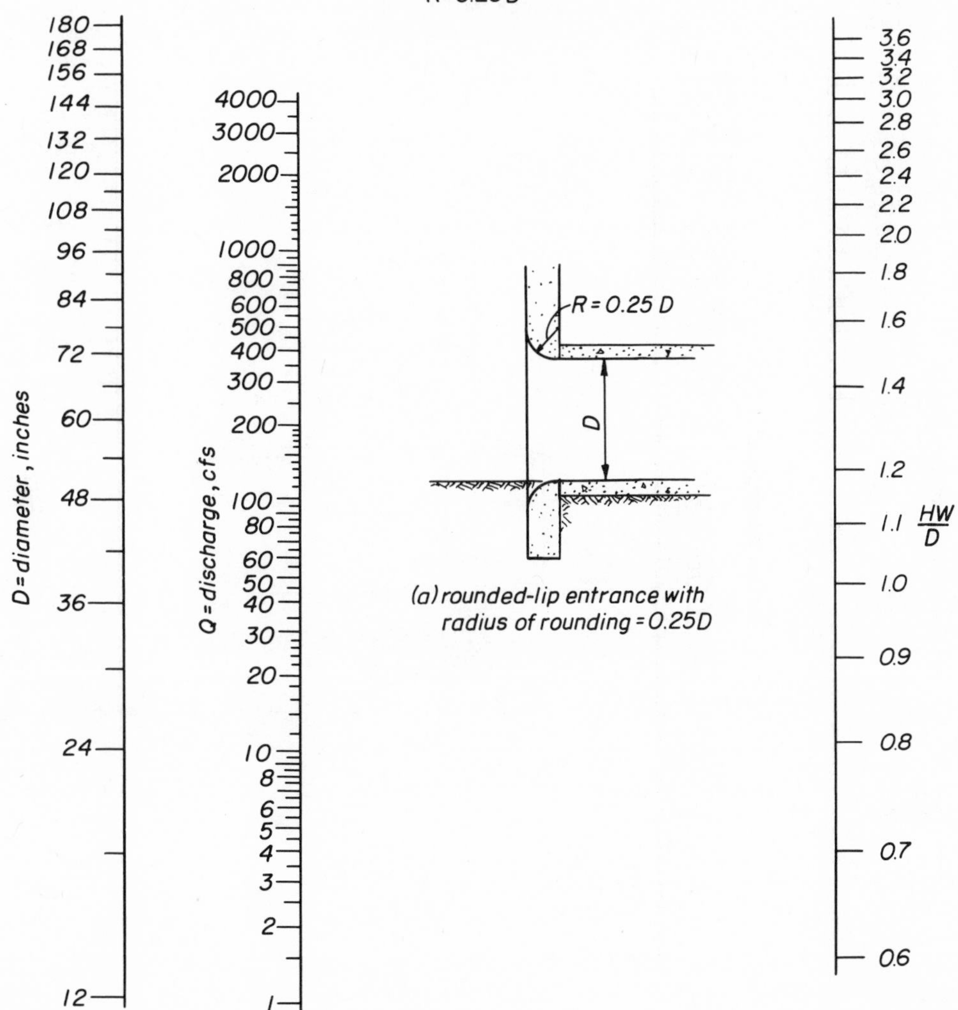
INLET CONTROL
NOMOGRAPH FOR ROUNDED-LIP ENTRANCE
R=0.25D
D=diameter, inches
180
168
156
144
132
120
108
96
84
72
60
48
36
24
12
Q=discharge, cfs
4000
3000
2000
1000
800
600
500
400
300
200
100
80
60
50
40
30
20
10
8
6
5
4
3
2
1
R = 0.25 D
D
(a) rounded-lip entrance with
radius of rounding = 0.25D
3.6
3.4
3.2
3.0
2.8
2.6
2.4
2.2
2.0
1.8
1.6
1.4
1.2
1.1
HW/D
1.0
0.9
0.8
0.7
0.6

Fig. B-10

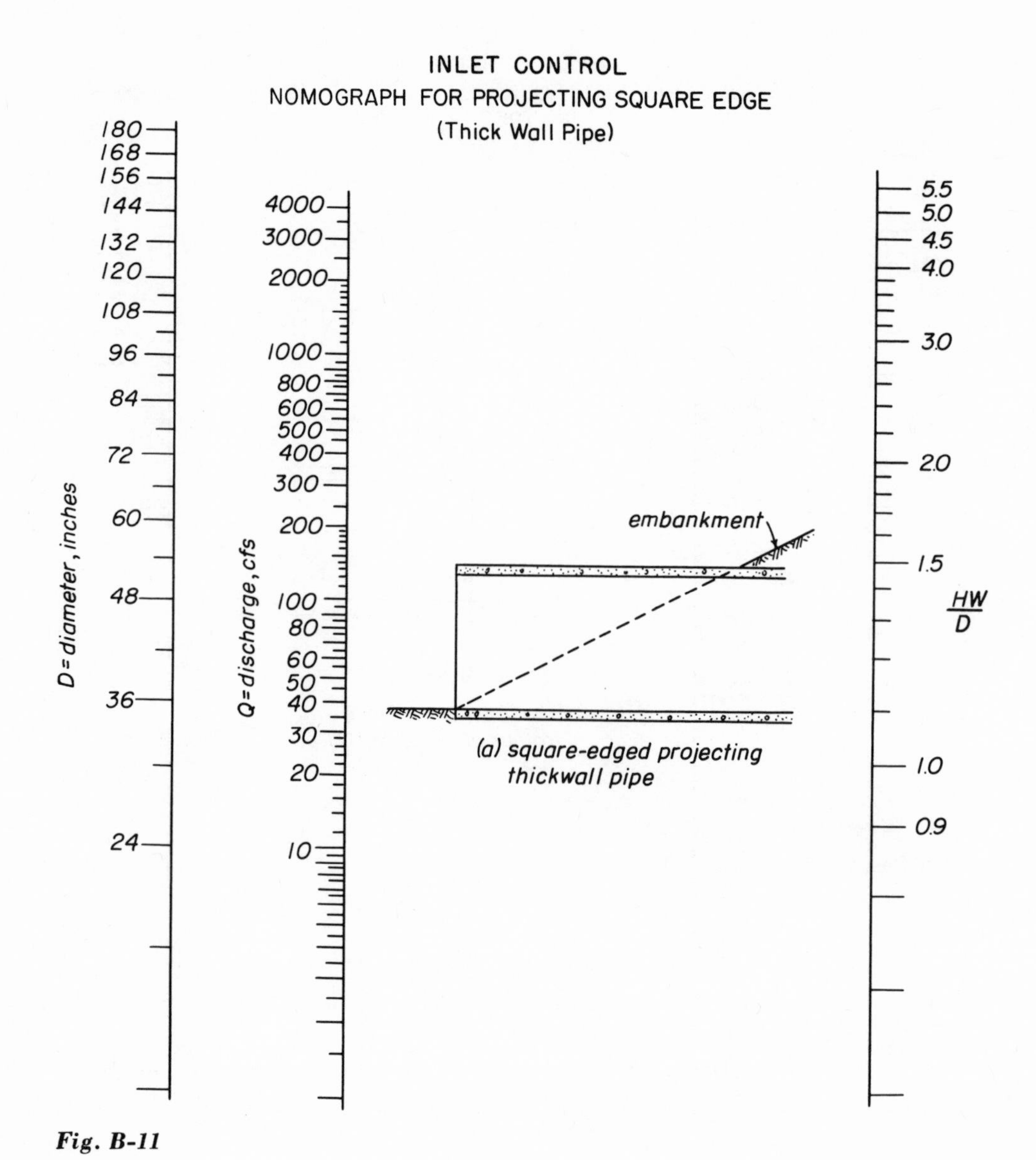
INLET CONTROL
NOMOGRAPH FOR PROJECTING SQUARE EDGE
(Thick Wall Pipe)
180
168
156
144
132
120
108
96
84
72
60
48
36
24
D=diameter, inches
4000
3000
2000
1000
800
600
500
400
300
200
100
80
60
50
40
30
20
10
Q=discharge, cfs
embankment
(a) square-edged projecting
thickwall pipe
5.5
5.0
4.5
4.0
3.0
2.0
1.5
HW
D
1.0
0.9

Fig. B-11

Appendix C

Nomographs for Outlet Control

THE FLOWING-FULL NOMOGRAPHS REDUCE THE MATHEMATICS involved in computing the headwater for a culvert flowing full. The term "flowing full" is used for these nomographs because the culvert barrel must be full for the correct application of the equation that is solved. In most cases the design procedure of Appendix A will refer to culvert headwater solutions by use of these nomographs. In other cases the flow control must be established by the procedures discussed in Chapter 4. Flowing-full nomographs consider all the factors that affect flow.

These nomographs have length scales, with entrance loss coefficients combined, that appear as arcs. The other scales on the nomographs are discharge on the left and, next to it, the diameter or pipe size scale. A turning line or reference line without division marks is needed in solving the two parts of the equation shown.

On the far right of each nomograph is the head scale—not to be confused with the headwater scale of the culvert capacity charts. The head H is converted to headwater HW by the equation shown on the nomograph. The head H is the difference between the elevation of the upstream pool level and the pressure head elevation at the culvert outlet. When the downstream tailwater submerges the culvert outlet, the pressure head elevation at the outlet is at the surface of the downstream tailwater. For other conditions, the pressure head elevation at the outlet is the projection of the hydraulic gradient to the plane of the outlet, which is the vertical distance above the invert of the outlet pipe.

For conservative design, the pressure head elevation can be assumed to be at the top of the pipe. For moderate size pipe, up to about 6-ft. diameter, this assumption provides adequate accuracy. For larger size pipe, a closer approximation to the true pressure head elevation is given by the average of critical depth and pipe size $(d_c + D)/2$. This formula provides a close approximation to the true pressure head elevation in that the true pressure elevation will always lie between the crown of the pipe and critical depth.

The location of the true pressure head elevation is obtained from experimental data. Fig. C-3 is the result of experimental data and may be used for pressure head calculations where more accuracy is desired for flowing-full conduits. One condition for the use of this figure is that the flow at the culvert outlet must pass through critical depth inside the conduit barrel. This is the general case for flowing-full conduits in culvert design.

Data Necessary to Use Flowing-Full Nomographs

The proper use of the flowing-full nomographs requires knowledge of the flow condition. As noted above, in most cases the capacity charts of Appendix A can be used as a guide on when to use these nomographs. In other cases the information in Chapter 4 will be needed.

To select a culvert size from these nomographs, certain basic data concerning the site must be established:

1. Flood discharge Q in cubic feet per second.
2. Outlet channel depth in relation to critical depth in the barrel.
3. Allowable headwater AHW in feet.
4. Length L of the culvert in feet.
5. Slope S_o of the culvert barrel in feet per foot.
6. Index number $L/100S_o$.

Procedure for Using Flowing-Full Nomographs

These nomographs can be used only for outlet control, flowing-full design. The following is a step-by-step procedure:

1. Determine if these nomographs are applicable by:
   a. Following the procedure outlined in Appendix A for culvert capacity charts, or

   b. Following the procedure outlined in Chapter 4 to determine type of flow control.
2. Select the appropriate nomograph, depending on the type of barrel and entrance.
3. Enter the nomograph with discharge, entrance loss coefficient, length, and an assumed pipe size. In most cases an approximate size can be determined from culvert capacity charts.
4. With a straightedge, connect the assumed pipe size and culvert length, using the appropriate entrance loss coefficient, and make a reference mark on the turning line.
5. Rotate the straightedge to connect discharge and the reference mark on the turning line, and extend the line to the head scale. Read the head H.
6. Determine pressure head elevation from Fig. C-3.
   a. Enter Fig. C-3 with the discharge parameter $Q/D^{5/2}$. Tables in Appendix D aid in computing $Q/D^{5/2}$.
   b. Select appropriate chart for type of material; read upwards to intersection of curve. Read across to the pressure head h_o/D and record.
   c. Compute h_o by multiplying value from b by pipe diameter in feet.
   d. Simplified pressure terms discussed at the beginning of this appendix may be used.
7. Compute S_oL for the culvert site.
8. Compute HW by equation $HW = H + h_o - S_oL$.

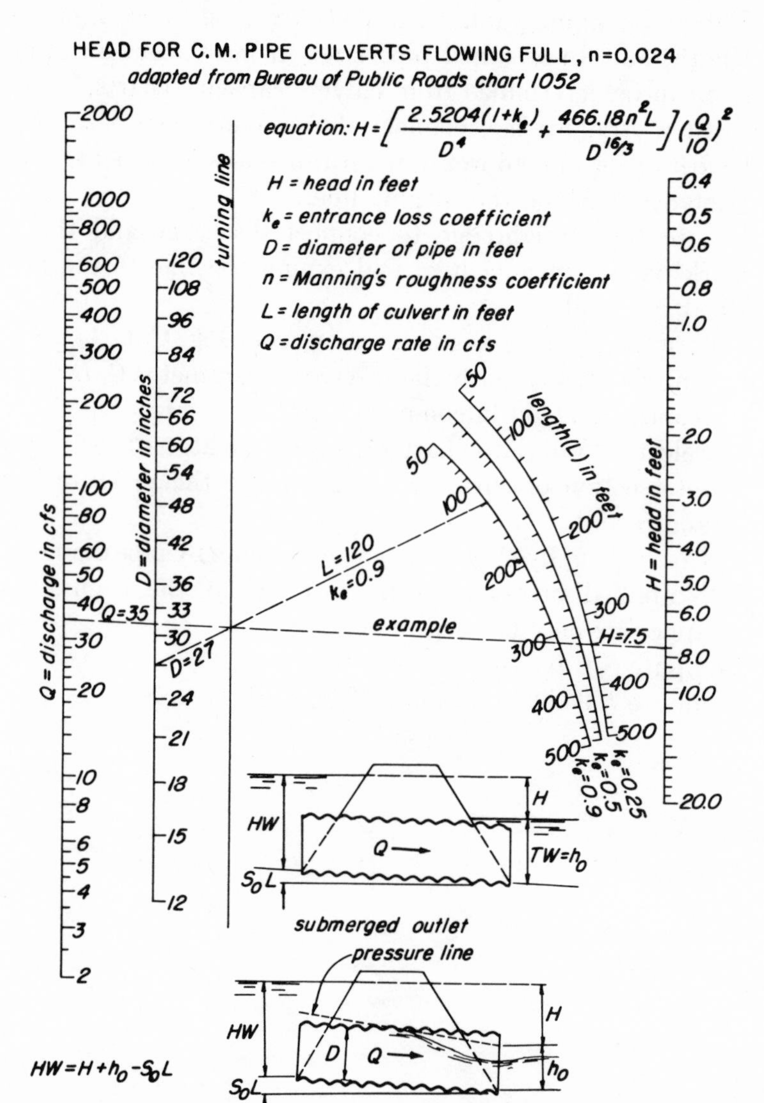

HEAD FOR C.M. PIPE CULVERTS FLOWING FULL, n=0.024
adapted from Bureau of Public Roads chart 1052
equation: $H = \left[\frac{2.5204(1+k_e)}{D^4} + \frac{466.18n^2L}{D^{16/3}}\right]\left(\frac{Q}{10}\right)^2$
H = head in feet
k_e = entrance loss coefficient
D = diameter of pipe in feet
n = Manning's roughness coefficient
L = length of culvert in feet
Q = discharge rate in cfs
Q = discharge in cfs
D = diameter in inches
turning line
length (L) in feet
H = head in feet
L=120
k_e=0.9
example
Q=35
D=27
H=7.5
k_e=0.25
k_e=0.5
k_e=0.9
HW
H
Q
TW=h_o
S_oL
submerged outlet
pressure line
D
h_o
unsubmerged outlet
HW=H+h_o-S_oL

Fig. C-1

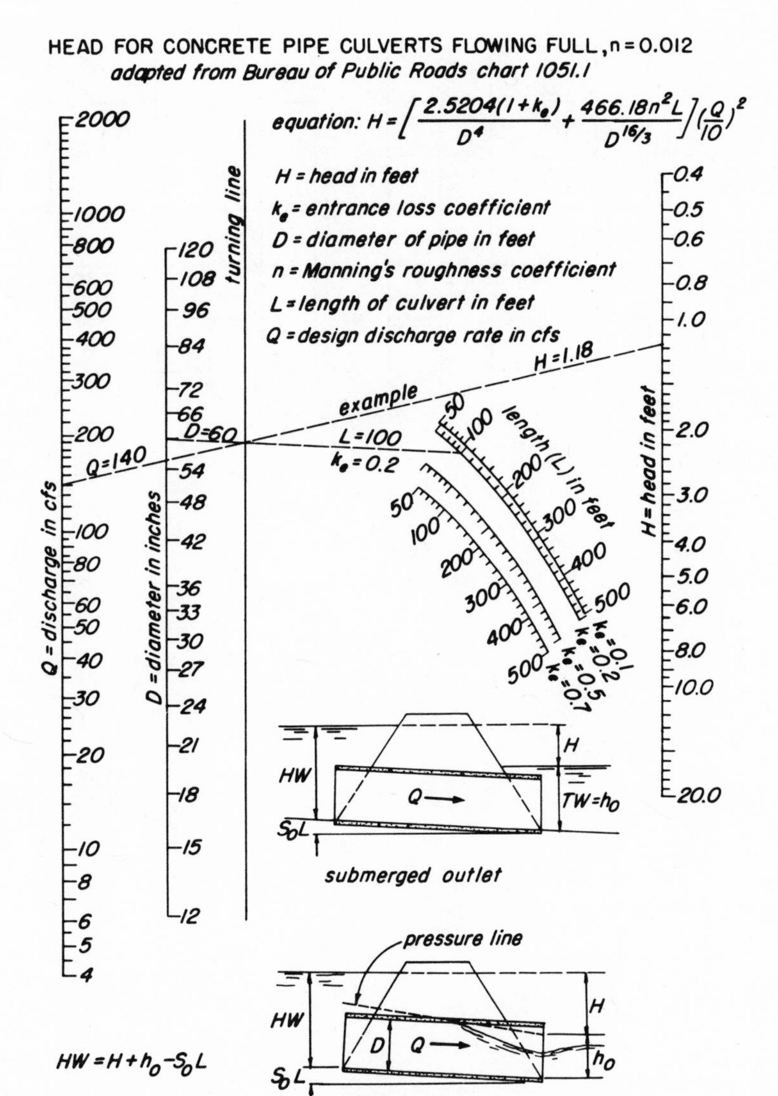

HEAD FOR CONCRETE PIPE CULVERTS FLOWING FULL, n = 0.012
adapted from Bureau of Public Roads chart 1051.1
equation: $H = \left[\frac{2.5204(1+k_e)}{D^4} + \frac{466.18n^2L}{D^{16/3}}\right]\left(\frac{Q}{10}\right)^2$
H = head in feet
k_e = entrance loss coefficient
D = diameter of pipe in feet
n = Manning's roughness coefficient
L = length of culvert in feet
Q = design discharge rate in cfs
Q = discharge in cfs
D = diameter in inches
turning line
H = head in feet
example
Q=140
D=60
L=100
k_e = 0.2
H=1.18
length (L) in feet
k_e = 0.1
k_e = 0.2
k_e = 0.5
k_e = 0.7
HW
H
TW=h_o
Q
S_oL
submerged outlet
pressure line
HW
H
D
Q
h_o
S_oL
unsubmerged outlet
HW = H + h_o − S_oL

Fig. C-2

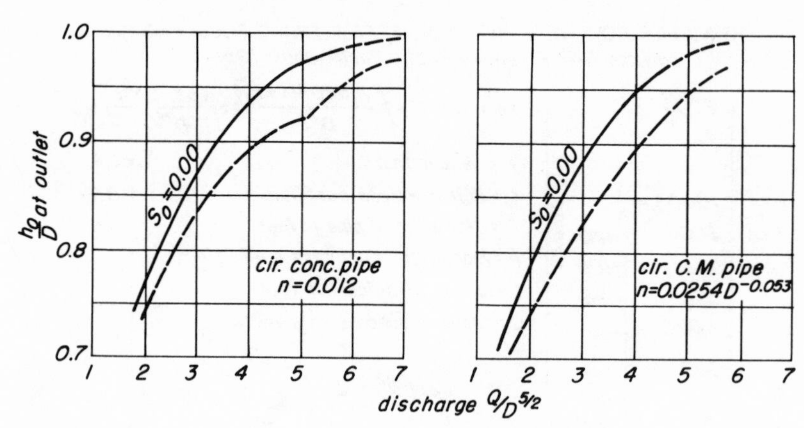
PRESSURE TERM AT CULVERT OUTLET FOR FLOWING-FULL CONDITIONS
1.0
0.9
0.8
0.7
ho/D at outlet
So=0.00
cir. conc. pipe
n=0.012
cir. C. M. pipe
n=0.0254D^-0.053
1 2 3 4 5 6 7
1 2 3 4 5 6 7
discharge Q/D^5/2

Fig. C-3

Appendix D

Discharge Factors and Functions of Circular Sections

TABLES 1 THROUGH 4 ARE PROVIDED FOR RAPID COMPUTATION of the functions required for solving problems in culvert hydraulics. The tabulated values of the discharge factor are in terms of cubic feet per second of discharge and feet of diameter. Similarly, the other tables include a conversion to feet for listed values of diameter in inches.

Table 1 is used to compute the discharge factor $Q/D^{5/2}$ for various discharges in standard pipe ranging in size from 12 to 96 in. Linear interpolation may be used for intermediate discharges. The discharge factor for pipe sizes not listed may be determined by linear interpolation for $D^{5/2}$.

Table 2 is used to determine the actual discharge for various values of the discharge factor for standard 6-in. pipe sizes. Linear interpolation may be used to determine discharge for the same size pipe. Interpolation for unlisted pipe sizes should be made in terms of $D^{5/2}$.

Table 3 lists the various functions of pipe diameter that are used in culvert hydraulics from time to time.

Table 4 is a tabulation of the geometric elements of partly filled pipe. The listed values are ratios of the particular function for the partly filled section to the value of the same function for a full pipe. These functions are: *d*, depth; *D*, diameter; *a*, area; *r*, hydraulic radius; and *p*, wetted perimeter. Actual values of the function are determined by multiplying the value for a full pipe by the ratio determined from the table. As an example, the cross-sectional area of a 24-in. pipe flowing 12 in. deep is determined by selecting the area ratio a/A corresponding to a depth ratio d/D of 12/24 and multiplying by the cross-sectional area of the

24-in. pipe. For d/D of 0.5, the a/A from the table is 0.500; to determine the part-full flow area a, solve

$$a = 0.5 \frac{\pi D^2}{4}$$

$$a = 0.500 \times \frac{\pi}{4} \left(\frac{24}{12}\right)^2$$

$$a = 1.57 \text{ sq.ft.}$$

Computations for the other functions are performed similarly.

TABLE 1. Values of $Q/D^{5/2}$ for Various Combinations of D, In., and Q, cfs

Q \ D	12	18	24	30	36	42	48	54	60	66	72	78	84	90	96
2	2.00	.72	.35	.20	.12	.08	.06	.04	—	—	—	—	—	—	—
4	4.00	1.45	.70	.40	.25	.17	.12	.09	—	—	—	—	—	—	—
6	6.00	2.17	1.06	.60	.38	.26	.18	.13	—	—	—	—	—	—	—
8	8.00	2.90	1.41	.80	.51	.34	.25	.18	—	—	—	—	—	—	—
10	10.00	3.62	1.76	1.01	.64	.43	.31	.23	—	—	—	—	—	—	—
12		4.35	2.12	1.21	.76	.52	.37	.27	—	—	—	—	—	—	—
14		5.08	2.47	1.41	.89	.61	.43	.32	—	—	—	—	—	—	—
16		5.80	2.82	1.61	1.02	.69	.50	.37	—	—	—	—	—	—	—
18		6.53	3.18	1.82	1.15	.78	.56	.41	—	—	—	—	—	—	—
20		7.25	3.53	2.02	1.28	.87	.62	.46	.35	.28	.22	.18	.15	.12	.11
40			7.07	4.04	2.56	1.74	1.25	.93	.71	.56	.45	.37	.30	.25	.22
60				6.07	3.84	2.61	1.87	1.39	1.07	.84	.68	.55	.46	.38	.33
80				8.09	5.13	3.49	2.50	1.86	1.43	1.12	.90	.74	.61	.51	.44
100					6.41	4.36	3.12	2.32	1.78	1.40	1.13	.92	.77	.64	.55
120					7.69	5.23	3.75	2.79	2.14	1.69	1.36	1.11	.92	.77	.66
140					8.98	6.10	4.37	3.25	2.50	1.97	1.58	1.29	1.07	.90	.77
160						6.98	5.00	3.72	2.86	2.25	1.81	1.48	1.23	1.03	.88
180						7.85	5.62	4.19	3.21	2.53	2.04	1.67	1.38	1.16	.99
200						8.72	6.25	4.65	3.57	2.81	2.26	1.85	1.54	1.29	1.10
220						9.59	6.87	5.12	3.93	3.10	2.49	2.04	1.69	1.42	1.21
240							7.50	5.58	4.29	3.38	2.72	2.22	1.85	1.55	1.32
260	>10						8.12	6.05	4.65	3.66	2.94	2.41	2.00	1.68	1.43
280							8.75	6.51	5.00	3.94	3.17	2.59	2.15	1.81	1.54
300							9.37	6.98	5.36	4.22	3.40	2.78	2.31	1.94	1.65
350		>10	>10					8.14	6.26	4.93	3.96	3.24	2.69	2.27	1.93
400								9.31	7.15	5.63	4.53	3.71	3.08	2.59	2.20
450				>10					8.04	6.34	5.10	4.17	3.47	2.92	2.48
500					>10				8.94	7.04	5.67	4.64	3.85	3.24	2.76
550									9.83	7.75	6.23	5.10	4.24	3.57	3.03
600						>10				8.45	6.80	5.57	4.62	3.89	3.31
650							>10			9.16	7.37	6.03	5.01	4.21	3.59
700										9.86	7.93	6.49	5.39	4.54	3.86
750								>10			8.50	6.96	5.78	4.86	4.14
800											9.07	7.42	6.17	5.19	4.41
850									>10		9.63	7.89	6.55	5.51	4.69
900										>10		8.35	6.94	5.84	4.97
950											>10	8.81	7.32	6.16	5.24
1000												9.28	7.71	6.49	5.52
1500												>10	>10	9.73	8.28

TABLE 2. Discharge (Q, cfs) for Various Values of Q/D^{5/2} and Pipe Size (D, In.)

$Q/D^{5/2}$ \ D	12	18	24	30	36	42	48	54	60	66	72	78	84	90	96
.2	.2	.5	1.1	1.9	3.1	4.5	6.4	8.5	11.1	14.1	17.6	21.5	25.9	30.8	36.2
.4	.4	1.1	2.2	3.9	6.2	9.1	12.8	17.1	22.3	28.3	35.2	43.0	51.8	61.6	72.4
.6	.6	1.6	3.3	5.9	9.3	13.7	19.2	25.7	33.5	42.5	52.9	64.6	77.7	92.4	108.6
.8	.8	2.2	4.5	7.9	12.4	18.3	25.6	34.3	44.7	56.7	70.5	86.1	103.7	123.2	144.8
1.0	1.0	2.7	5.6	9.8	15.5	22.9	32.0	42.9	55.9	70.9	88.1	107.7	129.6	154.0	181.0
1.2	1.2	3.3	6.7	11.8	18.7	27.5	38.4	51.5	67.0	85.1	105.8	129.2	155.5	184.8	217.2
1.4	1.4	3.8	7.9	13.8	21.8	32.0	44.8	60.1	78.2	99.3	123.4	150.8	181.5	215.6	253.4
1.6	1.6	4.4	9.0	15.8	24.9	36.6	51.2	68.7	89.4	113.5	141.0	172.3	207.4	246.4	289.6
1.8	1.8	4.9	10.1	17.7	28.0	41.2	57.6	77.3	100.6	127.7	158.7	193.8	233.3	277.2	325.8
2.0	2.0	5.5	11.3	19.7	31.1	45.8	64.0	85.9	111.8	141.8	176.3	215.4	259.2	308.0	362.0
2.2	2.2	6.0	12.4	21.7	34.2	50.4	70.4	94.5	122.9	156.0	194.0	236.9	285.2	338.9	398.2
2.4	2.4	6.6	13.5	23.7	37.4	55.0	76.8	103.1	134.1	170.2	211.6	258.5	311.1	369.7	434.4
2.6	2.6	7.1	14.7	25.6	40.5	59.5	83.2	111.6	145.3	184.4	229.2	280.0	337.0	400.5	470.6
2.8	2.8	7.7	15.8	27.6	43.6	64.1	89.6	120.2	156.5	198.6	246.9	301.6	362.9	431.3	506.8
3.0	3.0	8.2	16.9	29.6	46.7	68.7	96.0	128.8	167.7	212.8	264.5	323.1	388.9	462.1	543.0
3.2	3.2	8.8	18.1	31.6	49.8	73.3	102.4	137.4	178.8	227.0	282.1	344.6	414.8	492.9	579.2
3.4	3.4	9.3	19.2	33.5	53.0	77.9	108.8	146.0	190.0	241.2	299.8	366.2	440.7	523.7	615.4
3.6	3.6	9.9	20.3	35.5	56.1	82.5	115.2	154.6	201.2	255.3	317.4	387.7	466.7	554.5	651.6
3.8	3.8	10.4	21.4	37.5	59.2	87.0	121.6	163.2	212.4	269.5	335.0	409.3	492.6	585.3	687.8
4.0	4.0	11.0	22.6	39.5	62.3	91.6	128.0	171.8	223.6	283.7	352.7	430.8	518.5	616.1	724.0
4.2	4.2	11.5	23.7	41.5	65.4	96.2	134.4	180.4	234.7	297.9	370.3	452.4	544.4	646.9	760.2
4.4	4.4	12.1	24.8	43.4	68.5	100.8	140.8	189.0	245.9	312.1	388.0	473.9	570.4	677.8	796.4
4.6	4.6	12.6	26.0	45.4	71.7	105.4	147.2	197.6	257.1	326.3	405.6	495.5	596.3	708.6	832.6
4.8	4.8	13.2	27.1	47.4	74.8	110.0	153.6	206.1	268.3	340.5	423.2	517.0	622.2	739.4	868.8
5.0	5.0	13.7	28.2	49.4	77.9	114.5	160.0	214.7	279.5	354.7	440.9	538.5	648.2	770.2	905.0
5.2	5.2	14.3	29.4	51.3	81.0	119.1	166.4	223.3	290.6	368.9	458.5	560.1	674.1	801.0	941.3
5.4	5.4	14.8	30.5	53.3	84.1	123.7	172.8	231.9	301.8	383.0	476.1	581.6	700.0	831.8	977.5
5.6	5.6	15.4	31.6	55.3	87.2	128.3	179.2	240.5	313.0	397.2	493.8	603.2	725.9	862.6	1013.7
5.8	5.8	15.9	32.8	57.3	90.4	132.9	185.6	249.1	324.2	411.4	511.4	624.7	751.9	893.4	1049.9
6.0	6.0	16.5	33.9	59.2	93.5	137.5	192.0	257.7	335.4	425.6	529.0	646.3	777.8	924.2	1086.1
6.5	6.5	17.9	36.7	64.2	101.3	148.9	208.0	279.2	363.3	461.1	573.1	700.1	842.6	1001.3	1176.6
7.0	7.0	19.2	39.5	69.1	109.1	160.4	224.0	300.7	391.3	496.6	617.2	754.0	907.4	1078.3	1267.1
7.5	7.5	20.6	42.4	74.1	116.9	171.8	240.0	322.1	419.2	532.0	661.3	807.8	972.3	1155.3	1357.6
8.0	8.0	22.0	45.2	79.0	124.7	183.3	256.0	343.6	447.2	567.5	705.4	861.7	1037.1	1232.4	1448.1
8.5	8.5	23.4	48.0	83.9	132.5	194.8	272.0	365.1	475.1	603.0	749.5	915.5	1101.9	1309.4	1538.7
9.0	9.0	24.8	50.9	88.9	140.3	206.2	288.0	386.6	503.1	638.4	793.6	969.4	1166.8	1386.4	1629.2
9.5	9.5	26.1	53.7	93.8	148.0	217.7	304.0	408.0	531.0	673.9	837.7	1023.3	1231.6	1463.4	1719.7
10.0	10.0	27.5	56.5	98.8	155.8	229.1	320.0	429.5	559.0	709.4	881.8	1077.2	1296.4	1540.5	1810.2

TABLE 3. Functions of* D *for Standard Pipe Sizes

Diam., in.	$D^{1/3}$	$D^{1/2}$	$D^{5/2}$	$D^{8/3}$
12	1.00	1.00	1.00	1.00
18	1.14	1.22	2.76	2.95
24	1.26	1.41	5.65	6.35
30	1.36	1.58	9.88	11.51
36	1.44	1.73	15.6	18.7
42	1.52	1.87	22.9	28.2
48	1.59	2.00	32.0	40.3
54	1.65	2.12	43.0	55.2
60	1.71	2.24	55.9	73.1
66	1.77	2.34	70.9	94.3
72	1.82	2.45	88.2	119
78	1.87	2.55	107.7	147
84	1.91	2.64	129.6	179
90	1.96	2.74	154.0	216
96	2.00	2.83	181.0	256

TABLE 4. Properties of Partly Filled Pipe

d/D	a/A	r/R	p/P
0.0	.000	.000	.000
.1	.052	.252	.206
.2	.143	.484	.296
.3	.252	.685	.368
.4	.373	.855	.436
.5	.500	1.000	.500
.6	.626	1.11	.564
.7	.748	1.18	.634
.8	.858	1.22	.704
.9	.950	1.19	.798
1.0	1.000	1.00	1.000

Appendix E

References for Determining Earth Loads and Supporting Strengths

WHILE THIS HANDBOOK IS DEVOTED ENTIRELY TO CULVERT hydraulics, it is recognized that some engineers would like sources of design information pertaining to the calculation of loads on culverts. The following list contains readily available references that will enable the designer to broaden his knowledge, calculate loads, and select pipe of proper strength and bedding conditions to support those loads.

Portland Cement Association Publications

Concrete Sewers
Embankment Conduit D-Loads for Reinforced Concrete Pipe
Trench Loads and Concrete Pipe Supporting Strength (mimeograph)
Sewer Loads and Pipe Bedding (mimeograph)

Other References

Reinforced Concrete Pipe Culverts—Criteria for Structural Design and Installation, Washington, D.C., Bureau of Public Roads, August 1963.

Concrete Pipe Handbook, Chicago, American Concrete Pipe Association, 1959.

Concrete Pipe Field Manual, Chicago, American Concrete Pipe Association, 1960.

Rowe, R. Robinson, "Rigid Culverts Under High Overfills," ASCE *Transactions*, Vol. 122, 1957, p. 410.

Spangler, M. G., "A Theory on Loads on Negative Projecting Conduits," Highway Research Board *Proceedings*, Vol. 30, 1950, pp. 153-161.

Schlick, W. J., "Loads on Negative-Projecting Conduits," Highway Research Board *Proceedings*, Vol. 31, 1952, pp. 308-319.

Spangler, M. G., "A Practical Application of the Imperfect Ditch Method of Construction," Highway Research Board *Proceedings*, Vol. 37, 1958, pp. 271-277.

Spangler, M. G., *Soil Engineering*, Scranton, Pa., International Textbook Co., 1951.

Appendix F

The Use of Forms in Culvert Design

DATA SHEETS AND DESIGN EXAMPLES USING THE HYDRAULIC charts in the preceding appendices are presented in this section.

The hydraulic design of a culvert requires the passing of flow from the upstream side of the highway embankment to the downstream side with the most economical structure meeting predetermined risk requirements. These data sheets were developed to facilitate selection of culvert designs that will pass the design flow. With the various sizes, shapes, and entrance conditions selected to pass the flow, the engineer can appraise each culvert site and make a culvert design that will meet the other requirements of strength and economy.

The design information to be entered on the upper half of the data sheet is obtained from various sources. Data on hydrology must be related to the traffic facility and design risk. Estimates of flood runoff and risk evaluation are made by methods such as those suggested in Chapter 2.

The location and alignment of culverts discussed in Chapter 1 are determined from appropriate maps, photos, and field inspections. Controlling elevations, length, slope, and distance from pavement to the top of the culvert (for load restrictions) are determined from plans and field inspections. The information is summarized on the data sheet. By use of this information, culvert sizes with appropriate entrances are selected to pass the flow through the embankment.

The lower half of the data sheet tabulates the various culvert designs that meet the requirements shown on the upper half. The designer generally assumes an entrance condition and pipe material, and with these assumptions he determines the size of pipe to carry the flow within the maximum permissible headwater. Since most designs will be accomplished with the culvert capacity charts, the operating headwater from these charts is placed first. These charts also indicate which type of nomograph to use for designs outside the limits of the charts, and appropriate places are provided on the data sheet for nomograph solutions.

The remarks column can be used in many ways. One use is in checking designs for greater discharges to aid in developing damage estimates. Another use is to compare costs, including those of headwalls. Outlet structures, when needed, are generally necessary for all materials and must be included in final cost figures. The lower right-hand square is used by the engineer to tabulate the data on the final culvert selection.

The selected designs are readily transferred from the data sheets to the plans and profiles of the project. Work sheets should be filed separately for future reference.

Three examples are shown representing typical culvert design problems. A discussion of certain points about the examples, which may not be readily apparent from studying each problem, follows.

Example 1

The upper half of the page is filled in from previously discussed information sources. In this example, an expressway or Interstate highway design requires at least a 50-year frequency flood magnitude. A small safety factor is maintained by not allowing the flow to come onto the roadway shoulder since it is 1 ft. from the elevation of the center of the roadway at the low point of the vertical curve. The stream channel is determined from field inspection or topographic interpretation as approaching perpendicular to the embankment; therefore, headwalls are not necessary unless the designer wishes to shorten the culvert length.

The hydraulic designs are first tried by using the culvert capacity charts. The concrete pipe designs are readily determined from these charts. The charts indicate design solutions for corrugated metal pipe, but final headwater depths must be checked using the nomograph indicated by the charts (head for corrugated metal pipe flowing full).

In the remarks column the cost data shown are not necessarily representative of a particular area. The cost figures used are for illustrative purposes.

A study of the designs that will perform the task imposed by the requirements illustrated on the upper part of the data sheet indicates that a 60-in. circular concrete pipe, groove end projecting upstream into the flow, is the most economical choice. The cost of concrete pipe will vary somewhat with the class (strength requirements) of pipe. The cost estimate may be modified after the strength of pipe and bedding conditions are determined.

Example 2

This example is assumed to be on the Interstate Highway System. The problem illustrates a low fill condition over at least part of the pipe, and this must be considered in the hydraulic selections.

A first trial for size to carry the flow indicates an 84-in. pipe, which is too large for the fill restrictions. The design is carried out in this case by dividing the flow in half, selecting a culvert to carry this flow, and putting in two culverts. It is necessary at times to take some proportionate share of the discharge (1/2, 1/3, 1/4, $1/n$), design a single culvert for this share, and then install multiple culverts to handle the total discharge.

Example 3

This example illustrates common design practices on many highway routes other than Interstate. Assume the traffic to be on a secondary road that has a rather high volume of traffic. It is advisable to investigate floods greater than the standard design flood for this project.

The 30-in. circular concrete pipe is selected for this site because of the safety afforded at the larger flood. In this case, the 30-in. corrugated metal pipe and concrete pipe were assumed to have the same cost per linear foot of diameter. If the large flood had not been considered pertinent, a 24-in. concrete pipe would have been sufficient. In most cases, the design for the larger flood will control the culvert selection.

Also note in the location comments that residential property could be damaged by an extreme flood if the culvert were not properly selected. Potential property damage will very often control the maximum pool elevation upstream of the culvert.

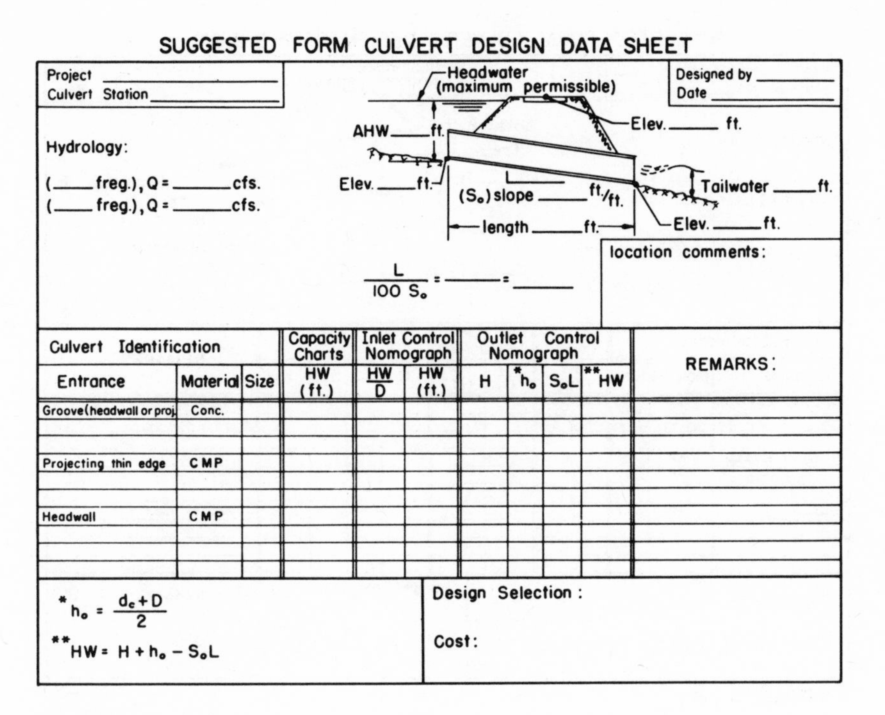

SUGGESTED FORM CULVERT DESIGN DATA SHEET

Project ____________
Culvert Station ____________

Designed by ____________
Date ____________

Hydrology:

(____ freq.), Q = ______ cfs.
(____ freq.), Q = ______ cfs.

Headwater (maximum permissible)
AHW ____ ft.
Elev. ____ ft.
Elev. ____ ft.
(S_o) slope ____ ft./ft.
length ____ ft.
Tailwater ____ ft.
Elev. ____ ft.

$\frac{L}{100\ S_o}$ = ______ = ______

location comments:

Culvert Identification			Capacity Charts	Inlet Control Nomograph		Outlet Control Nomograph				REMARKS:
Entrance	Material	Size	HW (ft.)	$\frac{HW}{D}$	HW (ft.)	H	* h_o	S_oL	** HW	
Groove (headwall or proj.	Conc.									
Projecting thin edge	CMP									
Headwall	CMP									

$^{*}h_o = \frac{d_c + D}{2}$

$^{**}HW = H + h_o - S_oL$

Design Selection:

Cost:

Fig. F-1

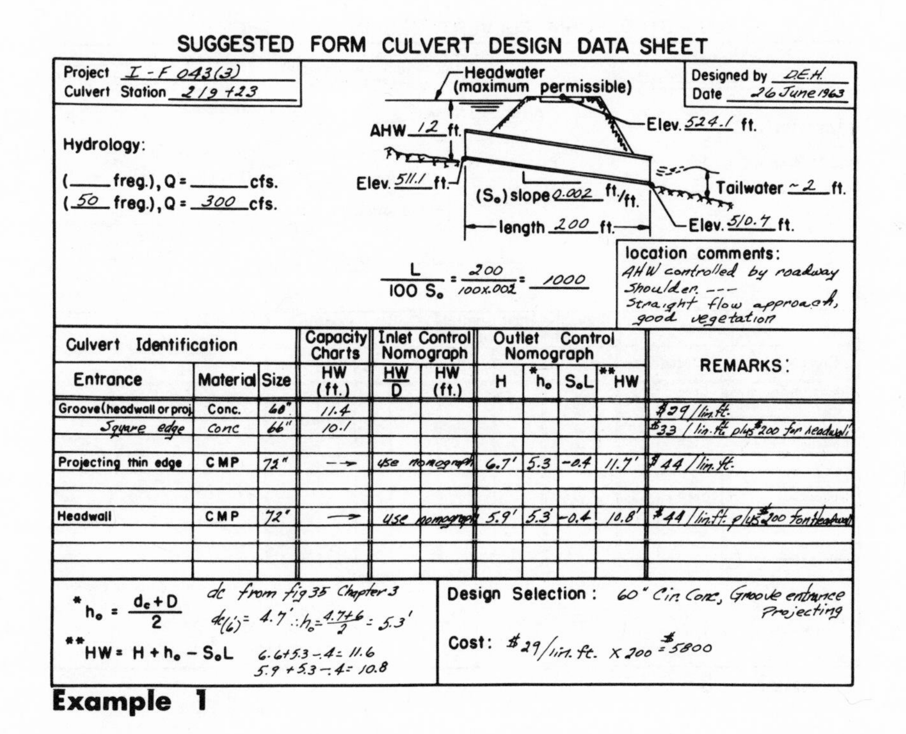

SUGGESTED FORM CULVERT DESIGN DATA SHEET

Project I-F 043(3)
Culvert Station 219+23

Designed by D.E.H.
Date 26 June 1963

Hydrology:

(____ freq.), Q = ______ cfs.
(50 freq.), Q = 300 cfs.

Headwater (maximum permissible)
AHW 12 ft.
Elev. 524.1 ft.
Elev. 511.1 ft.
(S_o) slope 0.002 ft./ft.
length 200 ft.
Tailwater ~2 ft.
Elev. 510.7 ft.

$\frac{L}{100\ S_o} = \frac{200}{100 \times .002} = 1000$

location comments:
AHW controlled by roadway Shoulder. ---
Straight flow approach, good vegetation

Culvert Identification			Capacity Charts	Inlet Control Nomograph		Outlet Control Nomograph				REMARKS:
Entrance	Material	Size	HW (ft.)	$\frac{HW}{D}$	HW (ft.)	H	* h_o	S_oL	** HW	
Groove (headwall or proj.	Conc.	60"	11.4							$29/lin.ft.
Square edge	Conc	66"	10.1							$33/lin.ft. plus $200 for headwall
Projecting thin edge	CMP	72"	-->	use nomograph		6.7'	5.3	-0.4	11.7'	$44/lin.ft.
Headwall	CMP	72"	-->	use nomograph		5.9'	5.3'	-0.4	10.8'	$44/lin.ft. plus $200 for headwall

$^{*}h_o = \frac{d_c + D}{2}$ — dc from fig 35 Chapter 3; $d_c(6') = 4.7' \therefore h_o = \frac{4.7+6}{2} = 5.3'$

$^{**}HW = H + h_o - S_oL$ — $6.6 + 5.3 - .4 = 11.6$; $5.9 + 5.3 - .4 = 10.8$

Design Selection: 60" Cir. Conc., Groove entrance Projecting

Cost: $29/lin.ft. × 200 = $5800

Example 1

Fig. F-2

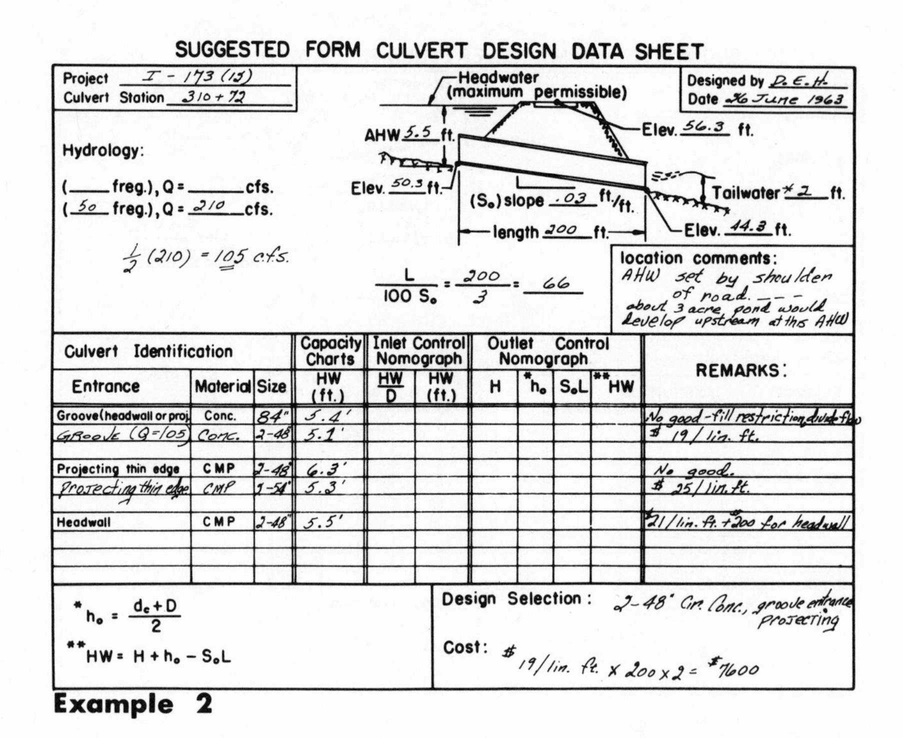

SUGGESTED FORM CULVERT DESIGN DATA SHEET

Project I - 173 (13)
Culvert Station 310 + 72

Designed by D. E. H.
Date 26 June 1963

Hydrology:

(____ freq.), Q = ____ cfs.
(50 freq.), Q = 210 cfs.

$\frac{1}{2}(210) = 105$ c.f.s.

$\frac{L}{100\ S_o} = \frac{200}{3} = 66$

location comments: AHW set by shoulder of road. --- about 3 acre pond would develop upstream at this AHW

Culvert Identification			Capacity Charts	Inlet Control Nomograph		Outlet Control Nomograph				REMARKS:
Entrance	Material	Size	HW (ft.)	HW/D	HW (ft.)	H	*h_o	S_oL	**HW	
Groove (headwall or proj.	Conc.	84"	5.4'							No good - fill restriction, divide flow
Groove (Q=105)	Conc.	2-48"	5.1'							$ 19 / lin. ft.
Projecting thin edge	CMP	2-48"	6.3'							No good.
Projecting thin edge	CMP	1-54"	5.3'							$ 25 / lin. ft.
Headwall	CMP	2-48"	5.5'							$21 / lin. ft. + $200 for headwall

$$^*h_o = \frac{d_c + D}{2}$$

$$^{**}HW = H + h_o - S_oL$$

Design Selection: 2-48" Cir. Conc., groove entrance projecting

Cost: $ 19 / lin. ft. × 200 × 2 = $7600

Example 2

Fig. F-3

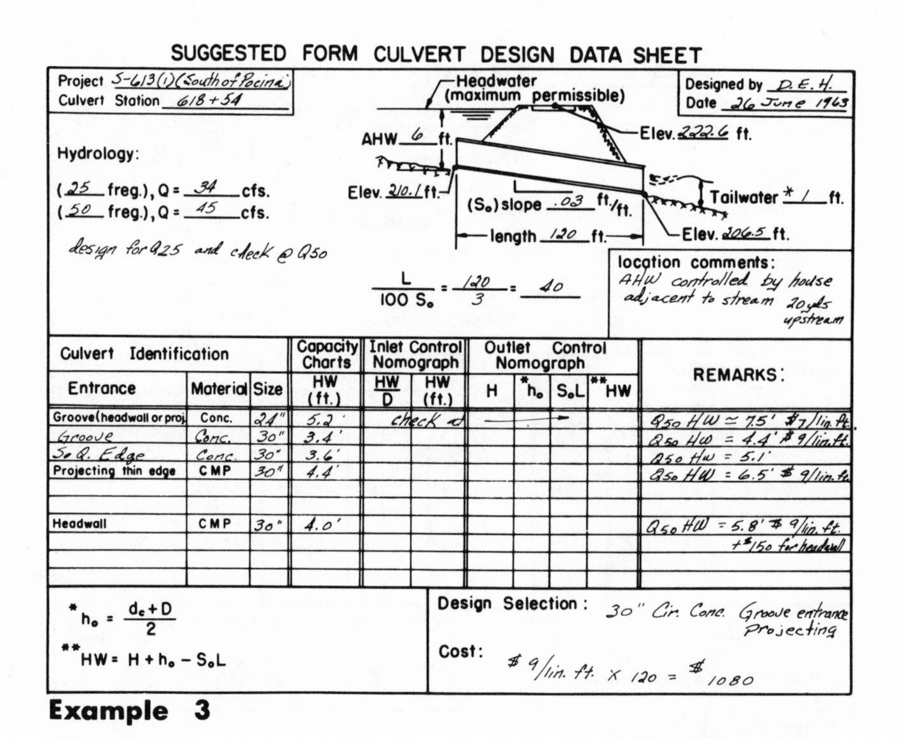

SUGGESTED FORM CULVERT DESIGN DATA SHEET

Project S-613(1) (South of Pocina)
Culvert Station 618 + 54

Designed by D. E. H.
Date 26 June 1963

Hydrology:

(25 freq.), Q = 34 cfs.
(50 freq.), Q = 45 cfs.

design for Q25 and check @ Q50

$\frac{L}{100\ S_o} = \frac{120}{3} = 40$

location comments: AHW controlled by house adjacent to stream 20 yds upstream

Culvert Identification			Capacity Charts	Inlet Control Nomograph		Outlet Control Nomograph				REMARKS:
Entrance	Material	Size	HW (ft.)	HW/D	HW (ft.)	H	*h_o	S_oL	**HW	
Groove (headwall or proj.	Conc.	24"	5.2'	check at		→				Q50 HW ≃ 7.5' $7 / lin. ft.
Groove	Conc.	30"	3.4'							Q50 HW = 4.4' $ 9 / lin. ft.
Sq. Edge	Conc.	30"	3.6'							Q50 HW = 5.1'
Projecting thin edge	CMP	30"	4.4'							Q50 HW = 6.5' $ 9 / lin. ft.
Headwall	CMP	30"	4.0'							Q50 HW = 5.8' $ 9 / lin. ft.
										+ $150 for headwall

$$^*h_o = \frac{d_c + D}{2}$$

$$^{**}HW = H + h_o - S_oL$$

Design Selection: 30" Cir. Conc. Groove entrance Projecting

Cost: $ 9 / lin. ft. × 120 = $ 1080

Example 3

Fig. F-4

Index